UNDERSTANDING ANTIBACTERIAL ACTION AND RESISTANCE

ELLIS HORWOOD SERIES IN PHARMACEUTICAL TECHNOLOGY
(incorporating Pharmacological Sciences)

Editor: Professor M. H. RUBINSTEIN, School of Health Sciences, Liverpool Polytechnic

UNDERSTANDING ANTIBACTERIAL ACTION AND RESISTANCE

A. D. RUSSELL B.Pharm., Ph.D., D.Sc., F.R.Pharm.S., F.R.C.Path.
Welsh School of Pharmacy
University of Wales College of Cardiff, UK

I. CHOPRA M.A., Ph.D., D.Sc.
Department of Microbiology
University of Bristol, UK

ELLIS HORWOOD
NEW YORK   LONDON   TORONTO   SYDNEY   TOKYO   SINGAPORE

First published in 1990 by
ELLIS HORWOOD LIMITED
Market Cross House, Cooper Street,
Chichester, West Sussex, PO19 1EB, England
A division of
Simon & Schuster International Group

Typeset in Times by Ellis Horwood
Printed and bound in Great Britain
by The Camelot Press, Southampton

British Library Cataloguing in Publication Data

Russell, A. D.
Understanding antibacterial action and resistance.
1. Antibacterials
I. Title II. Chopra, I.
615.1
ISBN 0–13–946930–3 (Library Ed.)
ISBN 0–13–946922–2 (Student Pkb. Ed.)

Library of Congress Cataloging-in-Publication Data

Russell, A. D. (Allan Denver), 1936–
Understanding antibacterial action and resistance/
A. D. Russell, I. Chopra
p. cm. — (Ellis Horwood series in pharmaceutical technology)
ISBN 0–13–946930–3 (Library Ed.)
ISBN 0–13–946922–2 (Student Pkb. Ed.)
1. Antibacterial agents—Physiological effect.
2. Drug resistance in microorganisms. I. Chopra, I. (Ian),
1946– . II. Title. III. Series: Ellis Horwood books in biological
sciences. Series in pharmaceutical technology.
[DNLM: 1. Antibiotics—pharmacology. 2. Bacteria–drug
effects. 3. Drug Resistance, Microbial. QW 52 R961u]
RM409.R87 1990
616'.014—dc20
DNLM/DLC
for Library of Congress   89–71647
                                                           CIP

Contents

6 **Contents**

**6   Genetic and biochemical basis of resistance to antiseptics, disinfectants
and preservatives**

*Those parts of this book written by Ian Chopra
are dedicated to his family.*

*Those parts of this book written by Denver Russell
are dedicated to his wife and son.*

Preface: scope of the book

The development and widespread use of antibacterial agents in the twentieth century has had a profound impact on society and in this book we consider the properties of the agents and how they work. We open the book with a general chapter on the structure of bacteria and spores and indicate those targets that are susceptible to antibacterial agents. More detailed accounts of the inhibitors, their modes of action and how they reach their targets are presented in Chapters 2 and 3. Emphasis is placed on those agents of applied value to man, i.e. bacterial inhibitors used in chemotherapy, disinfection or preservation.

The emergence of bacterial resistance to some of the agents has posed fresh challenges requiring new strategies to try to circumvent the problems of resistance. Since an understanding of bacterial resistance is important in many fields of biology and medicine, the remainder of the book is devoted to aspects of bacterial resistance. The genetic and biochemical basis of resistance is described and consideration given to the evolution and spread of resistance genes in bacterial populations.

1

Introduction

1. DEVOLOPMENT AND GENERAL NATURE OF ANTIBACTERIAL AGENTS

Bacteria comprise a large group of unicellular, prokaryotic, microorganisms some of which are also able to form spores, i.e. dormant forms produced under adverse conditions, but with the potential to germinate or revert to the cellular, replicating, bacterial form in a favourable environment. Some bacterial activities are beneficial to man while others, notably the capacity to cause disease, are detrimental. Undoubtedly one of the most important scientific achievements of this century has been man's ability to control the detrimental activities of bacteria by the judicious use of antibacterial agents. This relates not only to the prevention of bacterial growth *per se*, but also to the destruction of bacterial spores. The impact on society has been felt in many ways. For example, the era of antibacterial chemotherapy, heralded by the introduction of the sulphonamides and penicillin in the 1930s, has led to a dramatic decline in the incidence of numerous life-threatening bacterial infections such as endocarditis, meningitis and pneumonia, and the use of disinfectants and antiseptics has removed the hazards of infection during surgery. Although the types of antibacterial agent and their mechanisms of action will be considered in more detail in Chapters 2 and 3, it will be useful at this stage to make various general statements about the inhibitors.

Antibacterial agents comprise a large group of substances that either inhibit bacterial growth (bacteriostatic agents), cause bacterial death (bactericidal agents), or destroy spores (sporicidal agents). Some bactericidal agents are also sporicidal and vice versa, but bacteriostatic agents are ineffective against resting spores. Antibacterial agents include disinfectants, antiseptics, preservatives and antibiotics. The various terms are now described more fully.

By tradition, bactericidal agents which are used on inanimate objects are termed disinfectants. Disinfectants include antibacterial agents that are usually too toxic, irritant or corrosive to be applied to body surfaces or tissues, but are suitable for disinfection of equipment or the inanimate environment. Antiseptics include bacterial inhibitors that are sufficiently free from toxic effects to be applied to body surfaces or exposed tissues and are agents which should assist and not impair natural defence systems of the body. Although antiseptics have greater selective activity against bacteria than disinfectants, they are not suitable for the treatment of infections by systemic administration. Preservatives are frequently added to pharmaceutical, cosmetic and food products to inhibit bacterial contamination and proliferation and hence prevent infectivity or spoilage. Some, but not all, of the chemicals used as disinfectants and antiseptics may also act as preservatives. However, there are additional antibacterial agents which are only used as preservatives. The term 'biocide' is a general term that encompasses antiseptic, disinfectant and preservative activity and denotes a non-chemotherapeutic agent that kills microorganisms.

The term antibiotic includes a variety of naturally occurring and synthetic organic molecules many of which have sufficient selective activity against bacteria to permit systemic administration as chemotherapeutic agents for the treatment of bacterial infections. The establishment of an infection in man and animals by a pathogenic bacterium usually involves the following steps: (a) attachment to the epithelial surfaces of the respiratory, alimentary or urogenital tracts; (b) penetration of the epithelial surfaces by the pathogen; (c) interference with, or evasion of, host defence mechanisms; (d) multiplication in the environment of the host's tissues; (e) damage of the host's tissues. Steps (a) and (b) do not occur if the bacterium is introduced into the host directly through the skin by trauma or vector bite. Antibiotics usually prevent step (d) either by killing the pathogens or slowing their growth to the point where host defence mechanisms can clear the infection. Recently, however, there have been attempts to develop antibiotics capable of inhibiting bacterial attachment, i.e. at step (a) above. This is a reasonable strategy for disease control since step (a) usually represents the first step in the chain of events associated with a bacterial infection.

Although the basis of selectivity varies from one antibiotic to another it usually results from one, or both, of the following: (a) the target inhibited is only found in bacteria so that host (animal) cells remain insusceptible to the drug, (b) the antibiotic is concentrated within the bacterial cell, but not in the host cell. Therefore, although the antibiotic may potentially inhibit both bacterial and host cell targets, the higher concentration in bacteria ensures selectivity. However, it should be remembered that not all antibiotics are suitable for the chemotherapy of infections because some of them fail to meet the criteria for selectivity outlined above. Although such antibiotics (e.g. puromycin) may be useful biochemical tools, we will not specifically consider them here since we only wish to address antibiotics of value in the chemotherapy of infectious diseases. Readers wishing to learn more about the antibiotics that lack selectivity should consult the texts by Gale *et al.* (1981) and Franklin and Snow (1989) listed at the end of this chapter.

Effective antibacterial agents inactivate bacteria or their spores by interacting with susceptible targets within these structures. It is therefore appropriate at this stage to provide a brief outline of the structure and composition of bacteria and spores to prepare the reader for the more detailed approach to antibacterial targets in Chapters 2 and 3.

2. STRUCTURE OF BACTERIA

2.1 Introduction

Bacteria can be divided into two main classes, Gram-positive and Gram-negative on the basis of their differential abilities to retain an iodine-crystal violet stain when treated with organic solvents (e.g. alcohol or acetone). Bacteria that retain the stain are termed Gram-positive and those that do not, Gram-negative. The staining response depends primarily on the morphology and composition of the bacterial cell wall, in particular the possession by Gram-negative bacteria of an outer membrane within the wall. Apart from the outer membrane the composition of Gram-positive and Gram-negative bacteria is fundamentally similar and Fig. 1.1 shows the

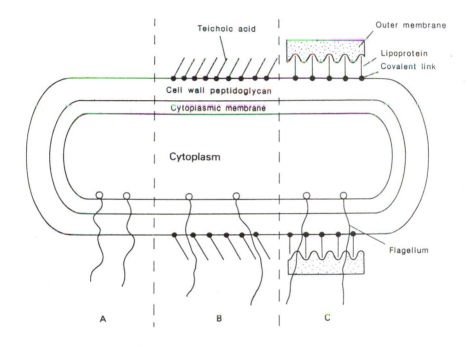

Fig. 1.1. — Diagram of the bacterial cell. A, The generalized structure of the bacterial cell; B, Gram-positive structure; C, Gram-negative structure. (Reproduced, with permission, from Hugo & Russell (1987).)

generalized structures of Gram-positive and Gram-negative bacteria. However, there are differences in detailed structural and compositional features between different bacterial species and even between strains of the same species. A description of cellular components now follows.

2.2   Cell wall

2.2.1   *General structure*
The cell wall surrounds the inner, cytoplasmic membrane. It maintains the shape of the cell and protects the mechanically fragile cytoplasmic membrane from rupture due to the high internal osmotic pressure generated by the cytoplasm. As noted, wall composition differs fundamentally between Gram-negative and Gram-positive organisms. In Gram-negative bacteria (Fig. 1.2) the inner region of the wall is a thin

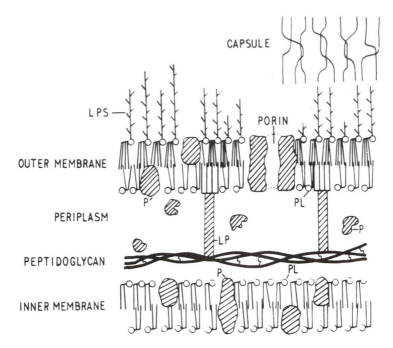

CAPSULE

LPS

PORIN

OUTER MEMBRANE

PERIPLASM

PEPTIDOGLYCAN

INNER MEMBRANE

Fig. 1.2 — The cell envelope of a Gram-negative bacterium. LP, lipoprotein; LPS, lipopolysaccharide; P, protein; PL, phospholipid. Flagella are not illustrated. (Reproduced, with permission, from Hancock & Poxton (1988).)

layer of peptidoglycan. The outer region of the wall in some respects resembles the
cytoplasmic membrane and is therefore commonly called the outer membrane. The
region between the inner and outer wall layers is termed the periplasm and found
only in Gram-negative bacteria. In Gram-positive bacteria (Fig. 1.3) the wall also
contains peptidoglycan, but in addition it contains 'accessory' or secondary wall
polymers, e.g. teichoic acids, polysaccharides and proteins that are covalently linked
to the peptidoglycan throughout its thickness. The walls of Gram-positive bacteria
can also contain loosely associated lipocarbohydrates (Fig. 1.3). In Gram-positive
cells the wall is not bounded by the outer membranous layer that is found in Gram-
negative bacteria, and hence there is no periplasm. Various surface appendages such
as pili, capsules and flagellae may also be attached to the wall. These frequently play
a role in the pathogenesis of bacterial infections, for example pili mediate adhesion
of pathogens to epithelial surfaces, capsules can prevent phagocytosis and flagellae,
by virtue of chemotactic responses, can propel bacteria through mucus layers that
overlie epithelial surfaces.

Capsules, which are discrete, tightly bound, polysaccharide layers are quite
distinct from the extracellular mucoid substance (glycocalyx or muco-exopolysac-
charide), loosely associated with the surface of some types of bacteria, e.g. *Ps.
aeruginosa*. The glycocalyx, composed of fibrous polysaccharides or globular glyco-
proteins, plays an important role in bacterial adhesion, both to sister cells and to
other strata to produce microcolonies in the form of biofilms. The formation of
biofilms may protect organisms from inhibition by antibacterial agents.

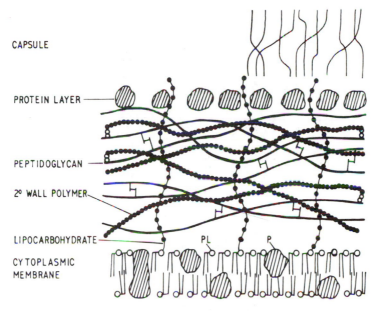

CAPSULE

PROTEIN LAYER

PEPTIDOGLYCAN

2° WALL POLYMER

LIPOCARBOHYDRATE

CYTOPLASMIC
MEMBRANE

Fig. 1.3 — The cell envelope of a Gram-positive bacterium. Note that not all the components shown occur in every strain of Gram-positive bacterium. P, protein; PL, phospholipid. Flagella are not illustrated. The secondary wall polymer is frequently teichoic acid. (Reproduced, with permission, from Hancock & Poxton (1988).)

2.2.2 Peptidoglycan

Peptidoglycan, which contributes to the mechanical stability of cell walls, is a polymer consisting of a disaccharide repeating unit of two different N-acetylated amino sugars, to one of which is attached a short peptide chain. Individual glycan strands are cross-linked through peptide bonds between the peptide chains to create a covalent network with great mechanical strength. The same types of cross-link also serve to join together sheets of peptidoglycan in bacteria that have multiple sheets. Fig. 1.4 shows the structure of E. coli peptidoglycan illustrating a repeating N-acetylglucosamine-N-acetylmuramic acid disaccharide unit, a tetrapeptide side-chain and one of the frequent types of cross-link found, i.e. the carboxyl group of D-alanine residue four in one primary chain is linked directly to another amino acid, meso-diaminopimelic acid, at the third position of a neighbouring chain. There is considerable diversity among bacteria in the nature and frequency of the cross-linking bridges as well as the composition of the tetrapeptides, particularly at positions 2 and 3. Until recently the traditional view of bacterial peptidoglycan structure has emphasized that in many particular bacterial species only one type of cross-link is found, e.g. the well-known tetrapeptide–tetrapeptide pattern in E. coli (Fig. 1.4). However, the recent introduction of sophisticated methods for bacterial peptidoglycan analysis reveal that other types of cross-linkage can also occur alongside the well recognized ones, e.g. in E. coli cross-links involving two diamino-pimelic acid residues have now been identified.

The peptidoglycan layer is not covalently attached to the underlying cytoplasmic

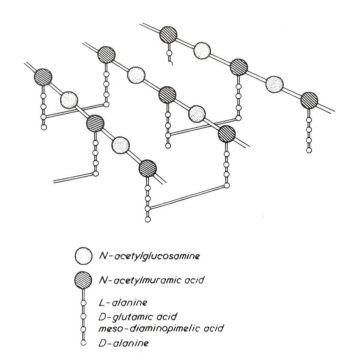

Fig. 1.4 — The structure of *E. coli* peptidoglycan showing one of the frequent types of cross-link. (Reproduced, with permission, from Hammond *et al.* (1984).)

membrane but, in the case of Gram-negative bacteria, it is firmly bound to the outer membrane of the wall by covalent linkage of occasional side-chains to an abundant outer membrane protein called murein lipoprotein (Fig 1.2 and 1.5).

Nearly all bacteria have an absolute requirement for peptidoglycan in their walls in contrast to mammalian cells which are only surrounded by a cytoplasmic membrane which does not contain peptidoglycan. Peptidoglycan synthesis therefore comprises a good selective target for antibiotic action and we shall see later (Chapter 2) that there are indeed many clinically useful compounds that inhibit peptidoglycan synthesis at various stages in its production. Without doubt the most important of these antibiotics are the beta-lactams.

2.2.3   Outer membrane of the Gram-negative cell wall

The outer membrane of the Gram-negative cell wall has a bilayer structure (Fig. 1.2), but in contrast to the cytoplasmic membrane (see below), only the inner leaflet contains phospholipid molecules. The lipid content of the outer leaflet derives exclusively from lipopolysaccharide, a molecule unique to the outer membrane. The lipopolysaccharide molecule consists of three regions (Figs. 1.6 and 1.7). The lipid moiety of the lipopolysaccharide, called lipid A, is integrated into the outer membrane bilayer with its fatty acid residues projecting towards the centre. The core polysaccharide with its attached O-polysaccharide side-chain (O antigen) projects outwards.

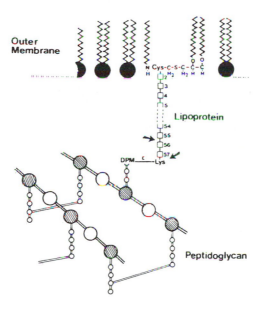

Phospholipid molecule consisting of polar head group (●) and fatty acids (〰〰).

Fatty acids attached to lipoprotein.

Fig. 1.5 — Diagrammatic representation of the insertion of lipoprotein into outer membrane. The diagram shows a lipoprotein molecule linked to the diaminopimelic acid residue (DPM) of peptidoglycan by its terminal lysine. The symbols used for peptidoglycan structure are as in Fig. 1.4. (Reproduced, with permission, from Hammond et al. (1984).)

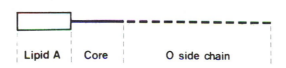

Fig. 1.6— Representation of the three regions of bacterial lipopolysaccharides (LPS). The lipid A region is embedded in the phospholipid bilayer, the core and O side-chain polysaccharide extending outwards from the cell. (Reproduced, with permission, from Hammond et al. (1984).)

If the outer leaflet of the outer membrane was only composed of lipopolysaccharide very few molecules (e.g. essential solutes) would be able to cross it to reach the cytoplasmic membrane. However, interspersed throughout the outer membrane are a number of proteins, in particular the porins, that considerably modify its permeabi-

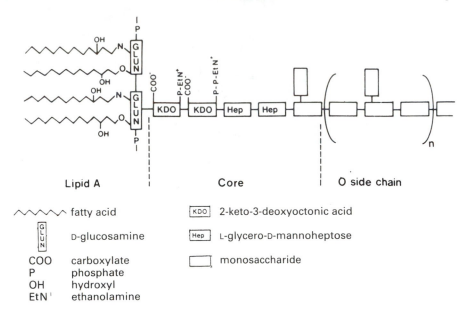

Fig. 1.7 — Generalized structure of bacterial lipopolysaccharide. The structure of the lipid A region is highly conserved amongst a wide range of Gram-negative bacteria. Similarly little variation is found in the inner core (KDO-heptose) region. Considerable variation is present in the monosaccharides that constitute the outer core and O side-chain regions and consequently they have been left as empty blocks. (Reproduced, with permission, from Hammond *et al.* (1984).)

lity characteristics. The *E. coli* proteins OmpC, OmpF and PhoE (and their counterparts in other species) form abundant non-specific transmembrane pores that allow the diffusion of small hydrophilic molecules (including antibiotics), within a limited size range (generally up to 600 daltons), across the membrane. PhoE channels are particularly involved with the passage of negatively charged molecules (e.g. compounds containing carboxylate, sulphate or phosphate residues). The OmpC and F channels contain three Omp protein molecules each of which open at the surface of the outer membrane (Fig. 1.8). However, the three separate openings merge into a single channel near the mid-point of the membrane (Fig. 1.8). In contrast, individual PhoE protein molecules can form transmembrane channels in their own right, but tend to aggregate in groups of three within the outer membrane (Fig. 1.8). Some molecules that pass through the outer membrane do so by routes that do not involve diffusion through the non-specific pores mentioned above. Many of the less abundant proteins of the outer membrane are specific transport proteins or receptors that mediate the entry of molecules unable to pass through the regular porins. These proteins are responsible for the entry of ferric iron chelates, maltose and maltodextrins, nucleosides and vitamin B12. In some cases these transport proteins form specialized pores, but in other cases the molecular mechanism by which transmembrane transport is achieved is unknown.

Certain chelating agents, e.g. ethylenediamine tetraacetic acid (EDTA) at

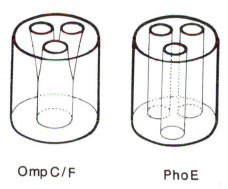

OmpC/F   PhoE

Fig. 1.8 — Schematic three-dimensional representations of the structures of different porin proteins. The porins are oriented such that the top of the figure is the portion exposed in the external environment, whereas the bottom is the portion extending into the periplasm. The plane of the outer membrane would run horizontal to these channels. (Reproduced, with permission, from Hancock (1987).)

alkaline pH, are particularly active against *Pseudomonas aeruginosa* and *Neisseria* spp. This is attributable to effects on the structural integrity of the outer membrane. For example, EDTA, by virtue of its chelating properties causes release of Mg^{2+} and Ca^{2+} from the outer membrane resulting in secondary loss of up to 50% of the lipopolysaccharide.

2.2.4   Cell walls of nocardiform bacteria
Although the nocardiform bacteria are difficult to stain, they do nevertheless give a Gram-positive staining response. However, the cell walls of the nocardiforms differ considerably from those of the more typical Gram-positive bacteria described above. Since the unusual nature of the cell wall in these organisms is responsible for intrinsic resistance to certain antibiotics and biocides, a brief description of wall structure in nocardiform bacteria, which includes corynebacteria, mycobacteria and nocardia, is presented here.

The main cell wall polysaccharide is arabinogalactan which is a copolymer of arabinose and galactose covalently bound to the acetyl (e.g. corynebacteria) or glycosyl (e.g. mycobacteria, nocardia) moieties of peptidoglycan. Distinctive lipids, known as mycolic acids, which are 2-branched, 3-hydroxy fatty acids (general structure Fig. 1.9) are esterified to the arabinogalactan, which thus forms a bridge

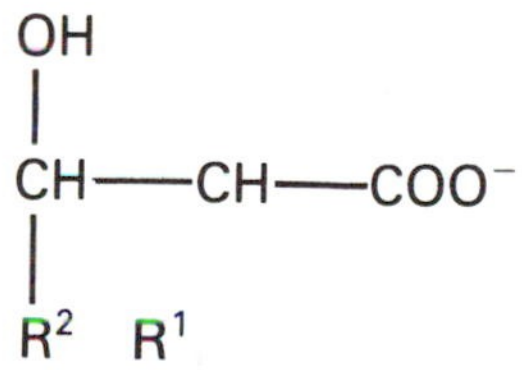

$$
\begin{array}{c}
\text{OH} \\
| \\
\text{CH}\!-\!\!-\!\text{CH}\!-\!\!-\!\text{COO}^- \\
| \quad\;\; | \\
\text{R}^2 \quad \text{R}^1
\end{array}
$$

Fig. 1.9 — General structure of mycolic acids. R^1 and R^2 are alkyl groups that may be saturated or unsaturated.

between the rigid peptidoglycan layer and the outer hydrophobic cell wall layers. Apart from mycolic acids, other lipids are also present and the lipid content accounts for up to 60% of the cell wall dry weight in nocardiform bacteria. The lipids account for the relative impermeability of the cells to normal staining procedures, their acid fastness and their intrinsic resistance to certain antibiotics and biocides.

2.3   Cytoplasmic membrane

The cytoplasmic membrane lies directly outside the cytoplasm (Fig. 1.1). It acts as a selective permeability barrier between the cytoplasm and the cell environment and is also the site at which many important and indispensable cellular activities occur. Cytoplasmic membranes primarily consist of phospholipids and proteins, although the exact membrane composition depends on the cell of origin. The phospholipid molecules are arranged in a bilayer with polar groups directed outwards on both sides (Figs. 1.2, 1.3). The membrane proteins are enzymes and carrier proteins, the latter mediating specific transport of nutrients and ions. Membrane enzymes perform the following reactions: (a) energy generation through electron transport and oxidative phosphorylation, (b) synthesis of complex lipids, (c) the final stages of peptidoglycan synthesis, (d) synthesis of external envelope components such as lipopolysaccharides and capsular polysaccharides, (e) transduction of sensory signals for motility and chemotaxis and (f) secretion of exo-proteins.

The bacterial cytoplasmic membrane is a vital cellular component since it provides the matrix by which metabolism is linked to solute transport, flagellar movement and the generation of ATP (Fig. 1.10). The electron transport system, the cytochromes, quinones, iron sulphur proteins and flavine adenine dinucleotides are embedded in the cytoplasmic membrane, which acts as an insulator. During metabolism, protons are extruded to the exterior of the bacterial cell, the net result being acidification of the cell exterior which also becomes positively charged relative to the interior. This combined potential, the concentration or osmotic effect of the proton and its electropositivity, is the electrochemical potential of the proton (μ_{H^+}), which can be quantified and expressed in terms of electrical units (mV). It is this potential, termed the proton-motive force (pmf) which drives those ancillary activities described above.

Chemical potential is measured in joules, which can be converted to volts by dividing by F (Faraday constant). This factor, μ_{H^+}/F, is the pmf, termed p by Mitchell. If ψ represents the membrane potential due to the distribution of the positively charged proton, then $\Delta p = \Delta\psi - Z\Delta pH$, all units electrical and expressed in millivolts. The symbol Z equals 2.303 RT/F and has a value of 61 at 37°C, and the pH difference (ΔpH) measures the contribution to Δp of the osmotic gradient due to the proton concentration potential.

Several antibacterial compounds affect the cytoplasmic membrane. They include the polymyxin group of antibiotics, the ionophorous antibiotics and various types of antiseptics, disinfectants and preservatives. The polymyxins, which disrupt cytoplasmic membrane integrity, have some limited uses in antibacterial chemotherapy (Chapter 2), but the ionophores, e.g. valinomycin which is a specific conductor of K$^+$, interact both with bacterial cytoplasmic membranes and mammalian membranes and therefore cannot be used clinically. The various antiseptics, disinfectants and preservatives that act at the level of the bacterial cytoplasmic membrane may

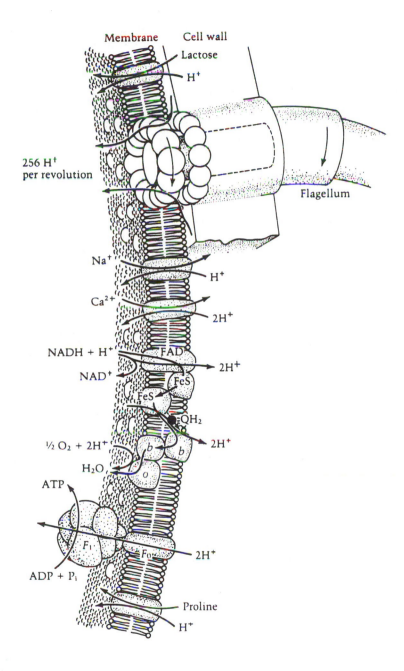

Fig. 1.10 — Chemiosmosis and the bacterial membrane. A proton gradient is generated by the operation of the respiratory chain. The passage of protons down this gradient can be coupled to ATP synthesis, active transport and flagellar motion. FeS, iron sulphur protein; QH_2, hydroquinone; b,o cytochromes b and o; F_1, F_0, components of ATPase. (Reproduced, with permission, from Hinkle and McCarthy (1978).)

inhibit specific membrane-bound enzymes or perturb homeostatic mechanisms by (a) inducing leakage of intracellular constituents, (b) inducing lysis, or (c) dissipating the proton-motive force. The cytoplasmic membrane might be a primary site of action of the cross-linking agent glutaraldehyde (used as a chemical sterilizing agent for specific purposes). Although this compound rapidly inhibits DNA, RNA and protein synthesis (and indeed combines with these macromolecules) its antibacterial activity is likely to occur via aldehyde–protein reactions in the cell wall or membrane which 'seal' the surface thereby preventing uptake of macromolecular precursors into the cell.

2.4   Cytoplasm

The cytoplasm (or cytosol) is the region lying within the bacterial cytoplasmic membrane. It contains DNA, RNA and protein synthesizing complexes, a variety of enzymes, macromolecular precursors and other low molecular weight metabolites. Together these components participate in a variety of catabolic and anabolic processes (e.g. see Fig. 1.11) that are essential for bacterial growth. We shall

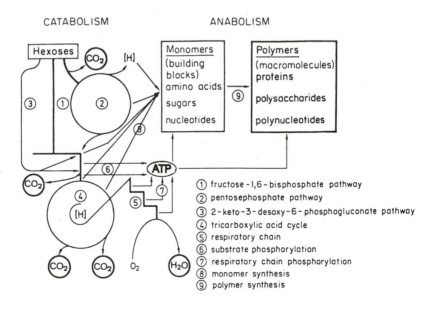

Fig. 1.11 — Metabolic map of aerobically respiring cells catabolizing hexoses. (Reproduced, with permission, from Schlegel (1986).)

concentrate in particular on the structure and synthesis of nucleic acids and proteins since many clinically useful antibiotics interfere with these processes in bacteria, and some biocides combine strongly with these macromolecules. The biocides are not suitable for consideration as internal chemotherapeutic agents because of their lack of selective toxicity. Some are, however, important disinfectants or sterilizing agents (aldehydes, ethylene oxide) and hydrogen peroxide is used as a disinfectant for cleansing wounds.

2.4.1 Chromosome structure and DNA replication

The bacterial chromosome is a single circular DNA molecule consisting of two very long helical polynucleotide chains coiled around a common axis. It is not surrounded by a membrane and has no defined shape. Because DNA contains the genetic information of the cell, its replication and division must precede cell division so that the chromosome is distributed to the two new cells. Although the concept of DNA replication developed by Watson and Crick in the 1950s is of course still generally valid, the process is now known to be highly complex in that at least 18 different gene products participate directly in the replication of the *E. coli* chromosome. One of these gene products, the enzyme DNA gyrase, is a target for the quinolone antibiotics. Many of these antibiotics have only been developed very recently (see Chapter 2). Although mammalian cells have a similar enzyme, it differs sufficiently from the bacterial one to be unaffected by the quinolones. The acridines, which are biocides rather than chemotherapeutic agents, also inhibit DNA synthesis. In this case, however, inhibition results from intercalation of acridines into DNA molecules.

Although DNA synthesis can be blocked at the level of replication by quinolones and acridines, other antibacterial agents interfere with the synthesis of the nucleotides required for the formation of the polynucleotide chain in DNA. Antibiotics that interfere with the synthesis of tetrahydrofolate act in this manner because this compound acts as a donor of one-carbon units in several steps of nucleotide biosynthesis. Interruption of the supply of tetrahydrofolate soon brings nucleotide and nucleic acid synthesis to a halt. The reaction most severely affected is thymine synthesis, hence DNA synthesis is particularly susceptible to inhibition of tetrahydrofolate production. Although tetrahydrofolate is an essential coenzyme for all cells, the ability to synthesize it from simple constituents is restricted to bacteria (Fig. 1.12). Since mammalian cells are unable to synthesize folic acid (Fig. 1.12) it therefore becomes an essential vitamin for man and is obtained from the diet. Most pathogenic bacteria are unable to take up preformed folic acid derivatives from the environment and require the enzyme dihydropteroate synthetase (DHPS) to meet their need for tetrahydrofolic acid (Fig. 1.12). This enzyme (DHPS) is inhibited by a group of antibiotics known as the sulphonamides. Since DHPS is absent from mammalian cells, human tissues are unaffected by sulphonamide drugs. The action of sulphonamide and other antifolate agents will be considered in more detail in Chapter 2.

2.4.2 Synthesis of RNA and protein and the nature of ribosomes

DNA coding regions in the chromosomes are termed genes. Genes govern the synthesis of proteins, ribosomal and transfer RNAs. Proteins are made at the direction of structural genes by the coupled processes of transcription and translation. Transcription (messenger RNA synthesis) involves the copying of one strand of DNA into mRNA which is then decoded or translated at the ribosome in participation with aminoacyl-tRNA molecules (see below). A single enzyme, RNA poly-

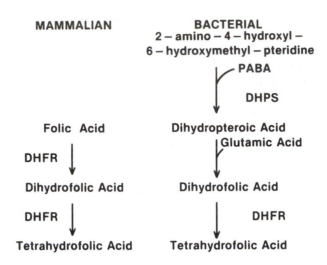

Fig. 1.12 — The tetrahydrofolic acid biosynthetic pathway in mammals and bacteria. PABA,
p-aminobenzoic acid; DHPS, dihydropteroate synthetase; DHFR dihydrofolate reductase.

merase, is responsible for all mRNA synthesis. Ribosomal and transfer RNAs are
also made by the same polymerase that makes mRNA.

Ribosomes are the complex organelles that catalyse the translation of information encoded in mRNA into protein. Polypeptide elongation is a cyclic process
whereby aminoacyl-tRNA molecules bind to the ribosome as dictated by the
mRNA. In growing bacteria approximately 80–90% of ribosomes are attached to
mRNA and are actively engaged in protein synthesis. The structure for synthesizing
protein, i.e. mRNA with attached ribosomes is termed a polysome. Proteins that are
to pass into or through the bacterial cytoplasmic membrane are invariably synthesized on polysomes that become attached by their nascent polypeptides to the inner
surface of the cytoplasmic membrane, whereas cytoplasmic proteins are synthesized
on polysomes that are not membrane associated.

An individual bacterial ribosome is a complex ribonucleoprotein particle which is
designated as a 70S ribosome since it sediments in centrifugation studies with a
velocity of 70 Svedberg (S) units. The molecular structure of bacterial ribosomes,
particularly those from *E. coli*, is well understood and a system of nomenclature to
describe them was adopted a number of years ago (Fig. 1.13). The 70S ribosome
comprises two subunits, the so-called 50S and 30S subunits. Each subunit contains
RNA and protein (Fig. 1.13). The small subunit contains one RNA molecule (16S)
and 21 different proteins numbered S (small subunit) 1–21. The large subunit
contains two RNA molecules (5S and 23S) and 32 different proteins numbered L
(large subunit) 1–34. Subsequently it was discovered that L8 is an aggregate of
proteins L7/L12/L10 and that L26 is identical to S20. Furthermore, L7 and L12 differ
only by the presence in L7 of an acetyl group at the amino terminus of the protein.

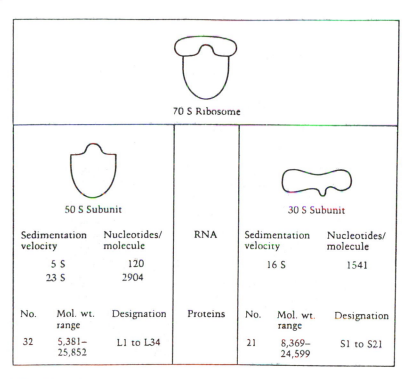

50 S Subunit		RNA	30 S Subunit	
Sedimentation velocity	Nucleotides/ molecule		Sedimentation velocity	Nucleotides/ molecule
5 S	120		16 S	1541
23 S	2904			

No.	Mol. wt. range	Designation	Proteins	No.	Mol. wt. range	Designation
32	5,381– 25,852	L1 to L34		21	8,369– 24,599	S1 to S21

Fig. 1.13 — The molecular structure of ribosomes from *E. coli*: based on the molecular weights of 19 proteins from the small subunit and 29 proteins from the large subunit, the primary structures of which are known. The discrepancy between numbers of proteins (32) in the large subunit and their designation (up to L34) derives from the fact that one protein, L8, which was thought to be unique when numbered as a spot on a chromatogram, is now known to be an association of L7, L12, and L10 and that another, L26, is identical to S20. Only small amounts of L26 remain associated with the large subunit upon dissociation of the 70S ribosome. (Reproduced, with permission, from Ingraham *et al.* (1983).)

Bacterial RNA synthesis can be selectively inhibited by the group of antibiotics known as rifamycins (Chapter 2). These antibiotics bind to and inhibit bacterial RNA polymerases but are without effect on the corresponding mammalian enzyme. Many antibacterial substances directly inhibit protein synthesis (Chapter 2). In most cases this is due to prevention of processes which take place on ribosomes. As we shall see, the specificity of clinically useful inhibitors of protein synthesis arises principally from their binding to bacterial 70S ribosomes, while mammalian ribosomes (80S particles) are left unaffected because the drugs usually fail to bind to this class of ribosome. The disinfectant hydrogen peroxide reversibly dissociates 70S ribosomes into 50S and 30S subunits. Peroxide does, however, have effects elsewhere in the cell which also contribute to its bactericidal activity.

3. STRUCTURE OF SPORES

The most important spore-formers are members of the genera *Bacillus* and *Clostridium*, but certain other bacteria, e.g. *Sporosarcina*, *Desulfomaculum* and *Sporolac-*

tobacillus can also form spores. True endospores are also produced by thermophilic actinomyces, e.g. *Thermoactinomyces vulgaris*. Only spores produced by *Bacillus* spp. and *Clostridium* spp. will be considered here and subsequently.

The structure (Figs 1.14 and 1.15) and composition (Table 1.1) of spores differ

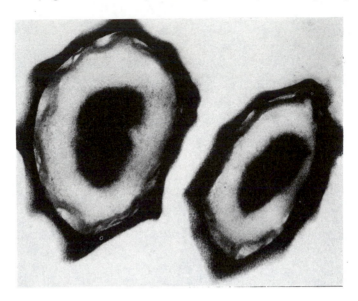

Fig. 1.14 — *Bacillus subtilis* spores showing the core, cortex and spore coats. Magnification ×80 000.

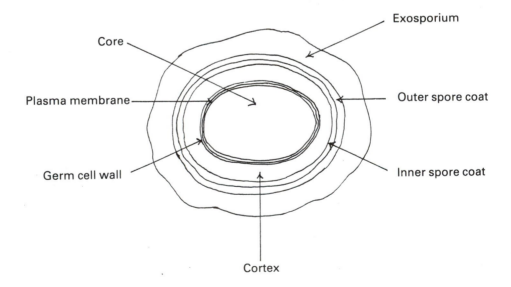

Fig. 1.15 — A diagrammatic representation of a typical bacterial spore.

Table 1.1 — Chemical composition of spore structures

Spore structure	Chemical composition	Comment
Outer spore coat (OSC)	Predominantly protein: a preponderance of disulphide (–S–S) bonds) in cystine-rich protein	Alkali-resistant, the OSC may be removed by di-sulphide bond-disrupting agents
Inner spore coat (ISC)	Predominantly protein: mainly acidic polypeptides	Alkali-sensitive, the acidic polypeptides can be dissociated to unit components by treatment with SDS[a]
Cortex	Mainly peptidoglycan	Presence of internal amide (muramic lactam: see Fig. 1.17)
Core	Protein, DNA, RNA, DPA, divalent metals	Spore-unique protein associated with DNA
		DNA in A-form

[a] Sodium dodecyl sulphate.

fundamentally from vegetative cells. The germ cell (protoplast or core) and germ cell wall are surrounded by the cortex. The cortex itself is surrounded by spore coats, the outer coat being the most dense. In some spores, e.g. *B. polymyxa*, a layer known as the exosporium exists outside the spore coats, whereas in other spores, e.g. *B. cereus*, an exosporium surrounds only one dense spore coat. Under certain conditions, spores will germinate and outgrow to produce vegetative cells, which have the typical form and composition of non-sporing bacteria.

Bacterial spores are amongst the most resistant of all microbial forms to inactivation by chemical or physical (e.g. heat, radiation) agents. This aspect will be dealt with in considerably more detail in Chapter 7, and suffice to state here that the outer coats appear to present a barrier to the intracellular penetration of many biocides, whereas the comparatively dry interior of the spore is associated with resistance to heat and radiation. Since spores develop from vegetative cells that are themselves sensitive to most chemical and physical processes, it follows that resistance will be expressed during sporulation. However, during the germination and/or outgrowth stages, the organisms may, like vegetative cells, be susceptible to inhibitors. These aspects are also considered in depth in Chapter 7. The remainder of the present section is devoted to a description of spore structure and the sequence of changes during endospore formation and germination.

3.1 Spore core (protoplast)
In terms of its macromolecular constituents, the core is a relatively normal cell and most, if not all, spore enzymes are structurally similar to the corresponding enzymes in germinated cells. However, when located inside the spore, enzymes are protected

from denaturation by heat. The core is the location of DNA and RNA and a substantial amount of low molecular weight, basic proteins which are associated with the DNA. During germination the proteins are rapidly degraded.

The spore core is a comparatively dry compartment with a low water activity (A_w value). Therefore the environment surrounding DNA in spores and vegetative cells differ. The biologically important form of DNA in vegetative cells is the B-form, in which there are ten base pairs for each turn of the double helix. However, within the comparatively dry spore, the bases tilt to produce a more compact structure, the A-form, where there are eleven base pairs per turn. Interestingly, compared with DNA in vegetative cells, the DNA in spores responds differently to ultraviolet and ionizing radiations, but DNA extracted from spores shows the same *in vitro* response as vegetative cell DNA.

Dipicolinic acid (DPA, Fig. 1.16) is a unique spore constituent the majority of

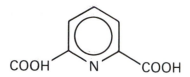

Fig. 1.16 — Chemical structure of dipicolinic acid.

which is associated in a chelated form with calcium, thereby preserving electrical neutrality. For many years DPA was considered to be a component of the spore cortex, but more recent evidence demonstrates that DPA is located in the core and not in the cortex. DPA is lost during germination and its specific role in the spore remains a subject of conjecture.

3.2   Spore membranes
During sporulation, two membranes surround the forespore. These are:

(a) the inner forespore membrane (IFSM), which eventually becomes the cytoplas-
     mic membrane of the germinating spore, and
(b) the outer forespore membrane (OFSM) which persists in the spore integuments
     i.e. outer spore layers.

Initially, the ISFM and OSFM are extensions of the mother cell membrane, but later they are differentiated both in composition and function and the specialized spore integument is formed between the two.

3.3   Spore cortex
The cortex lies between the core and the coat(s). It consists largely of peptidoglycan which is similar to, but not identical with, that found in vegetative cell forms. A dense

inner layer of the cortex known as the germ cell wall (also termed the spore cell wall, primordial cell wall, or cortical membrane) develops into the cell wall of the emergent cell when the cortex is degraded during germination and outgrowth. The germ cell wall has the chemical structure of vegetative rather than spore peptidoglycan. In disrupted spores, the cortex and usually the germ cell wall are degraded by lysozyme and the repeating unit of peptidoglycan depicted in Fig. 1.17 has been obtained from the digestion products of several *Bacillus* spp.

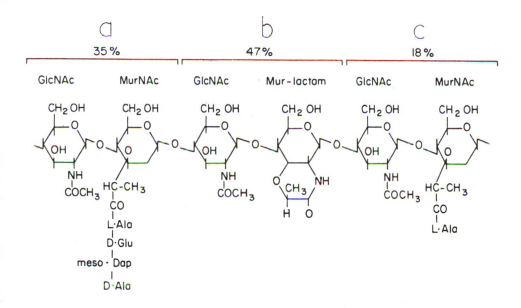

Fig. 1.17 — Chemical structure of spore peptidoglycan. Part (a) corresponds to vegetative cell peptidoglycan, (b) consists partly of muramic lactam (Mur-lactam), (c) contains an incomplete peptide. GlcNAc, *N*-acetylglucosamine; MurNAc, *N*-acetylmuramic acid.

The osmotically dehydrated nature of the mature spore is maintained by means of the electronegatively charged peptidoglycan and positively charged counterions in the cortex. Heating in the presence of acids results in protonation of the peptidoglycan with a consequent fall in its osmotic effectiveness.

3.4   Spore coats
Spore coat synthesis commences fairly early in sporulation, but completion is a much later event, occurring at the same time as the development of refractility. The spore coats play an important role in the resistance of bacterial spores to disinfectants and preservatives. They comprise a major portion of the spore, occupying about 50% of the spore volume, and consist mainly of protein and inorganic phosphorus with smaller amounts of complex carbohydrates and lipid. Proteins in the inner and outer

coats differ quite substantially. An alkali-soluble fraction resides in the inner coat and consists predominantly of acid polypeptides, whereas the outer coat contains an alkali-resistant fraction associated with the presence of cystine-rich protein. The removal of spore coats by various procedures (described in Chapter 7, section 3.5) has been used to define their role as barriers to the intracellular penetration of chemical agents.

3.5   Sporulation, germination and outgrowth

Sporulation is a complex process which commonly takes about 8 hours from the end of vegetative growth to the release of a mature spore (Table 1.2). In contrast,

Table 1.2 — Sequence of major changes accompanying endospore formation and germination[a]

Spore formation[b]	Spore germination[c]
End of vegetative growth	Addition of germinants
Chromatin filament formed	Heat resistance lost
Spore protease excreted	
Forespore septum formed	Calcium and DPA excreted
Forespore protoplast engulfed	Temporary rise in resistance to
Heat resistant catalase formed	ultraviolet irradiation
Peptidoglycan cortex synthesized	Refractility loss observable by
Spore becomes refractile	contrast microscopy (see
Dipicolinic acid (DPA) synthesized	Chapter 4)
Uptake of calcium	Resistance to stains lost
Spore coats assembled	Release of fragments of hydro-
Resistance to organic solvents acquired	lysed peptidoglycan
Resistance to heat acquired	Fall in optical density of spore
Resistance to some biocides	suspensions
Mother cell lyses to release mature spore	Onset of metabolism
	Fall in ultraviolet resistance.

[a] Based on G. W. Gould (1984). In *The Revival of Injured Microbes* (eds M. H. E. Andrew and A. D. Russell). Academic Press, London.
[b] Spore formation, time-scale about 8 hours. Resistance to biocides is discussed in Chapter 7.
[c] Spore germination, time-scale about 5 minutes. Effect of biocides is discussed in Chapter 4.

germination is more rapid (Table 1.2) and is followed by an outgrowth phase in which macromolecular synthesis takes place leading to the development of a vegetative cell culture. The stages involved in sporulation and germination and their influence on the activity of biocides will be considered in detail in Chapter 7.

4. SUMMARY

This chapter has outlined the structure and metabolism of bacteria and their spores and indicated those targets that are susceptible to inhibition or destruction by antibacterial agents. It has been noted that some antibacterial agents are also inhibitory to mammalian systems and are therefore used primarily to disinfect inanimate objects. Other agents with a low level of toxicity can be used as antiseptics, while agents (i.e. antibiotics) with a high degree of selectivity towards bacteria are used systemically as chemotherapeutic agents. The material that has been presented in this chapter is intended primarily to provide a general background for the more detailed discussion of bacterial targets to be found in Chapters 2 and 3.

FURTHER READING

General works on bacterial structure and metabolism

Books

Hammond, S. M., Lambert, P. A. & Rycroft, A. N. (1984). *The Bacterial Cell Surface*. Croom Helm, London and Sydney.

Hancock, I. & Poxton, I. (1988). *Bacterial Cell Surface Techniques*. John Wiley & Sons, London.

Ingraham, J. L., Maaloe, O. & Neidhardt, F. C. (1983). *Growth of the Bacterial Cell*. Sinauer Associates Inc., Sunderland, USA.

Mandelstam, J., McQuillen, K. & Dawes, I. (1982). *Biochemistry of Bacterial Growth*. Third edition. Blackwell Scientific Publications, Oxford.

Rogers, H. J. (1983). *Bacterial Cell Structure. Aspects of Microbiology*, Volume 6. Van Nostrand Reinhold, Wokingham.

Schlegel, H. G. (1986). *General Microbiology*. Sixth edition. Cambridge University Press.

Review articles

Hancock, R. E. W. (1987). Role of porins in outer membrane permeability. *Journal of Bacteriology* **169**: 929–933.

Lambert, P. A. (1988). Enterobacteriaceae: composition, structure and function of the cell envelope. Symposium Supplement to the *Journal of Applied Bacteriology* **65**: 21S–34S.

McMacken, R., Silver, L. & Georgopoulos, C. (1987). DNA replication. In *Escherichia coli* and *Salmonella typhimurium, Cellular and Molecular Biology, Volume* 1 (ed. F. C. Neidhardt) pp. 564–612. American Society for Microbiology, Washington.

General works on the nature of spores

Books

Dring, G. J., Ellar, D. J. & Gould, G. W. (1985). *Fundamental and Applied Aspects of Bacterial Spores*. Academic Press, London.

Hurst, A. & Gould, G. W. (1984). *The Bacterial Spore*. Second edition. Academic Press, London.

Review articles

Mandelstam, J. (1976). Bacterial sporulation: a problem in the biochemistry and genetics of a primitive developmental system. *Proceedings of the Royal Society* **193B**: 89.

Warth, A. D. (1978). Molecular structure of the bacterial endospore. *Advances in Microbial Physiology* **17**: 1–38.

General works on antibacterial compounds and their action

Books

Franklin, T. J. & Snow, G. A. (1989). *Biochemistry of Antimicrobial Action*. Fourth edition. Chapman & Hall, London.

Gale, E. F., Cundliffe, E., Reynolds, P. E., Richmond, M. H. & Waring, M. J. (1981). *The Molecular Basis of Antibiotic Action*. John Wiley & Sons, London.

Greenwood, D. (1989). *Antimicrobial Chemotherapy*. Second edition. Ballière Tindall, London.

Greenwood, D. & O'Grady, F. (1985). *The Scientific Basis of Antimicrobial Chemotherapy*. Symposium 38 of the Society for General Microbiology, Cambridge University Press.

Hugo, W. B. & Russell, A. D. (1987). *Pharmaceutical Microbiology*. Fourth edition. Blackwell Scientific Publications, Oxford.

Lorian, V. (1986). *Antibiotics in Laboratory Medicine*. Second edition. Williams & Wilkins, Baltimore.

Russell, A. D. (1982). *The Destruction of Bacterial Spores*. Academic Press, London.

Russell, A. D., Hugo, W. B. & Ayliffe, G. A. J. (1982). *Principles and Practice of Disinfection, Preservation and Sterilization*. Blackwell Scientific Publications, Oxford.

2

Mode of action of antibiotics and their uptake into bacteria

1. INTRODUCTION

In the previous chapter the modes of action of antibacterial antibiotics were outlined. In this chapter the molecular basis of their action and the mechanisms by which the drug molecules reach their intracellular target sites are dealt with more extensively.

It is convenient to consider antibiotics in groups as inhibitors respectively of: (a) nucleic acid synthesis, (b) protein synthesis, (c) peptidoglycan synthesis, (d) membrane integrity.

2. INHIBITORS OF NUCLEIC ACID SYNTHESIS

2.1 Introduction

The growth and division of bacterial cells depends, amongst other factors, upon DNA and RNA syntheses. Antibiotics that interfere with these syntheses fall into three main categories:

(a) Compounds that interrupt nucleotide metabolism, usually by interference with nucleotide synthesis or nucleotide interconversion.
(b) Compounds that interfere with the role of DNA as a template in replication and transcription, either by reacting with it directly to form a complex, or by causing structural alterations such as strand breakage or removal of bases.
(c) Agents which directly inhibit enzymic processes in nucleic acid synthesis.

Although there are many antibiotics capable of inhibiting bacterial nucleic acid synthesis by the three mechanisms described, relatively few of the inhibitors are used clinically as antibacterial agents because most of them do not distinguish between nucleic acid synthesis conducted by the host and that by the pathogen. However, even though some of these antibiotics may not be appropriate for the treatment of infectious diseases they can be used as anticancer drugs. Since anticancer drugs fall outside the scope of this book, attention will be focused only upon the relatively few inhibitors that have sufficient selectivity of action ('selective toxicity') to be used for antibacterial chemotherapy.

2.2   Compounds that interrupt nucleotide metabolism
2.2.1   Introduction

Antibiotics that interfere with the biosynthesis of tetrahydrofolic acid (THFA) are powerful indirect inhibitors of nucleotide biosynthesis because THFA is required as a donor of one-carbon units at several stages in purine and pyrimidine synthesis. Synthesis of THFA in bacteria proceeds as shown in Fig. 2.1 and its production is subject to inhibition by two groups of compound, the sulphonamides (e.g. sulphamethoxazole, Sx) and the 2,4-diaminopyrimidines (e.g. trimethoprim, Tp).

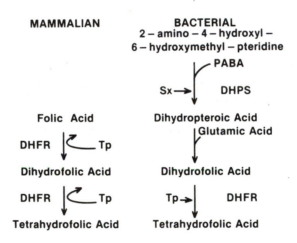

Fig. 2.1 — The tetrahydrofolic acid biosynthetic pathway in mammals and bacteria. PABA, *p*-aminobenzoic acid; DHPS, Dihydropteroate synthase; DHFR, Dihydrofolate reductase; Sx→, Sulphamethoxazole inhibits; Tp→, Trimethoprim inhibits, Tp↺, Trimethoprim does not inhibit. (Reproduced, with permission, from Smith & Amyes (1984), *British Medical Bulletin* **40**, 42–46.)

2.2.2   Sulphonamides

Sulphamethoxazole (Sx) and other sulphonamides (Fig. 2.2) are structural analogues of *p*(4)-aminobenzoic acid (PABA) (Fig. 2.2) acting as alternative substrates that bind more tightly to dihydropreroate synthase (DHPS) than PABA itself. This results in the formation of inactive folate-like analogues. As noted in Chapter 1, DHPS is absent from mammalian cells (see also Fig. 2.1) thereby explaining the selective activity of sulphonamides towards bacteria.

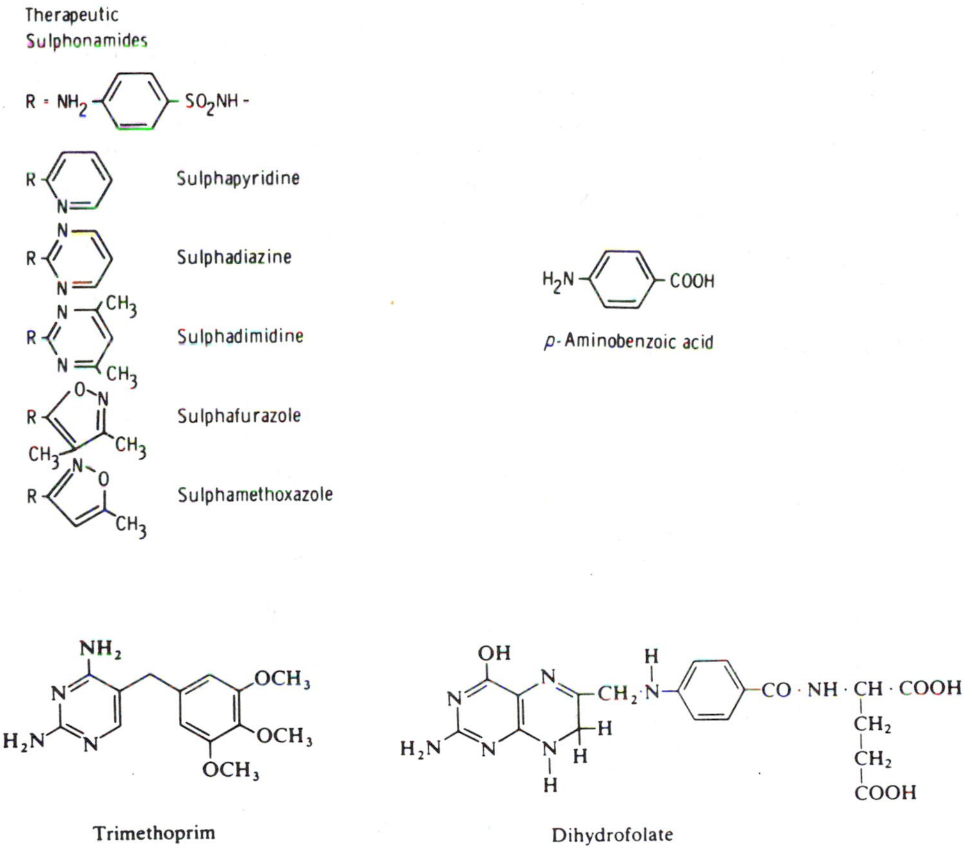

Therapeutic
Sulphonamides

R = NH₂ ⟨benzene ring⟩ SO₂NH –

R ⟨pyridine⟩   Sulphapyridine

R ⟨pyrimidine⟩   Sulphadiazine

R ⟨pyrimidine with CH₃⟩   Sulphadimidine

R ⟨isoxazole with CH₃, CH₃⟩   Sulphafurazole

R ⟨isoxazole with CH₃⟩   Sulphamethoxazole

H₂N ⟨benzene ring⟩ COOH

p-Aminobenzoic acid

Trimethoprim

Dihydrofolate

Fig. 2.2 — Structure of sulphonamide antibiotics, trimethoprim (a 2,4-diamino-pyrimidine antibiotic) and the naturally occurring molecules *p*-aminobenzoic acid and dihydrofolate.

2.2.3   2,4-diaminopyrimidines

The second group of compounds that inhibit synthesis of bacterial THFA are the 2,4-diaminopyrimidines, e.g. trimethoprim (Tp) (Fig. 2.2) and tetroxoprim which competitively inhibit bacterial dihydrofolate reductase (DHFR) (Fig. 2.1). Although mammalian cells possess DHFR enzymes, these drugs are highly selective towards the bacterial enzymes, e.g. Tp and tetroxoprim are respectively 80 000 and 50 000 times more active against *E. coli* DHFR than against mammalian DHFR.

2.2.4   Sulphonamide–2,4-diaminopyrimidine combinations

Since sulphonamides and 2,4-diaminopyrimidines inhibit sequential stages in THFA synthesis it was initially believed that administration of a combination of appropriate inhibitors (e.g. Sx plus Tp, the combination known as cotrimoxazole) would offer therapeutic advantages over the single agents, through double blockade of the folate pathway (Fig. 2.1). However, this concept has not been entirely borne out in practice. Thus, although some laboratory studies demonstrate synergy between the two components when each is present at sublethal concentrations, other *in vitro* experiments have failed to detect synergy, especially when the concentration of Tp alone is inhibitory. Synergy therefore depends upon exposure of bacteria to an optimal ratio of Sx:Tp, a situation apparently rarely achieved in the body due to differences in the pharmacokinetic properties of the two compounds. Other studies also support the view that laboratory synergy is irrelevant *in vivo* and the continued use of sulphonamide–2,4-diaminopyrimidine combinations is now being seriously challenged.

2.3   Compounds that interfere with DNA template functions
A variety of antibiotics interfere with DNA template functions, but they do not have sufficient selective toxicity to be considered as therapeutic antibacterial agents.

2.4   Agents that inhibit enzymic processes in nucleic acid synthesis
2.4.1   Inhibitors of RNA polymerase

The rifamycins comprise a group of closely related antibiotics of which rifampicin (Fig. 2.3), a semi-synthetic compound, is the most widely-known member of the group. Rifampicin binds to and specifically inhibits bacterial DNA-dependent RNA

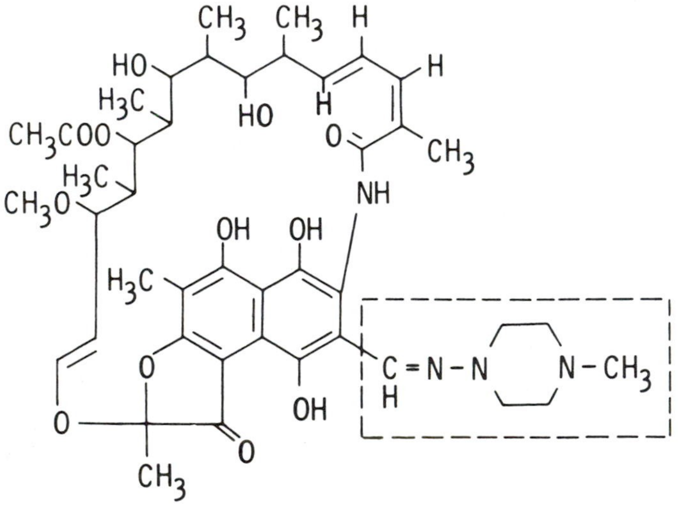

Fig. 2.3 — Structure of rifampicin. This antibiotic is a semi-synthetic member of the rifamycin group; the synthetic side chain is enclosed by the dotted line.

polymerase, by inhibiting the initiation process. If added after initiation of polymerization it is without effect. Rifampicin has no effect on nuclear or mitochondrial DNA-dependent RNA polymerases from mammalian cells. These properties explain its selective action for bacteria.

RNA polymerases catalyse the initiation and elongation of RNA molecules using DNA as a template. The reaction performed by the enzyme is:

$$(RNA)_n \text{ residues} + \text{ribonucleoside triphosphate}$$

$$\Updownarrow$$

$$(RNA)_{n+1} \text{ residue} + PPi$$

The RNA polymerase from *E. coli* consists of two major components, the CORE (containing 4 polypeptide chains: 2α, β, and β') which associates with another subunit, the SIGMA factor. The complete (holo)enzyme participates in selection of promoter sites on the DNA template and in initiation of RNA synthesis, whereas the core participates in elongation. Rifampicin binds to the β subunit and in so doing interferes with the ability of the holoenzyme to initiate RNA synthesis. Binding of RNA polymerase to the DNA template is not blocked and inhibition probably results from interference with the formation of the first phosphodiester bond in the RNA chain.

2.4.2   Inhibitors of DNA gyrase
2.4.2.1   Introduction
The principles of DNA replication were established by Watson and Crick in the 1950s, i.e. at the replication point the double-stranded DNA molecule separates and nucleotides pair with their complementary bases on the two exposed single strands and are then linked by polymerization. Although subsequent studies have confirmed that DNA replication does indeed proceed in this manner, they have revealed that the process is biochemically complex. For instance, in *E. coli* at least 18 different gene products have been identified that participate directly in the replication of the bacterial chromosome. Some of these are indicated in Fig. 2.4.

One of the enzymes involved in bacterial DNA replication, DNA gyrase (DNA topisomerase II) is of particular interest in the context of the action of quinolone antibiotics (Section 2.4.2.2). Replication of the bacterial chromosome, a circular duplex DNA molecule, requires separation of the two highly intertwined parental strands from one another. However, separation of strands wound in a helix generates loops, termed positive supercoiled twists, in the single strands. Unless prevented, positive superhelicity would increase until the rising torsional strain prevented further unwinding of parental DNA at the replication fork. DNA gyrase relaxes positively supercoiled DNA by periodically breaking a phosphodiester bond in one of the strands of the double helix, then introducing negative supercoils and finally resealing the nick. Fig. 2.4 presents a diagrammatic representation of bacterial DNA strand separation and supercoil relaxation at the replication fork.

E. coli DNA gyrase is composed of four subunits: two gyrase A subunits (each of molecular weight 97 000) and two gyrase B subunits (each of molecular weight 90 000). The A and B subunits are the products of the *gyr*A and *gyr*B genes located at 48 min and 83 min respectively on the *E. coli* chromosome. The gyrase A subunits mediate the transient breakage-rejoining reactions mediated by DNA gyrase while the B subunits are responsible for introduction of negative supercoils into duplex DNA which has been nicked by the action of the A subunits. The DNA dependent

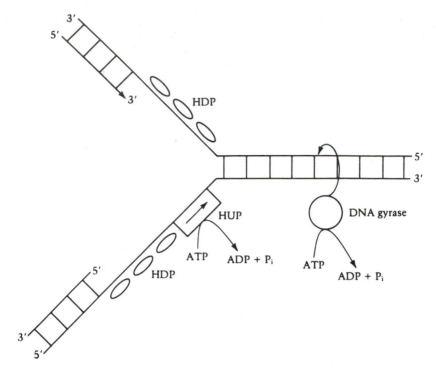

Fig. 2.4 — Schematic representation of the process of strand separation at the replication fork. The action of DNA gyrase in allowing free rotation within the double helix is illustrated by the circular arrow. A helix-unwinding protein (HUP) is shown at the point of separation; its direction of movement is indicated by the arrow. Molecules of helix-destabilizing proteins (HDP) are shown attached to the single-stranded regions. As indicated, the action of DNA gyrase and unwinding proteins involve hydrolysis of ATP. (Reproduced, with permission, from Ingraham *et al.* (1983); for reference see Further Reading, Chapter 1.)

ATPase activity of DNA gyrase resides in the B subunits. However, the individual subunits alone do not demonstrate enzymic activity and must therefore be part of the complete tetramer to function properly. Recent work suggests that in the absence of ATP a single turn of DNA is wrapped around DNA gyrase with DNA tails entering and leaving the complex in close proximity. Binding of ATP to DNA gyrase probably causes a conformational change in the protein and a single round of negative supercoiling occurs. Hydrolysis of ATP returns DNA gyrase to its original conformation, thereby permitting enzyme turnover. Various studies indicate that DNA gyrase is essential for replication of the bacterial chromosome.

2.4.2.2 Quinolones
Various quinolone derivatives (Fig. 2.5) inhibit bacterial DNA gyrase. Nalidixic acid, an 8-aza-4-quinolone (Fig. 2.5) was synthesized in the early 1960s and was the first 4-quinolone to be introduced to clinical practice. Since the introduction of nalidixic acid several other chemically related drugs have been developed for therapeutic use including norfloxacin, enoxacin, ofloxacin and ciprofloxacin (Fig.

2.5). Compared with nalidixic acid these new compounds often exhibit enhanced antibacterial activity towards a wider spectrum of organisms. Currently there is much interest in the therapeutic potential of the 4-quinolone agents.

The quinolones characteristically kill bacteria rapidly with as much as a thousand-fold decline in cell viability following exposure to drugs for 1–2 hours. However, the exact mechanism of killing is not known. The most immediate and striking effect on bacterial metabolism following addition of a 4-quinolone is inhibition of DNA synthesis, consistent with interference of DNA gyrase activity. Quinolones bind predominantly to the A subunits of DNA gyrase which impairs both A subunit activity and B subunit function. This damage to DNA leads to induction of the so-called 'SOS' response. Essentially this is a mechanism by which cells filament and prevent replication of damaged DNA to potential daughter cells until non-replicative DNA repair enzymes have had the opportunity to repair the DNA damage. Induction of the DNA repair system in the presence of continued gyrase interference may well be lethal to the cell.

The basis of the selective activity of 4-quinolones against bacteria has been examined. Mammalian cells possess a topoisomerase II that in some respects resembles bacterial gyrase. However, the mammalian enzyme differs in structure from the bacterial enzyme being composed of two subunits (rather than four) each of molecular weight 172 000. The structural differences between the bacterial and mammalian topoisomerase II enzymes are therefore substantial and provide a satisfactory explanation for the selective action of the 4-quinolones.

3.   INHIBITORS OF PROTEIN SYNTHESIS

3.1   Introduction

Protein synthesis is inhibited by several antibiotics, some of which are selectively toxic towards bacteria. Although these antibiotics have obvious chemotherapeutic application, it should be noted that some inhibitors of protein synthesis are selectively toxic for eukaryotes rather than bacteria. The latter are not considered here. As mentioned in Chapter 1, the selectivity of clinically useful inhibitors of bacterial protein synthesis arises principally from their ability to bind selectively to bacterial rather than mammalian ribosomes. In contrast to earlier views, a consensus is now emerging that ribosomal RNA is the primary target for a number of antibacterial drugs, rather than ribosomal protein.

Table 2.1 provides a summary of the mode of action of antibiotics that inhibit bacterial protein synthesis. However, in order to understand how antibiotics are inhibitory, it is necessary to consider ribosomal structure and the nature of protein synthesis in more detail than presented in Chapter 1.

3.2   Structure of bacterial ribosomes

As noted in Chapter 1, *E. coli* 30S ribosomal subunits contain one molecule of 16S RNA and 21 proteins (designated S1, S2 etc.) whereas 50S subunits contain one molecule each of 5S RNA and 23S RNA together with 32 proteins (designated L1, L2, etc.). Fig. 2.6(a–c) shows models of the *E. coli* ribosomal subunits and the 70S ribosome which have been constructed from electron microscopic studies. The

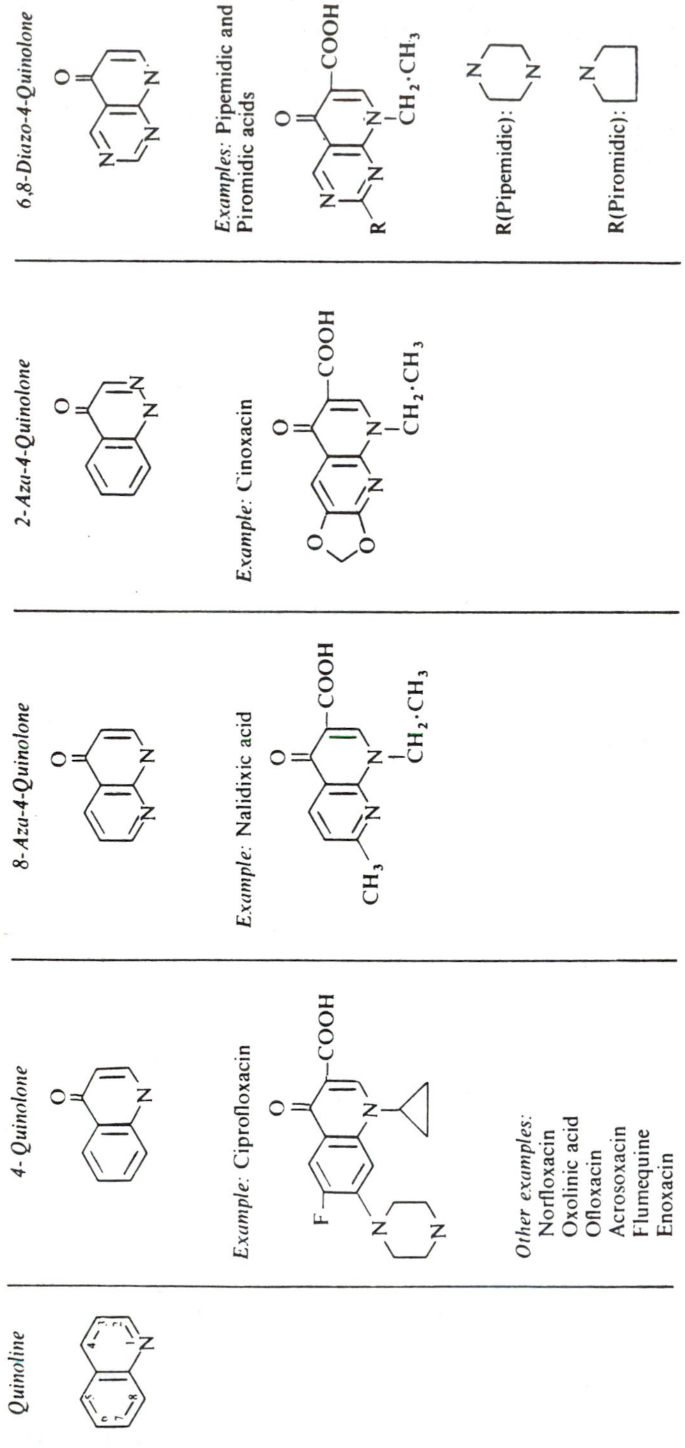

Fig. 2.5 — Quinoline and antibacterial 4-quinolones.

Table 2.1 — Antibiotic inhibitors of protein synthesis

Antibiotic	Mechanism of action
Mupirocin	Inhibits isoleucyl-tRNA synthetase
Streptomycin	Inhibits initiation and causes misreading of mRNA by binding to 30S ribosomal subunit
Neomycins Kanamycins Gentamicins Amikacin Tobramycin Spectinomycin	Inhibit translocation by binding to 30S ribosomal subunit
Chloramphenicol	Inhibits peptidyl transferase activity of 50S ribosomal subunit
Fusidic acid	Inhibits translocation by forming stable complex with EF-G, GDP and the ribosome
Lincomycin	Inhibits peptidyl transferase activity of 50S ribosomal subunit
Macrolides	Stimulate dissociation of peptidyl-tRNA from ribosomes by binding to 50S ribosomal subunit
Streptogramin A	Blocks peptide bond formation by distorting ribosomal A site
Streptogramin B	Blocks translocation of growing polypeptide from the A site to the P site
Tetracyclines	Bind to 30S ribosomal subunit and inhibit binding of aminoacyl-tRNAs

groove formed between the two subunits in the 70S ribosome (Fig. 2.6c) probably accommodates the mRNA. Other important functional sites on the 70S ribosome are the aminoacyl tRNA and peptidyl tRNA binding sites, also referred to respectively as the A and P sites.

Recently, considerable advances have been made in understanding the assembly and molecular organization of bacterial ribosomes. This has resulted principally from the ability to reconstitute ribosomal subunits *in vitro* from mixtures of the appropriate ribosomal RNA and protein molecules. Fig. 2.7 shows an assembly map for the *E. coli* 30S ribosomal proteins from which it can be seen that proteins S4, S8, S15 and S17 bind directly to 16S RNA and provide a matrix for the assembly of other proteins into the particle. Thus cooperative binding of proteins to the ribosomal particle is an essential feature of assembly because binding of certain proteins depends on prior binding or a simultaneous binding of other proteins. An assembly map for *E. coli* 50S ribosomal proteins has also been determined and those proteins that probably interact initially with 23S and 5S RNA have been identified. However it is likely that, in addition to the initial binding proteins, the majority of proteins in both subunits also interact with ribosomal RNA in the finished particles.

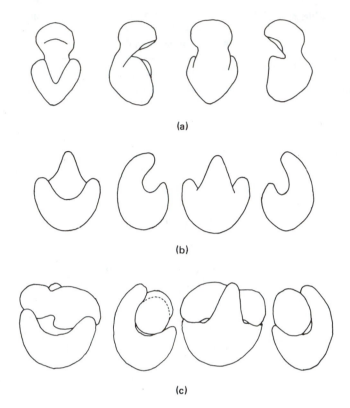

Fig. 2.6 — Models of the *E. coli* 30S ribosomal subunit (a), 50S ribosomal subunit (b), and 70S ribosome with the 30S subunit lying on the 50S subunit (c). The four views are derived by successive rotation through an angle of 90°. (Reproduced, with permission, from Chopra (1985).)

At present primary structures are known for all three ribosomal RNA molecules and reliable secondary structure models have been deduced (e.g. Fig. 2.8 shows a model of 16S ribosomal RNA secondary structure). The nature of tertiary folding in these molecules is also beginning to emerge together with identification (at least at the secondary structure level) of some regions that interact with ribosomal proteins. For instance it is now known that proteins S8 and S15 bind to the central domain of 16S RNA at positions 583–610/623–653 and 654–672/733–756 (Figs 2.8, 2.9). The general regions in 16S RNA to which other S proteins bind are also known (Fig. 2.9), but, to date, the precise binding sites have only been elucidated for S8 and S15.

3.3   Stages in protein synthesis
3.3.1   *Synthesis of aminoacyl-tRNAs*

Prior to incorporation into polypeptides, amino acids are attached to specific transfer RNA (tRNA) molecules. Each amino acid is converted by a specific aminoacyl-tRNA synthetase to an aminoacyladenylate-enzyme complex which then interacts

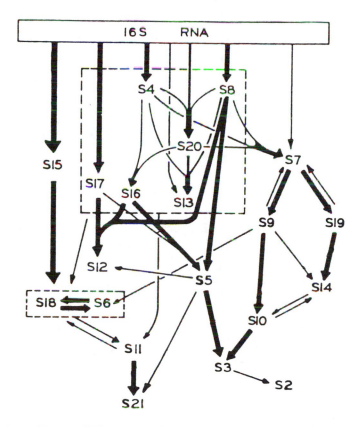

Fig. 2.7 — Assembly map of 30S r-proteins. Arrows between proteins indicate facilitating effect of one protein on the binding of another; a thick arrow indicates a major facilitating effect. The thick arrows from 16S RNA to S4, S8, S15 and S17 indicate that each of these proteins binds directly to 16S RNA. S7 and S20 also bind directly to 16S RNA, but binding is stimulated by other proteins as indicated in the map. The arrow from the large box to a small box containing S18 and S6 indicates that S8 (together with S15) stimulates binding of S18 and that S8 (together with S15 and S18) also stimulates binding of S6. Although the position of S1 is not shown, it is known that r-proteins S2, S9, S10 and S14, are required for the binding of S1. (From Noller & Nomura (1987), with modifications.)

with an amino acid-specific tRNA to form an aminoacyl-tRNA molecule. These steps can be represented as follows:

$$Enzyme_x + amino\ acid\ (aa)_x + ATP \rightleftharpoons Enzyme_x - (aa)_x\text{-}AMP + PPi$$

$$Enzyme_x - (aa)_x - AMP + tRNA_x \rightleftharpoons (aa)_x - tRNA_x + AMP + Enzyme_x$$

$$Overall:\ (aa)_x + ATP + tRNA_x \rightleftharpoons (aa)_x - tRNA_x + AMP + PPi$$

Aminoacyl-tRNA molecules are then linearly ordered by interacting with mRNA bound in the ribosome.

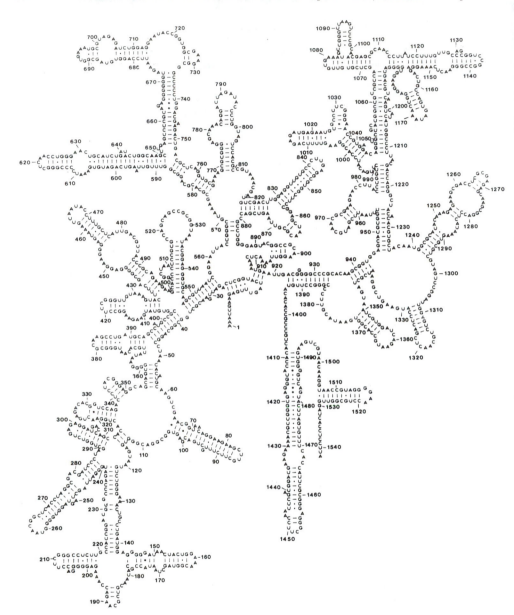

Fig. 2.8 — Secondary structure of *E. coli* 16S rRNA. (Reproduced, with permission, from Noller *et al*. (1987).)

3.3.2   Initiation of protein synthesis (Fig. 2.10, Steps I–IV)

Initiation of protein synthesis involves a series of reactions during which:

(1) The 30S ribosomal subunit binds to the region of the mRNA containing the initiation codon AUG.

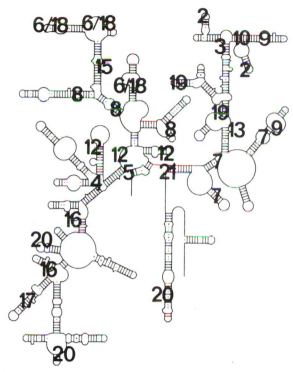

Fig. 2.9 — Location of 16S rRNA regions with which ribosomal proteins are associated. The number of each protein is centred on regions where significant protein interactions are observed. (Reproduced, with permission, from Noller *et al.* (1987).)

(2) Formylmethionyl tRNA (f-Met-tRNAfMet) is attached to the 30S-mRNA complex in response to the codon AUG. The resultant complex is called the '30S initiation complex'.

(3) The 50S ribosomal subunit is added to form 'the 70S initiation complex'.

Several initiation factors (Table 2.2), i.e. proteins playing an important role in initiation but only transiently bound to the ribosome, are involved in the above steps.

    Although the codon AUG acts as the initiation signal for translation of mRNA, the AUG codon is not itself the initiation codon recognized by ribosomes. Obviously the sequence AUG often occurs in and out of phase in a message, and the proper AUG corresponding to the beginning of the gene transcript has to be selected. Recognition involves a pyrimidine-rich sequence at the 3′ end of 16S ribosomal RNA that pairs directly with a polypurine stretch found 10–14 nucleotides upstream of the starter AUG codon. The so-called 'Shine-Dalgarno' sequences in prokaryotic mRNA comprise stretches of three to seven nucleotides which are complementary to the region HO A-U-U-C-C-U-C-C-A (5′) of the 16S RNA. In addition to the 'Shine-Dalgarno' region, nucleotides upstream from this area are probably important for the binding of mRNA to ribosomes. These nucleotides, some of which comprise

(A)   Initiation

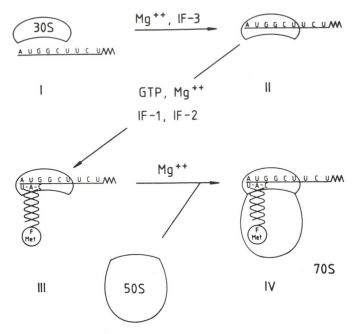

(B)   Recognition   of   internal   codons

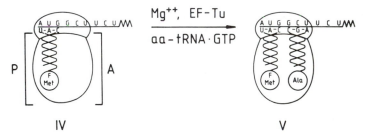

Fig. 2.10—Schematic summary of protein syntheis in *E. coli*. Details of the individual steps are described in the text and the nature of the soluble protein factors (IF-1, IF-2 etc.) in Table 2.2. *P*, peptidyl site; *A*, acceptor site. (Reproduced, with permission, from Chopra (1985).) (*cont.*)

comprise translated codons, probably stabilize the 30S-mRNA complex by interaction with ribosomal protein. In *E. coli* the proteins S1, S4, S12, S18 and S21 are particularly important in this context.

3.3.3 Recognition of internal codons (Fig. 2.10, Steps IV,V)
Upon addition of the 50S ribosomal subunit the 70S initiation complex is prepared for recognition of internal codons. The P-site is occupied by fMet-tRNAfMet and the A site is vacant. The codon present in the A-site determines the binding of cognate aminoacyl-tRNA to the ribosome. The affinity of aminoacyl-tRNA itself for the A-site is low and the aminoacyl-tRNA binding reaction involves the protein elongation

(C)   Peptide   bond   formation,   translocation

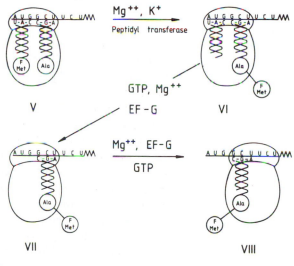

(D)   Termination

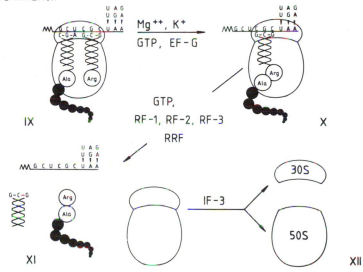

Fig. 2.10 (*cont.*) — Schematic summary of protein synthesis in *E. coli*. Details of the individual steps are described in the text and the nature of the soluble protein factors (IF-1, IF-2 etc.) in Table 2.2. *P*, peptidyl site; *A*, acceptor site. (Reproduced, with permission, from Chopra (1985).)

factor EF-Tu (Table 2.1). Aminoacyl-tRNA becomes bound to the A-site in the form of the ternary complex EF-Tu.aminoacyl-tRNA.GTP. fMet-tRNAfMet does not react with EF-Tu.GTP so that individual formylmethionine residues never enter the ribosomal A site.

Codon–anticodon interaction in the A-site is accompanied by hydrolysis of one

Table 2.2 — Soluble protein factors involved in the synthesis of *E. coli* polypeptides

Name of factor[a]	Molecular weight (daltons$\times 10^3$)	Function
IF-1	8	Promotes IF-2 and IF-3 activity
IF2 alpha	97	Hydrolyse GTP and promote fMet-tRNA
IF2 beta	78	binding to 30S subunits
IF3	21	Responsible for formation of mRNA.30S complex. Acts as anti-dissociation factor to prevent formation of 70S ribosomes
EF-Tu	43	Hydrolyses GTP and promotes aminoacyl-tRNA binding to 70S ribosomes
EF-Ts	30	Regeneration of EF-Tu.GTP complex
EF-G	77.4	Hydrolyses GTP and promotes translocation
RF-1	36 ⎫	Promote release of completed peptidyl
RF-2	38 ⎬	residues from the ribosome by
	⎭	recognizing UAA, UAG and UGA
RF-3	46	Hydrolyses GTP and stimulates RF-1 and RF-2
RRF	23.5	Ejection of mRNA and tRNA from ribosomes

[a]IF, initiation factor; EF, elongation factor; RF, release factor; RRF, ribosome release factor.

molecule of GTP for every molecule of aminoacyl-tRNA bound. This reaction results in release of EF-Tu.GDP from the ribosome. The binary complex itself cannot bind aminoacyl-tRNA, but regeneration of EF-Tu.GDP to EF-Tu.GTP is mediated by the elongation EF-Ts (Table 2.2). Thus GTP and GDP are allosteric effectors of EF-Tu. The EF-Tu.GDP complex cannot bind aminoacyl-tRNA and cannot be retained in the ribosome, whereas the EF-Tu.GTP complex binds aminoacyl-tRNA to form a ternary complex which interacts with the ribosomal A-site.

3.3.4 Peptide bond formation and translocation (Fig. 2.10, Steps V–VIII)
Following release of the EF-Tu.GDP complex from the ribosome, the formylmethionine residue (or peptidyl residue in subsequent chain elongation cycles) is cleaved from its tRNA in the P-site and transferred to the aminoacyl-tRNA in the A-site. The reaction is catalysed by peptidyltransferase which is located in the 50S subunit. The P-site is now occupied by a deacylated tRNA and the A-site contains peptidyl-tRNA that has been elongated by one aminoacyl residue. Several coordinated processes now occur known collectively as 'translocation':

(1) Deacylated tRNA is released from the P-site.
(2) The peptidyl-tRNA moves from the A- to the P-site, where it remains linked to the mRNA via codon–anticodon interaction.

(3) Movement of mRNA and ribosome with respect to each other causes a new codon to enter the A-site.

The starting point for recognition of a further internal codon is therefore reached and the sequence of events (V–VIII, Fig. 2.10) repeated.

Maximum rates of translocation depend upon elongation factor EF-G (Table 2.2) and GTP, which is converted to GDP during translocation. Translocation may occur as a result of binding of EF-G to the ribosome and hydrolysis of GTP may be needed to release EF-G for its recycling. Thus GTP may also be an allosteric effector of elongation factor EF-G.

3.3.5   Termination of protein synthesis (Fig. 2.10, Steps IX–XII)
Termination involves the arrival of termination codons (UAG, UGA or UAA) in the A-site and the release factors RF-1, RF-2 and RF-3 (Table 2.2.). RF-1 (in the presence of UAG or UAA) and RF-2 (in the presence of UGA or UAA) promote cleavage of the completed peptidyl residue from tRNA by activating peptidyl transferase. The polypeptide leaves the ribosome, eventually to become an active protein, or to become a subunit in an active protein. At this stage deacylated tRNA and mRNA are released from the 70S ribosome. This involves hydrolysis of GTP by RF-3 and the additional factor RRF (ribosome-release factor) (Table 2.2). Initiation factor IF3 (Table 2.2) prevents association of subunits to form 70S ribosomes, thus permitting the start of another initiation cycle.

3.4   Antibiotic inhibitors of protein synthesis and their mechanisms of action
3.4.1   Mupirocin

Mupirocin (Fig. 2.11) is a recently discovered antibiotic structurally unrelated to any of the other recognized antibiotic groups. It consists of a short fatty acid side chain linked to a larger molecule, monic acid, the tail-end of which mimics the amino acid iso-leucine (Fig. 2.11). Mupirocin, which is bacteriostatic, competitively inhibits isoleucyl transfer-RNA synthetase (Fig. 2.11) and thus, by preventing incorporation of iso-leucine into growing polypeptide chains, arrests protein synthesis. Although mupirocin appears to be non-toxic in animals and man, its use is restricted to topical applications, e.g. for treatment of skin infections. This situation arises because the antibiotic is metabolized to the inactive monic acid and its fatty acyl side chain in the body. Mupirocin is inactive against Gram-negative bacteria (Section 4.3.2).

3.4.2   Aminoglycoside-aminocyclitol group
3.4.2.1   Introduction

The aminoglycoside-aminocylitol (AGAC) group of antibiotics includes a large number of clinically useful drugs. These antibiotics can be divided into three groups on the basis of their structures:

(1) 4,5-disubstituted deoxystreptamines (e.g. neomycin B; Fig. 2.12),
(2) 4,6-disubstituted deoxystreptamines (e.g. kanamycin A, amikacin, tobramycin, gentamicins; Fig. 2.12),
(3) others (e.g. streptomycin, spectinomycin; Fig. 2.12).

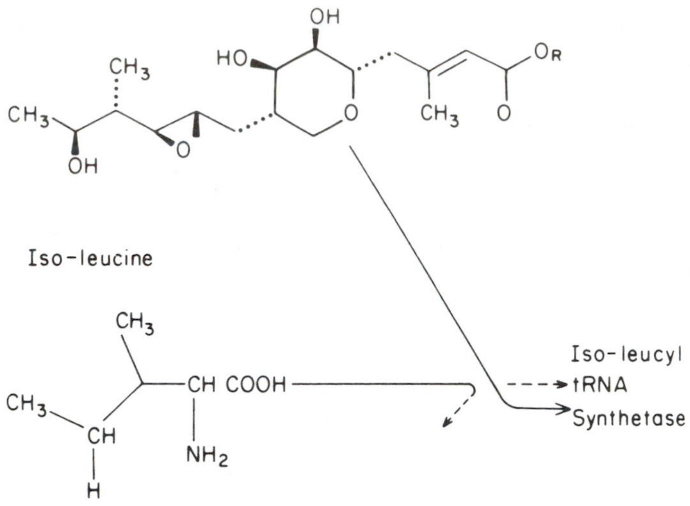

Fig. 2.11 — Structure and mode of action of mupirocin. R=(CH₂)₈ COOH: mupirocin (pseudomonic acid); R=H: monic acid. (Reproduced, with permission, from Casewell & Hill (1985).)

3.4.2.2 *Streptomycin*

Streptomycin, a bactericidal antibiotic, binds irreversibly to a single site in the bacterial 30S ribosomal subunit. This site (Fig. 2.13) is located close to the interface with the 50S particle in the intact 70S ribosome. Binding of streptomycin to free 30S ribosomal subunits about to initiate protein synthesis blocks their further progress. The initiation complexes which form with these ribosomes are non-productive. Seemingly amino acyl-tRNA cannot bind to the distorted acceptor site and f-Met-tRNAfMet is released. Binding of streptomycin to ribosomes already engaged in protein synthesis slows the chain elongation process and can cause misreading of the genetic code to produce misread or nonsense proteins. Misreading results from indirect distortion of 16S ribosomal RNA at a critical point in its structure (the so-called '530 loop' containing bases 517–534; Figs. 2.8 and 2.13). However, misreading effects are not thought to contribute directly to the bactericidal action of the drug and the killing action results from the irreversible block on protein synthesis mediated at the level of protein initiation.

Protein S12 of the 30S ribosomal subunit influences the binding of streptomycin to ribosomes, but the anti-initiation and misreading activities of streptomycin relate to perturbation of ribosomal RNA structure following binding of the antibiotic to its single site in the 30S ribosomal subunit. The streptomycin binding site (Fig. 2.13) includes adenosine residues 913–915 of the 16S RNA, a region to which protein S12 also binds (Fig. 2.9). Streptomycin therefore binds to ribosomal RNA, but its affinity for the site in 16S RNA is influenced by protein S12.

3.4.2.3 *Neomycins, gentamicins, kanamycins, amikacin and tobramycin*

In contrast to streptomycin, these bactericidal aminoglycosides bind to bacterial ribosomes at multiple sites. Binding to the 30S subunit is slightly tighter than binding

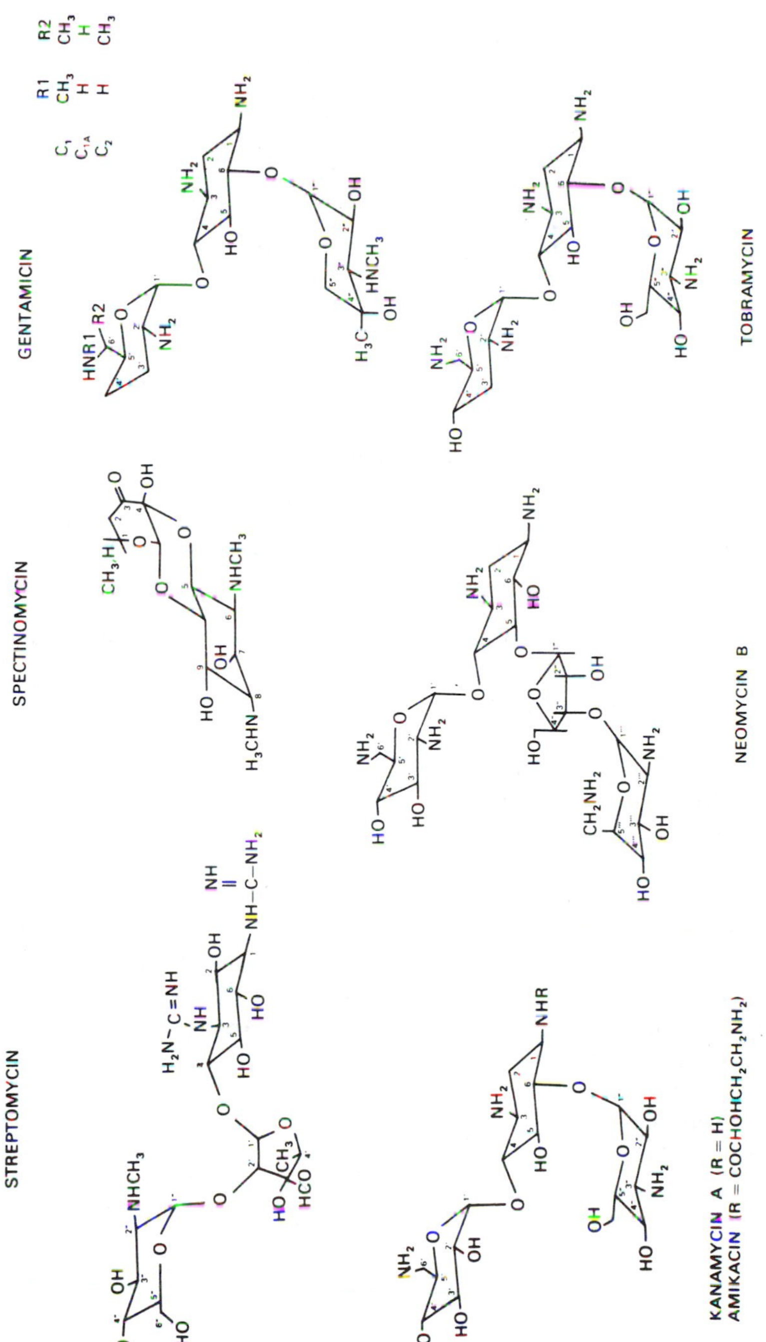

Fig. 2.12 — Structure of aminoglycoside-aminocyclitol (AGAC) antibiotics.

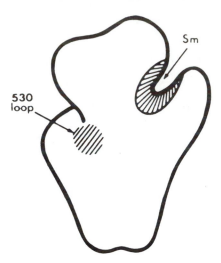

Fig. 2.13 — Site of streptomycin binding in the *E. coli* 30S ribosomal subunit. Binding of the antibiotic causes distortion of ribosomal RNA in the so-called '530' loop region (see text for further details). (Reproduced, with permission, from Melancon *et al.* (1988), *Nucleic Acids Research* **16**, p. 9637.)

to the 50S subunit, but none of these antibiotics utilize the streptomycin-binding site on the 30S subunit. Again, in contrast to streptomycin, these aminoglycosides inhibit translocation by preventing the binding of EF-G to the ribosome. The inhibitory activity of the antibiotics probably depends upon direct binding to ribosomal RNA and bases at positions 1408 and 1494 in 16S RNA (Fig. 2.8) have been implicated as binding sites for neomycins, gentamicins and kanamycin.

3.4.2.4   *Spectinomycin*
This aminocyclitol antibiotic is bacteriostatic and interacts reversibly with the 30S ribosomal subunit. Spectinomycin inhibits translocation possibly by preventing the relative movement between ribosomes and mRNA that occurs at this stage in polypeptide elongation. As with other AGAC antibiotics the inhibitory activity of spectinomycin seems to be related to binding to 16S ribosomal RNA, in particular to bases at positions 1063 and 1064 (Fig. 2.8).

3.4.3   Chloramphenicol
Chloramphenicol (Fig. 2.14) is a broad-spectrum bacteriostatic agent that binds to 70S (bacterial) ribosomes but not the 80S type. The antibiotic prevents peptide bond formation by inhibiting the peptidyl transferase reaction. Recent work suggests that peptidyl transferase activity is directly mediated by 23S ribosomal RNA. Hence the inhibitory activity of chloramphenicol probably relates to direct binding to ribosomal RNA.

3.4.4   Fusidic acid
Fusidic acid is a narrow-spectrum steroidal antibiotic (Fig. 2.15) that inhibits protein synthesis in prokaryotic and eukaryotic subcellular systems. The antibiotic forms a

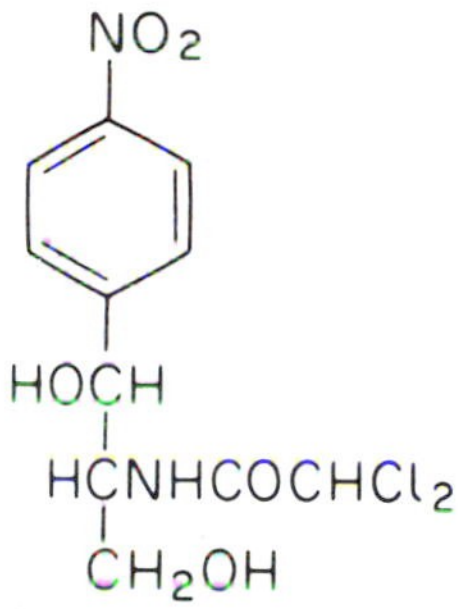

$$NO_2$$

HOCH

HCNHCOCHCl$_2$

CH$_2$OH

Fig. 2.14 — Structure of chloramphenicol.

stable complex with EF-G (or EF-2 in eukaryotes), GDP and the ribosome which is unable to release EFG for a further round of translocation. The lack of toxicity of fusidic acid against mammalian cells is probably explained by its poor accumulation in cells of this type.

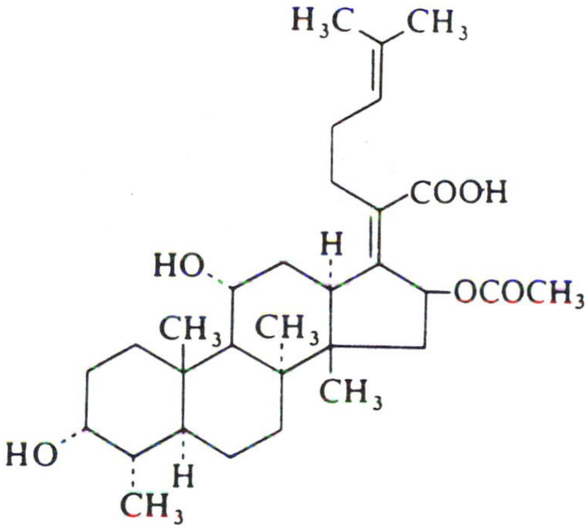

H$_3$C   CH$_3$

COOH

H

HO

CH$_3$ CH$_3$

-OCOCH$_3$

CH$_3$

HO

H

CH$_3$

Fig. 2.15 — Structure of fusidic acid.

3.4.5 Lincosamides
Lincomycin and its chlorinated derivative clindamycin (Fig. 2.16) are members of the lincosamide group of antibiotics. They inhibit the peptidyl transferase function of the bacterial 50S ribosomal subunit.

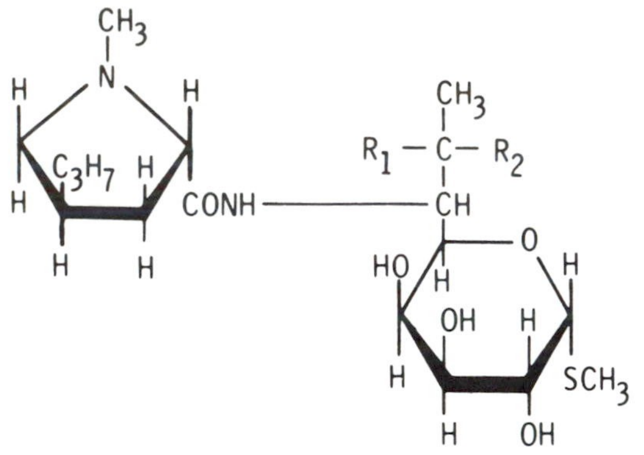

Fig. 2.16 — Structure of lincomycin (R_1=OH, R_2=H) and clindamycin (R_1=H, R_2=Cl).

3.4.6 Macrolides

Macrolide antibiotics contain a large lactone ring characterized by few double bonds and no nitrogen atoms. The ring is substituted with one or more sugar residues, some of which may be amino sugars. The structures of the more important macrolides are shown in Fig. 2.17.

These, predominantly bacteriostatic, antibiotics display selective toxicity towards bacteria by binding to 50S ribosomal subunits. The mode of action of macrolides has been a matter of controversy for some time but a consensus is now emerging that they act primarily by stimulating the dissociation of peptidyl-tRNA from ribosomes during translocation. Direct binding of macrolides to 23S ribosomal RNA has been demonstrated, involving sites in the 2058–2062 region of the molecule. However, although the actual macrolide target may be located in 23S RNA, the binding of macrolides to this site is influenced by certain L proteins, particularly L4.

3.4.7 Streptogramins

These antibiotics can be classified into two major groups, A and B. Antibiotics of the A group (e.g. streptogramin A; Fig. 2.18) possess a large non-peptide ring which is polyunsaturated. Members of the B group (e.g. streptogramin B; Fig. 2.18) are cyclic hexadepsipeptides containing unusual amino acids. Generally these antibiotics are bacteriostatic and inhibit protein synthesis directed by 70S ribosomes. Antibiotics of group A distort the ribosomal A site in such a way that both the binding of aminoacyl-tRNA and the peptidyl transferase reaction are inhibited. It has been postulated that antibiotics in group B block translocation of the growing polypeptide chain from the A site to the P site (although EF-G dependent GTPase activity is unaffected).

Group A and B antibiotics exhibit a marked synergism towards Gram-positive bacteria when both drugs are present in a mixture. This appears to result from an increased affinity of group A antibiotics for the ribosome in the presence of group B antibiotics.

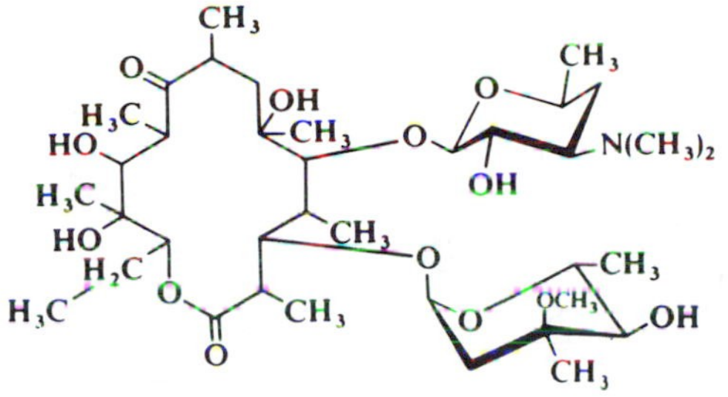

Erythromycin A

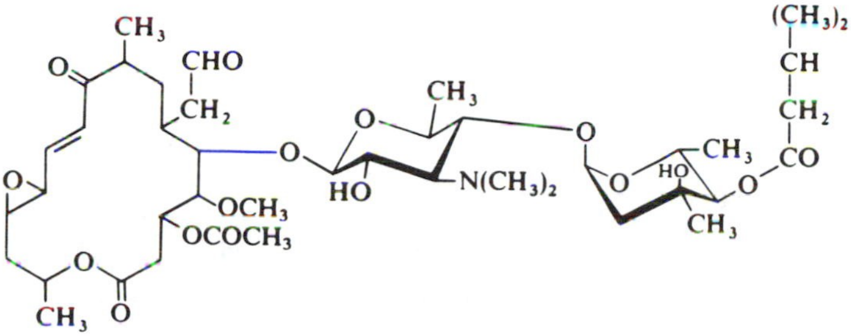

Carbomycin A

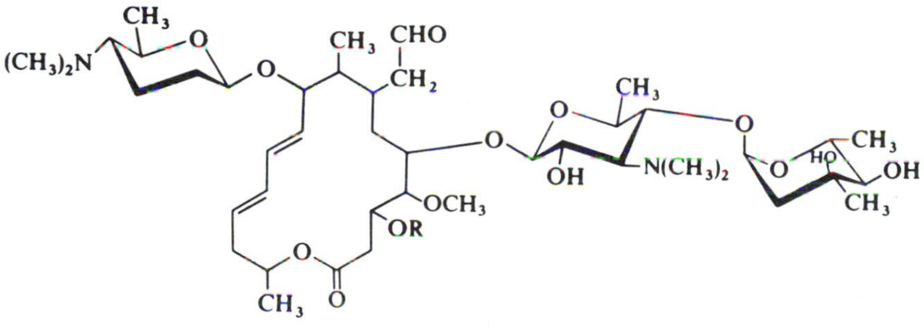

Spiramycin I   R = H
           II   R = COCH₃
           III   R = COCH₂CH₃

Fig. 2.17 — Structure of various macrolide antibiotics.

3.4.8 *Tetracyclines*

The tetracyclines (Fig. 2.19) comprise a group of clinically useful broad-spectrum bacteriostatic antibiotics that inhibit protein synthesis. These drugs prevent protein synthesis on both 70S and 80S ribosomes, although 70S ribosomes are more

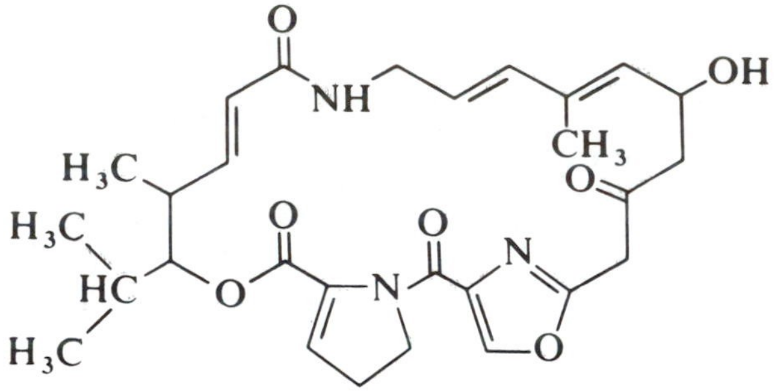

Streptogramin A

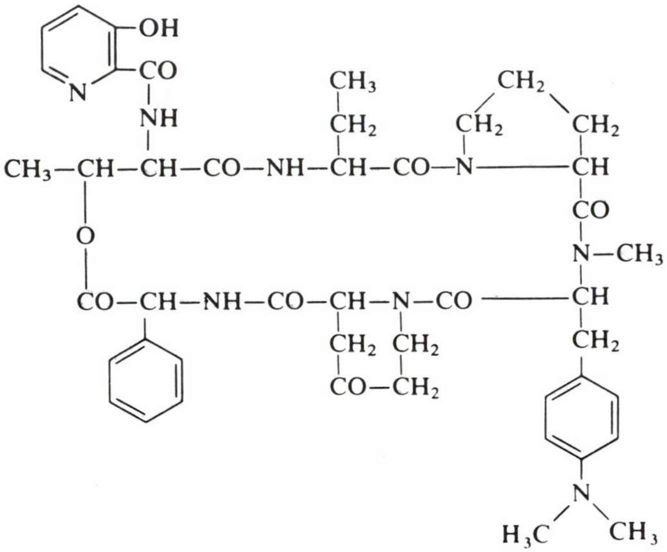

Streptogramin B

Fig. 2.18 — Structure of streptogramin A and B.

sensitive. Another factor explaining the selective activity of these antibiotics against bacteria arises from their concentration within bacterial but not mammalian cells.

Tetracyclines inhibit the binding of aminoacyl-tRNA to the ribosomal acceptor (A) site by disruption of codon–anticodon interaction between tRNA and mRNA. This inhibitory effect results from the binding of tetracycline to a single site in the 30S ribosomal subunit. This binding site involves a region of 16S ribosomal RNA which contains base A892. However, the anticodon of bound aminoacyl-tRNA is spatially proximal to the 16S RNA region containing base number 1400. This suggests that the tertiary folding of 16S ribosomal RNA brings the 892 and 1400 regions into close

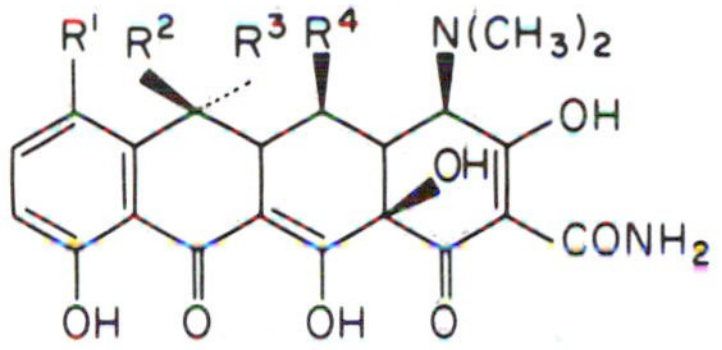

Antibiotic	R^1	R^2	R^3	R^4
Tetracycline	H	CH_3	OH	H
Oxytetracycline	H	CH_3	OH	OH
Chlortetracycline	Cl	CH_3	OH	H
Demethylchlortetracycline	Cl	H	OH	H
Methacycline	H	$=CH_2$		OH
Doxycycline	H	CH_3	H	OH
Minocycline	$-N(CH_3)_2$	H	H	H

Fig. 2.19 — Structure of tetracycline and some of its analogues.

proximity and that tetracyclines block aminoacyl-tRNA binding by interference with the folding of the 892–1400 region after binding of antibiotic to base number 892. Tetracycline also appears to interact with protein S7 during binding to 16S ribosomal RNA in the 30S particle. However, this protein does not associate with either the 892 or 1400 base regions (Fig. 2.9). Possibly the binding of tetracycline to base number 892 in 16S RNA leads to gross distortion of ribosome structure so that protein S7 is presented to the 892–1400 RNA domain.

3.5   Antibiotics that inhibit peptidoglycan synthesis
3.5.1   Introduction

As noted in Chapter 1, nearly all bacteria possess peptidoglycan in their cell walls, but this macromolecule is absent from mammalian cells. Consequently, the development of antibiotics that inhibit peptidoglycan synthesis can provide very useful chemotherapeutic agents. There are indeed a large number of antibiotics that inhibit peptidoglycan synthesis and in recent years much effort has been devoted to the development of new ones.

Peptidoglycan synthesis (Fig. 2.20) takes place in three major stages:

(1) Synthesis of precursors in the cytoplasm.
(2) Transfer of precursors to a lipid carrier molecule (undecaprenyl-phosphate) which transports them across the cytoplasmic membrane.
(3) Insertion of glycan units into the cell wall, attachment by transpeptidation and further final maturation steps.

The following section provide examples of antibiotics which inhibit peptidoglycan synthesis by interfering with reactions taking place during one of the stages outlined (Fig. 2.20).

3.5.2   Stage 1 inhibitors
3.5.2.1   D-cycloserine

D-cycloserine is an analogue of D-alanine (Fig. 2.21). The antibiotic blocks peptido-

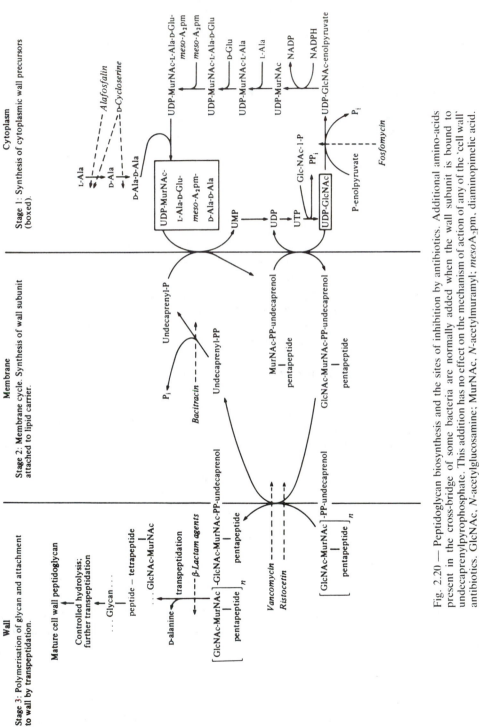

Fig. 2.20 — Peptidoglycan biosynthesis and the sites of inhibition by antibiotics. Additional amino-acids present in the cross-bridge of some bacteria are normally added when the wall subunit is bound to undecaprenylpyrophosphate. This addition has no effect on the mechanism of action of any of the 'cell wall' antibiotics. GlcNAc, N-acetylglucosamine; MurNAc, N-acetylmuramyl; $meso$-A$_2$pm, diaminopimelic acid. (Reproduced, with permission, from Reynolds (1985).)

glycan synthesis by competitive inhibition of two enzymes, alanine racemase and D-alanyl-D-alanine synthetase. Therefore, both the formation of D-alanine from L-alanine and the synthesis of the D-alanyl-D-alanine dipeptide prior to its addition to the UDP-MurNAc tripeptide are inhibited (Fig. 2.20).

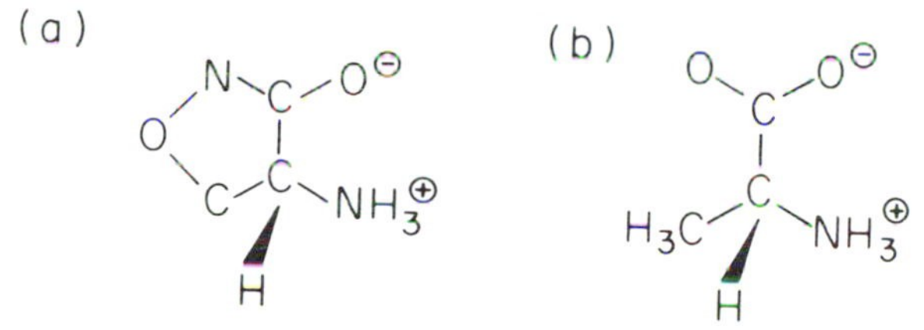

(a)   (b)

Fig. 2.21 — Structure of D-cycloserine (a) and D-alanine (b).

3.5.2.2   Fosfomycin

Fosfomycin (phosphonomycin) (Fig. 2.22) inhibits peptidoglycan synthesis by covalently binding to a cysteinyl residue in the enzyme phosphoenolpyruvate: UDP-GlcNAc-3-enolpyruvyltransferase ('pyruvyl transferase') (Fig. 2.20).

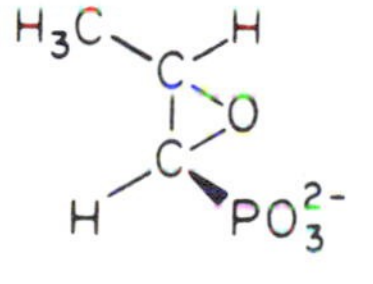

Fig. 2.22 — Structure of fosfomycin.

3.5.3   Bacitracin: a Stage 2 inhibitor

Bacitracin (Fig. 2.23) complexes with the membrane-bound pyrophosphate form of the undecaprenyl (C55-isoprenyl) lipid carrier molecule that remains after the discaccharide-pentapeptide unit has been transferred to the nascent peptidoglycan chain. Binding of bacitracin prevents the enzymic dephosphorylation of the carrier lipid to its monophosphate form, a step which is required for another round of synthesis and transfer of the discaccharide-peptide unit (Fig. 2.20). Inhibition by bacitracin is therefore associated with an interaction between antibiotic and substrate, rather than the antibiotic and the dephosphorylating enzyme.

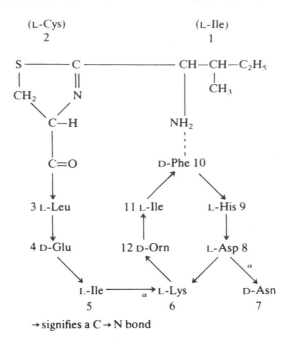

Fig. 2.23 — Structure of bacitracin.

3.5.4   Stage 3 inhibitors
3.5.4.1   Glycopeptide antibiotics

Vancomycin, ristocetin and teicoplanin (teichoplanin) are examples of glycopeptide antibiotics that interfere with glycan unit insertion (Fig. 2.20). Vancomycin (Fig. 2.24) undergoes hydrogen-bonding to the acyl-D-alanyl-D-alanine terminus of various peptidoglycan precursors (Fig. 2.24). In particular, it binds to the GlcNAc-MurNAc-pentapeptide-pyrophosphate-undecaprenol precursor and to the growing point of the peptidoglycan, thereby inhibiting the transglycosylation step by which glycan units are polymerized within the peptidoglycan (Fig. 2.20). Strictly speaking, the transglycosylase enzyme is not inhibited, but the complex of vancomycin with the peptide prevents the substrate from interacting with the active site of the enzyme. Vancomycin is therefore another example of an antibiotic that combines with a peptidoglycan substrate rather than an enzyme. The mode of action of ristocetin and teicoplanin is similar.

3.5.4.2   Beta-lactam antibiotics

(a)   *Introduction.*   Without doubt the beta-lactam antibiotics represent the most important group of drugs that inhibit the final stage of peptidoglycan synthesis. During the last decade there has been a dramatic increase in the number of beta-lactam antibiotics synthesized or discovered and in our understanding of how these antibacterial agents act as inhibitors of peptidoglycan synthesis. In view of their

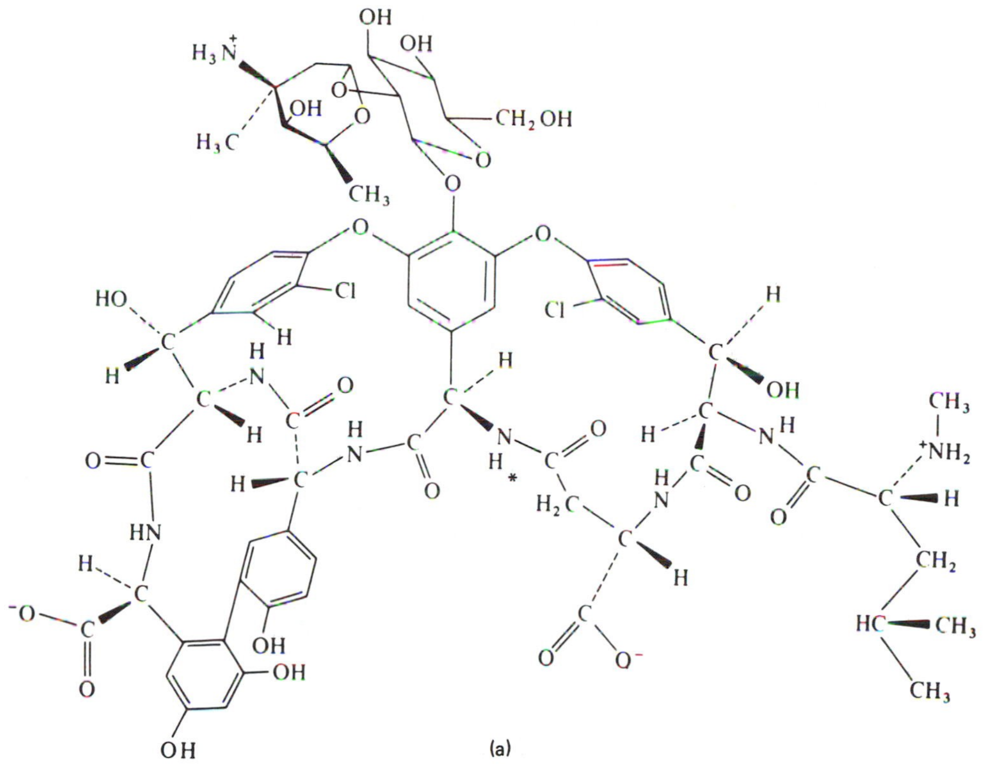

Fig. 2.24 — Structure of vancomycin (a) and proposed binding interactions between acetyl-D-alanyl-D-alanine and vancomycin (b). The same hydrogen atom is marked with an asterisk in (a) and (b) to allow the structures to be aligned. (Reproduced, with permission, from Rogers *et al.* (1980.)

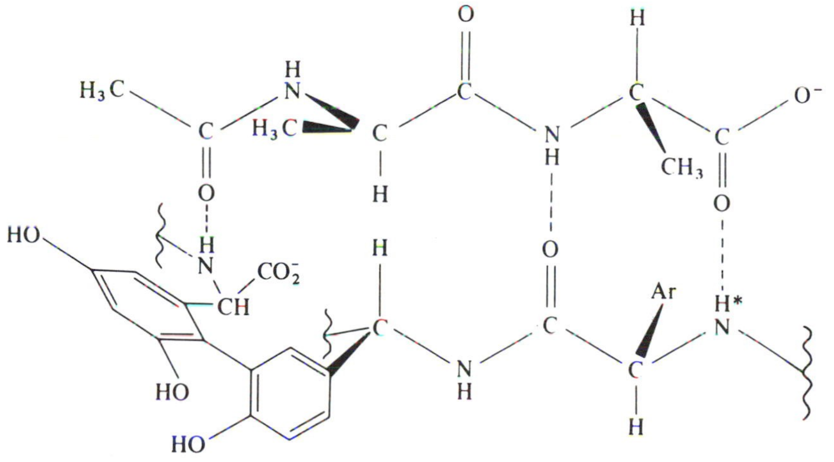

importance as clinically useful antibacterial agents, these antibiotics will be considered in detail.

Beta-lactams derive their name from the possession of a four-membered cyclic amide ring (Fig. 2.25). Until recently, beta-lactam antibiotics were defined and classified by a trivial nomenclature, the name of a compound usually relating to the producing organism and a chemical feature of the compound. More recently, beta-lactams have been categorized by a system based on a defined parent beta-lactam skeleton giving ten classes of compound (Fig. 2.25). Thus, the penicillins and cephalosporins, which are the best known members of the beta-lactam antibiotics, are now classified respectively as penams and cephems. Many semi-synthetic penam and cephem derivatives have been produced by varying the substituents attached either to the beta-lactam ring and/or (in the case of the cephems) to the six-membered dihydro-thiazine ring (Fig. 2.25).

(b) *Early studies (1950–65) on the mode of action of beta-lactams.*   Early work on the mode of action of penicillin culminated in the theory that its primary target was the transpeptidation reaction that cross-links neighbouring glycan strands (Fig. 2.26). This conclusion was based primarily upon studies with intact staphylococci treated with benzylpenicillin where it was shown that increased amounts of alanine were present in isolated walls while cross-linkage was decreased. Furthermore, Tipper and Strominger advanced the important hypothesis that penicillin might be a structural analogue of the acyl-D-alanyl-D-alanine portion of the peptide side chain (Fig. 2.27). It was therefore reasonable to suppose that an enzyme catalysing transpeptidation would mistake the antibiotic molecule for the genuine substrate, cleave the beta-lactam bond, and, in so doing, be rendered inactive due to the formation of a stable (covalent) antibiotic-enzyme intermediate. Aspects of this model are indeed still applicable today, although, as we shall see, various refinements are necessary in the light of more recent findings.

(c) *Multiplicity of penicillin-sensitive reactions in bacteria.*   Until the 1960s it was assumed that bacteria probably contained only a single type of transpeptidase enzyme and that this represented the unique target for penicillin. However, this simple picture had to be revised following the development of *in vitro* assays to examine transpeptidation reactions.

The first *in vitro* demonstration of peptidoglycan transpeptidase activity was achieved using *E. coli*. Unexpectedly, it was noted that in addition to transpeptidation, two further reactions occurred: removal of the carboxyl terminal D-alanine, but without formation of peptide bonds (i.e. a D,D, carboxypeptidase reaction) and cleavage of cross links between peptide chains (i.e. an endopeptidase reaction) (Fig. 2.28). All three reactions were inhibited by pencillin. Subsequently, similar types of pencillin-sensitive reactions were detected in a variety of other bacteria and in every case the substrate involved was either a D-alanyl-D-alanine bond, or a D-alanyl-meso-(D)-diaminopimelyl bond. Indeed, it is now apparent that any enzyme which metabolizes a D–D peptide bond is likely to be sensitive to beta-lactam antibiotics.

(d) *Penicillin-binding proteins (PBPs).*   The identification of more than one penicillin-sensitive reaction in the cell-free peptidoglycan synthetic systems described above implied that several proteins (enzymes) capable of interacting with

Structural type	Examples

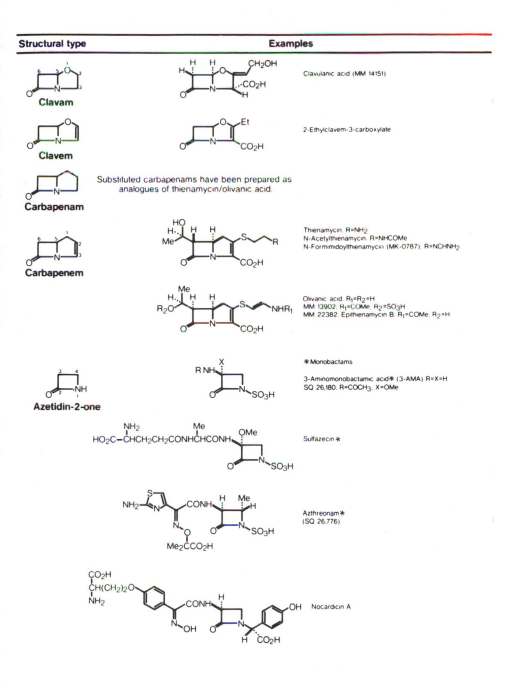

Clavam — Clavulanic acid (MM 14151)

Clavem — 2-Ethylclavem-3-carboxylate

Carbapenam — Substituted carbapenams have been prepared as analogues of thienamycin/olivanic acid.

Carbapenem —
Thienamycin: R=NH₂
N-Acetylthienamycin: R=NHCOMe
N-Formimidoylthienamycin (MK-0787): R=NCHNH₂

Olivanic acid: R₁=R₂=H
MM 13902: R₁=COMe, R₂=SO₃H
MM 22382: Epithienamycin B: R₁=COMe, R₂=H

Azetidin-2-one —
*Monobactams
3-Aminomonobactamic acid* (3-AMA) R=X=H
SQ 26,180: R=COCH₃, X=OMe

Sulfazecin*

Azthreonam*
(SQ 26,776)

Nocardicin A

Fig. 2.25 — Structure of beta-lactam antibiotics. (Reproduced, with permission, from Brown (1982).) (*cont.* on next page)

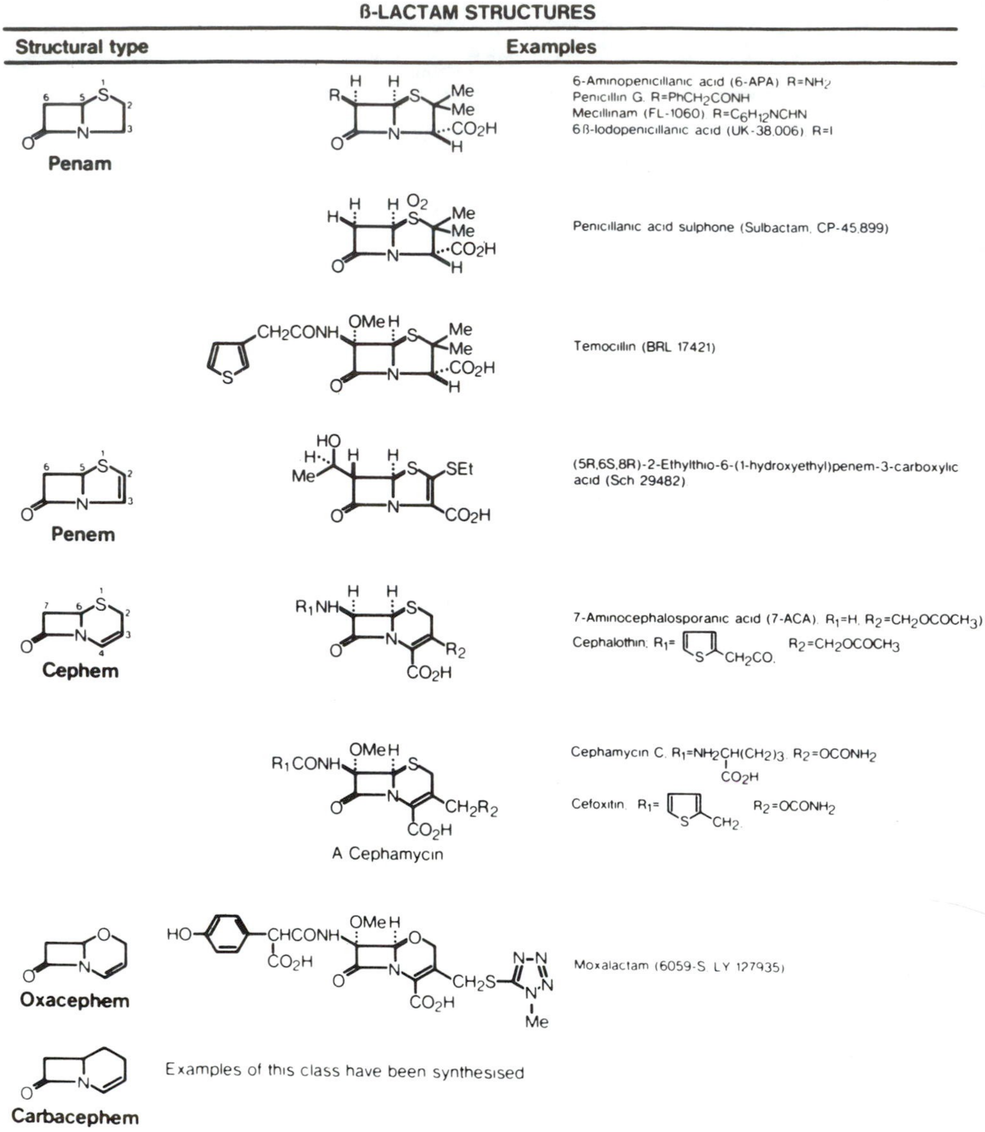

β-LACTAM STRUCTURES

Structural type	Examples	

Penam

6-Aminopenicillanic acid (6-APA) R=NH$_2$
Penicillin G. R=PhCH$_2$CONH
Mecillinam (FL-1060) R=C$_6$H$_{12}$NCHN
6β-Iodopenicillanic acid (UK-38,006) R=I

Penicillanic acid sulphone (Sulbactam, CP-45,899)

Temocillin (BRL 17421)

Penem

(5R,6S,8R)-2-Ethylthio-6-(1-hydroxyethyl)penem-3-carboxylic acid (Sch 29482)

Cephem

7-Aminocephalosporanic acid (7-ACA) R$_1$=H, R$_2$=CH$_2$OCOCH$_3$)
Cephalothin: R$_1$= [structure] CH$_2$CO,   R$_2$=CH$_2$OCOCH$_3$

Cephamycin C. R$_1$=NH$_2$CH(CH$_2$)$_3$, R$_2$=OCONH$_2$
                        CO$_2$H
Cefoxitin: R$_1$= [structure] CH$_2$ R$_2$=OCONH$_2$

A Cephamycin

Oxacephem

Moxalactam (6059-S. LY 127935)

Carbacephem

Examples of this class have been synthesised

Fig. 2.25 (cont.) — Structure of beta-lactam antibiotics (*=monobactams). (Reproduced, with permission, from Brown (1982).)

penicillin (and other beta-lactams) might be present in any individual bacterial species. The introduction of radioactive penicillin-labelling techniques for the visualization of bacterial proteins that covalently bind penicillin has confirmed this prediction.

Several (usually at least four) PBPs are present in most bacterial species. PBPs

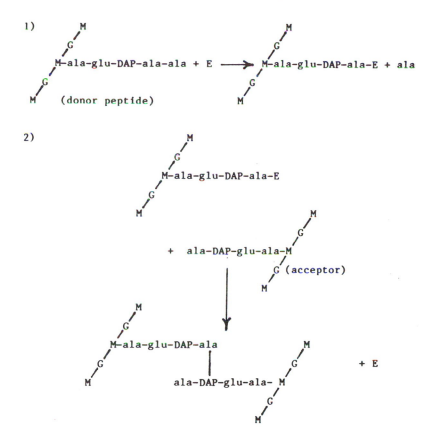

Fig. 2.26 — The transpeptidation reaction. G, NAcetylglucosamine; N, NAcetylmuramic acid; E, transpeptidase; DAP, diaminopimelic acid. The reaction shown applies to *E. coli*, but it should be remembered that some bacteria contain additional amino-acids in the cross bridge. However, the overall nature of transpetidation is similar in all bacteria containing peptidoglycan. (Reproduced, with permission, from Park (1987).)

are designated numerically, e.g. 1–7 in *E. coli* K12 (Table 2.3) The numerical description of PBPs is strictly a reference to their relative molecular size within the group of PBPs detected in a particular bacterium (PBP1 having the greatest molecular weight). Thus PBP3 of *E. coli* need not have anything in common with PBP3 of *S. aureus*. Nevertheless, within a closely related group of bacteria, e.g. the Enterobacteriaceae, at least some of the PBPs of comparable molecular size may have similar functions.

PBPs are minor components of the cytoplasmic membrane. For example, in *E. coli* they total about 3000 molecules per cell (Table 2.3), or 1% of total membrane proteins. The likely functions of several PBPs have been established by a combination of genetic and biochemical techniques. In view of the information presented in Section 3.5.4.2c it is not surprising to find that PBPs catalyse transpeptidase, carboxypeptidase and endopeptidase reactions. The PBPs of *E. coli* (Table 2.3)

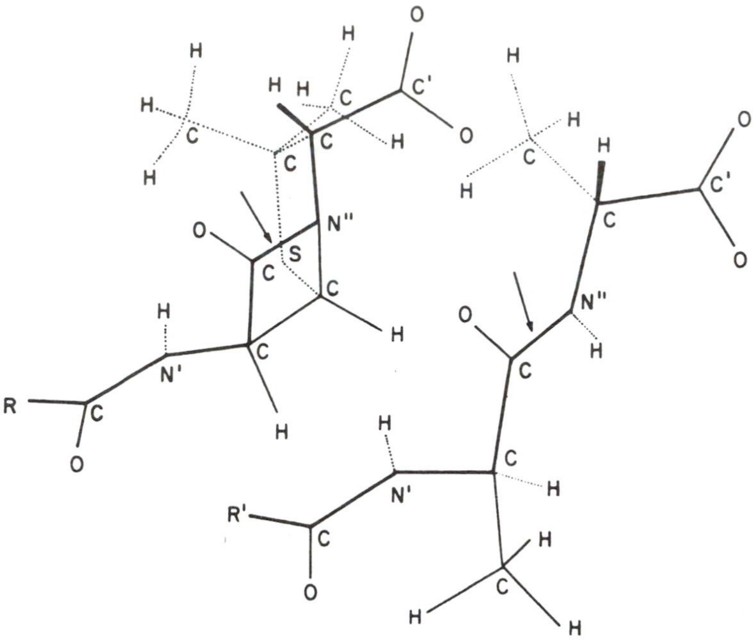

Fig. 2.27 — Dreiding stereomodels of penicillin (*upper left*) and of the acyl-D-alanyl-D-alanine end of the nascent peptidoglycan (*lower right*). Arrows indicate the position of the CO–N bond in the β-lactam ring of penicillin and of the CO–N peptide bond joining the two D-alanine residues. The portion of the penicillin molecule which is believed to resemble the peptide backbone of acyl-D-ala-D-ala is reproduced in heavy lines. (Reproduced with permission from Tipper, D. J., and Strominger, J. L. (1965) *Proceedings of the National Academy of Sciences* (*USA*) **54**, 1133 (Fig. 1).)

represent the most extensively studied set of PBPs. Their functions and the consequences of inhibition by beta-lactams are discussed more fully below. PBPs can conveniently be considered as two groups, the high molecular weight essential PBPs and the lower molecular weight, generally non-essential, PBPs that appear to play a minor role in peptidoglycan synthesis.

(e)   *High molecular weight* E. coli *PBPs.*   The high molecular weight PBPs (PBPs 1–3) are responsible for net synthesis of peptidoglycan *in vivo*, although their enzymic activities are often difficult to demonstrate *in vitro*. The proteins are products of separate structural genes (Table 2.3), the multiple components of PBP1B arising because alternative translational initiation codons are used within *mrc*B (*pon*B). The gene for each high-molecular weight *E. coli* PBP has been sequenced, thereby permitting prediction of the primary amino acid sequences of the respective PBPs.

PBPs 1–3 are enzymes which catalyse both the polymerization of the disaccharide units into glycan chains (transglycosylation) and also the cross-linking of their pentapeptide side chains (transpeptidation) i.e. they are bifunctional peptidoglycan transglycosylases/transpeptidases (Fig. 2.29). The transglycosylation activity of

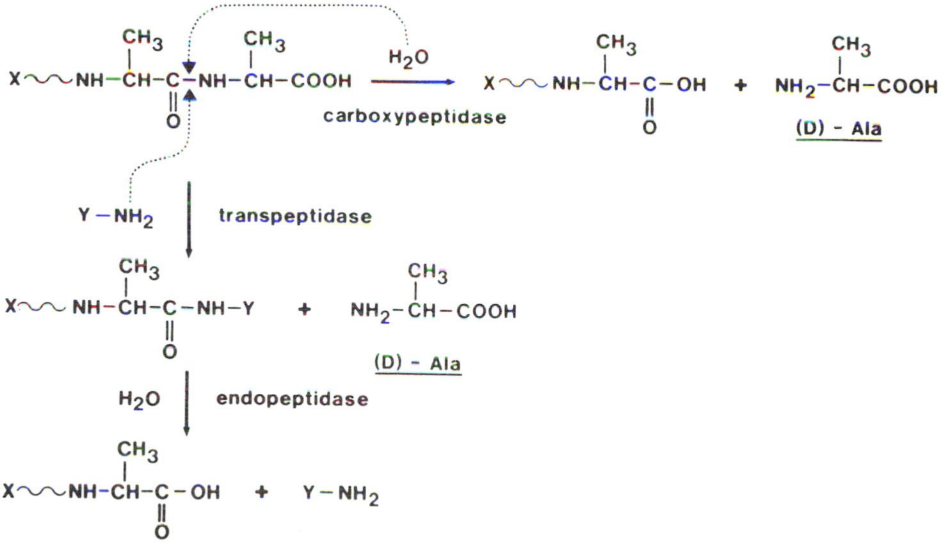

Fig. 2.28 — Carboxypeptidase, transpeptidase and endopeptidase reactions. All three types of reaction can be catalysed by bacterial penicillin-binding proteins (see text). Carboxypeptidase reactions are basically similar; in both cases the carbonyl of the penultimate D-alanine is transferred to an exogenous nucleophile. If the latter is water, hydrolysis occurs; if it is an amino group of another peptide, the product is a cross-linked dimer of the two peptides. Endopeptidase activity can hydrolyse such dimers. (Reproduced, with permission, from Tomasz (1983).)

these proteins is insusceptible to beta-lactams, unlike the transpeptidase activity (Fig. 2.29). The dual enzymatic activity expressed by these PBPs probably results from the presence of two distinct, catalytically-active, centres in the same polypeptide, i.e. an amino-terminal domain catalysing the transglycosylation reaction and a carboxyl-terminal domain carrying the beta-lactam sensitive transpeptidase activity. Presumably the presence of both enzymic activities in the same polypeptide permits close control over the insertion and cross-linking of glycan units into the growing peptidoglycan network.

Inhibition of the transpeptidase activity of the high-molecular weight PBPs of *E. coli* by beta-lactam antibiotics eventually leads to cell death. Concomitant inhibition of PBPs 1A and 1B leads to rapid cell lysis, inhibition of PBP2 to 'growth' as osmotically stable spherical or ovoid forms and inhibition of PBP3 to filamentation. 'Growth' as spheres following inhibition of PBP2 (e.g. by mecillinam), or as filaments following inhibition of PBP3 (e.g. by cephalexin) can continue for several generations before deformation and collapse (but not necessarily complete lysis) occurs.

(f)   *Low molecular weight* E. coli *PBPs.*   Apart from PBP7, the probable functions of the low molecular weight PBPs (i.e. PBPs 4–6) have been established (Table 2.3). Although PBP4 exhibits D-alanine carboxypeptidase activity *in vitro*, it may also act *in vivo* as an endopeptidase hydrolysing previously formed peptide cross-links in

Table 2.3 — Properties of the penicillin-binding proteins (PBPs) of *E. coli* K12

PBP	Molecular weight	Molecules/cell	Gene symbol	Proposed function	Examples of antibiotics showed marked affinity
1A	92 000	100	*mrcA* (*ponA*)	Bifunctional enzymes with transglycosylase and transpeptidase activities. Synthesize peptidoglycan at the growing zones of the side wall.	Benzylpenicillin and most cephalosporins
1B α	86 500	120	*mrcB* (*ponB*)		
β	84 000				
γ	81 500				
2	66 000	20	*pbpA*	Bifunctional enzyme with transglycoylase and transpeptidase activity. Initiates peptidoglycan insertion at new growth sites which are then further extended by PBPs 1A, 1B.	Mecillinam, imipenem
3	60 000	50	*ftsI* (*pbpB,sep*)	Bifunctional enzyme with transglycosylase and transpeptidase activity. Required specifically for formation of the cross-wall at cell division.	Cephalexin and many other cephalosporins, piperacillin, azthreonam
4	49 000	110	*dacB*	DD-carboxypeptidase and/or DD-endopeptidase. The first activity may control the extent of peptidoglycan cross-linking by transpeptidases, the second activity causing hydrolysis of cross-links during cell elongation.	Benzylpenicillin, ampicillin, imipenem
5	42 000	1800	*dacA*	DD-carboxypeptidases that may control the extent of peptidoglycan cross-linking by transpeptidases.	Cefoxitin
6	40 000	600	*dacC*		
7	29 000	?	?	Unknown	Penems

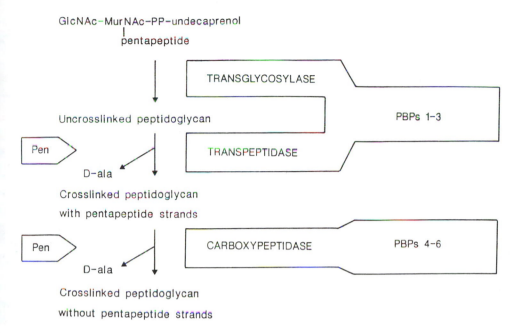

GlcNAc-MurNAc-PP-undecaprenol
│
pentapeptide

TRANSGLYCOSYLASE

PBPs 1-3

Uncrosslinked peptidoglycan

Pen

TRANSPEPTIDASE

D-ala

Crosslinked peptidoglycan

with pentapeptide strands

Pen

CARBOXYPEPTIDASE   PBPs 4-6

D-ala

Crosslinked peptidoglycan

without pentapeptide strands

Fig. 2.29 — Enzymatic formation of cross-linked peptidoglycan in *E. coli* showing the bifunctional activity of PBPs 1–3 as peptidoglycan transglycosylases and penicillin-sensitive transpeptidases. PBPs 4-6 may function as penicillin-sensitive DD-alanine carboxypeptidases to limit the cross-linking reaction.

peptidoglycan. The endopeptidase reaction is the reverse of transpeptidation except that the resulting product is a tetrapeptide, not possessing the terminal D-alanine. The endopeptidase activity of PBP4 probably contributes to the remodelling of peptidoglycan necessary for growth and division of the cell. PBPs 5 and 6 catalyse a D-alanine carboxypeptidase reaction (Fig. 2.29). This reaction probably controls the extent of peptidoglycan cross-linking by removing the terminal D-alanine residues from the pentapeptide side chains of nascent peptidoglycan, thereby preventing them from acting as peptide donors in transpeptidation.

Mutants of *E. coli* lacking the enzyme activities of PBPs 4 (*dac*B), 5 (*dac*A), or 6 (*dac*C) and a double mutant (*dac*A, *dac*B) have been isolated. Since these mutants grew normally it has been concluded that neither the carboxypeptidase nor the endopeptidase activities of the respective PBPs were essential for growth, at least under laboratory conditions. However, a role in normal growth for the carboxypeptidase activity provided by these PBPs cannot yet be completely excluded since even the *dac*A, *dac*B double mutant might have sufficient *dac*C-encoded carboxypeptidase activity to maintain growth. The nature of a triple *dac*A,B,C mutant (if it can be isolated) might resolve the question of whether PBP-mediated D-alanine carboxypeptidase activity is required for growth.

Although the enzymatic activity and function of the low molecular weight PBP7 are unknown, its inactivation, particularly by penems (e.g. impipenem) leads to bacterial lysis. However, the steps leading to lysis following inactivation of PBP7 differ from those when PBP1A and 1B are inactivated (see Section 3.5.5.2).

(g)   E. coli *PBPs that are killing targets for beta-lactams: a summary.*   In *E. coli* PBPs 4, 5 and 6 do not appear to be essential for growth and thus their interaction with beta-lactams is not considered to be responsible for the killing action of these antibiotics. The remaining proteins, particularly the high molecular weight PBPs 1A, 1B, 2 and 3, are the primary lethal targets. The binding of a beta-lactam, leading to inactivation of transpeptidase activity, is potentially lethal. Rapid lysis (death) results from inactivation of PBPs 1A and 1B, whereas antibiotics showing a preference for PBPs 2 or 3 produce distinct, but transient, morphological changes prior to cell death. Inhibition of bacterial growth by beta-lactams (e.g. benzylpenicillin, ampicillin) that have similar affinities for the target proteins is likely to result from the simultaneous inactivation of more than one of the lethal targets. The exact mechanisms leading to cell death are not entirely clear, but this topic is expanded in a later section (3.5.5).

(h)   *Enzymatic activities of PBPs in other bacteria and identification of beta-lactam killing targets.*   The enzymic activity of PBPs in Gram-negative bacteria other than *E. coli* is not well documented. However, transpeptidase, carboxypeptidase and endopeptidase activities have been ascribed to some PBPs. Only DD-carboxypeptidase activity has been associated with PBPs purified from Gram-positive bacteria, i.e. natural transpeptidation activity has not been directly demonstrated. Nevertheless, on the basis of findings with *E. coli* and other Gram-negative organisms, it can be assumed that at least some of the PBPs from Gram-positive bacteria mediate transpeptidation reactions *in vivo* that are susceptible to inhibition by beta-lactam antibiotics.

   Although the precise functions of the majority of PBPs found in bacteria other than *E. coli* have not yet been established, a more general approach to the identification of physiologically important PBPs (killing targets) in these organisms has been possible. If the multiple PBPs of bacteria include one or more killing targets for beta-lactams, while other PBPs perform less vital activities (e.g. PBPs 4–6 of *E. coli*), then it should be possible to identify the former from among all the detectable PBPs by comparing the extent of inhibition of PBPs to the overall susceptibility of the organism as a function of antibiotic concentration. The principle behind this method is that PBPs which are saturated at antibiotic concentrations that are either below, or far above, those required to inhibit bacterial growth do not qualify as killing targets. It is beyond the scope of this book to attempt to describe in detail the various conclusions drawn from studies of this type. Nevertheless, it is sufficient to comment that this general approach has identified likely PBP killing targets in *Ps. aeruginosa*, *K. aerogenes*, *Pr. rettgeri*, *E. cloacea*, *H. influenzae* and *B. megaterium*. However, this approach does not yield helpful information with those organisms (e.g. *S. aureus*, *Strep. pneumoniae* and *B. subtilis*) where several, or all, of the PBPs are saturated at similar beta-lactam concentrations which are themselves equivalent to the antibiotic concentrations inhibiting growth of the respective organisms.

   Although beta-lactam-promoted death in the majority of bacteria probably results from inactivation of PBPs that catalyse transpeptidation reactions, there is at least one example in which inhibition of a DD-carboxypeptidase is responsible for bacterial death. In *G. homari* peptidoglycan cross-linking is insensitive to penicillin, but a penicillin-sensitive DD-carboxypeptidase exists which is required for cleavage of some D-alanine residues from the nascent peptidoglycan prior to insertion of glycan units into the wall. Inhibition of the DD-carboxypeptidase by benzylpenicillin apparently prevents further peptidoglycan synthesis, leading to cell death.

(i)   *Nature of the substrate and beta-lactam binding sites in PBPs.* As discussed above, peptidoglycan carboxypeptidases, and in particular transpeptidases, are the targets of beta-lactam action. These enzymes utilize the D-alanyl-D-alanine moiety of the pentapeptide as a substrate and are believed to form an acyl-enzyme inter-mediate, with release of the terminal D-alanine during the course of the reaction (Fig. 2.30). The hypothesis of Tipper and Strominger (Section 3.5.4.2b) predicts that

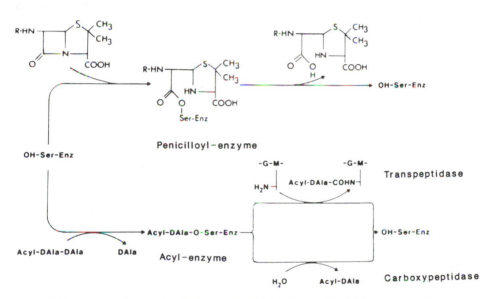

Fig. 2.30 — Proposed mechanism for the reaction of penicillin-sensitive enzymes with penicillin or acyl-D-Ala-D-Ala. A nucleophile in the enzyme active site (shown as a serine residue) reacts either with acyl-D-Ala-D-Ala or penicillin to yield either acyl-D-alanyl-enzyme or penicilloyl-enzyme intermediates. Serine has been established as the residue to which the substrate or inhibitor binds in PBPs 1,2,3,5 and 6 of *E. coli*, PBP5 of *B. subtilis* and *B. stearothermophilus* and certain carboxypeptidase/transpeptidases from streptomycetes. Subsequent reaction of the acyl-D-alanyl-enzymes with a suitable amino acceptor peptide results in formation of a cross-link and release of the enzyme (transpeptidase). Alternatively, reaction with water results in the release of acyl-D-alanine and enzyme (carboxypeptidase). Although both functions are shown for the same enzyme, individual proteins tend to favour one reaction, i.e. they are D,D-carboxypeptidases with inefficient transpeptidase activity or the reverse may be the case. The penicilloyl-enzyme is more stable than the acyl-D-alanyl-enzyme and consequently the antibio-tic residue is not transferred to an amino acceptor. Certain of these complexes do, however, react to release penicillin degradation products (e.g. penicilloic acid) and active enzyme (see Fig. 2.31). (Reproduced, with permission, from Lorian (1986).)

penicillin and other beta-lactams will bind covalently to the same group in the enzymes (PBPs) to which the natural substrate normally binds. Evidence for similar, if not identical, binding sites for substrate and beta-lactams has now been obtained, the enzyme active site containing a serine residue through which beta-lactams or substrate bind to the enzymes (Fig. 2.30).

The amino acid sequence in the active site regions of several PBPs have been determined. PBPs 1–6 of *E. coli* and PBP5 of *B. subtilis* contain the active site serine within the sequence Ala/Gly-Ser-X-X-Lys. Thus the sequence Ser-X-X-Lys is conserved in all the PBPs. By themselves these sequencing studies do not establish the three-dimensional architecture of the substrate and inhibitor binding sites. To investigate the contribution of different regions of the polypeptide to the active site it will be necessary to apply X-ray crystallographic techniques to purified PBPs. Such studies are still in their infancy, but it can be assumed that the different affinities displayed by beta-lactam antibiotics for the same PBP reflect the three-dimensional shapes of the active site and the drug molecules. Presumably certain pendant groups on the antibiotic molecules can be accommodated by the proteins more easily than others. Although there is considerable evidence for overlapping substrate and beta-lactam binding sites in PBPs, enzymological studies suggest that penicillin sensitive enzymes, in addition to the enzyme active site, may also have other drug recognition sites. Interaction of antibiotic molecules with these sites may influence the reactivity of the enzyme active site.

(j)   *Interaction of beta-lactams with PBPs: kinetic studies and fate of the antibiotic molecule.*   The association (binding and release) of beta-lactams with PBPs is represented by the following equation:

$$I + PBP \underset{k_2}{\overset{k_1}{\rightleftharpoons}} IPBP \overset{k_3}{\rightarrow} IPBP^* \overset{k_4}{\rightarrow} PBP(active) + antibiotic(inactive)$$

where I = inhibitor (beta-lactam), PBP = penicillin-binding protein, IPBP = initial non-covalent inhibitor-PBP complex, $IPBP^*$ = inhibitor–PBP complex (demonstrably covalent in most cases), k_1, k_2, k_3, k_4 = first order rate constants.

Beta-lactams with slow rates of acylation ($k_3 < k_2$), or fast rates of deacylation (k_4 high) will be poor inhibitors, in the latter case because the antibiotic is a substrate of the enzyme. However, even in the case of good PBP inhibitors, the penicilloyl complexes undergo deacylation. Decomposition can follow two routes (Fig. 2.31) depending on the PBP and the particular type of beta-lactam. The first reaction (formation of a penicilloic acid) is identical to that catalysed by beta-lactamases, enzymes distinct from PBPs that mediate bacterial resistance to beta-lactams (see Chapter 5).

3.5.5   Mechanisms by which inhibition of peptidoglycan synthesis leads to bacterial death

3.5.5.1   Introduction

Exposure of growing bacteria to inhibitors of peptidoglycan synthesis usually leads to cell death. This may result from lytic or non-lytic events (Fig. 2.32). The two types of response are considered more fully in the following sections.

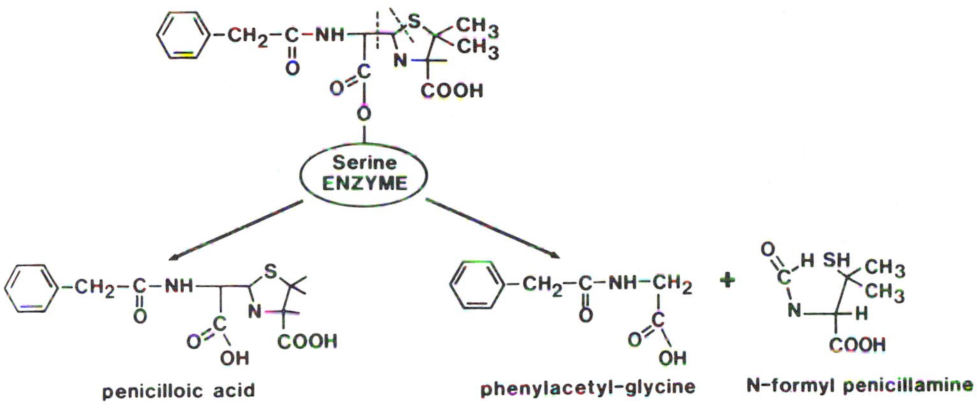

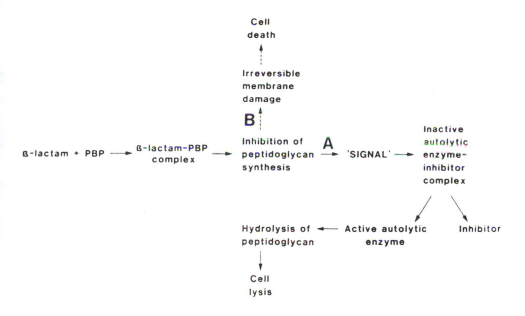

Fig. 2.31 — Alternative pathways for the degradation of the beta-lactam acyl-enzyme complexes. (Reproduced, with permission, from Tomasz (1983).)

Fig. 2.32 — Model for the mechanisms by which beta-lactam antibiotics kill bacteria by lytic death (route A), or non-lytic death (route B). The nature of the 'signal' resulting from inhibition of peptidoglycan synthesis and leading to lytic death (route A) is unknown. See text for further details. (Reproduced, with modifications, from Lorian (1986).)

3.5.5.2   Lytic death and the role of peptidoglycan degradative enzymes (autolysins)

It has been known for many years that inhibition of further peptidoglycan synthesis can result in the formation of osmotically fragile cells which lyse in the absence of a suitable non-penetrating stabilizer, such as sucrose. Furthermore, the participation of peptidoglycan degradative enzymes in the process had been established by the mid-1950s.

However, the findings summarized above do not explain why cessation of peptidoglycan synthesis can lead to enzymatic degradation of cell walls. The first hypothesis (advanced in the 1960s) considered that the effects of antibiotics like penicillin resulted primarily from 'unbalanced growth'. Bacterial autolysins, i.e. enzymes hydrolysing bonds in the glycan, or peptide side chains of peptidoglycan (Fig. 2.33) were considered to play an essential role in cell wall synthesis by providing space and acceptor sites for new material to be condensed into the growing wall by peptidoglycan synthetic enzymes. In the presence of penicillin, inhibition of cross-linkage (by transpeptidation) together with continued autolytic activity would, it was proposed, lead to a structurally weakened wall and eventual lysis of the cell because it would no longer be able to withstand the high internal osmotic pressure generated by the cytoplasmic contents. Under such circumstances bacterial lysis would not be due to any specific induction of autolysins, but due to the abrupt arrest of peptidogly-can synthesis leading to the unbalanced state where autolysins continue unabated to cleave peptidoglycan.

The first direct evidence for involvment of autolysins in penicillin-induced lysis of bacteria came from studies with a *Strep.pneumoniae* mutant defective in *N*-acetylmuramyl-L-alanine amidase activity. The parent (wild-type) organism lysed rapidly on treatment with beta-lactam antibiotics, but the mutant, although prevented from growing by the drugs, remained viable for much longer periods than the parent strain in the presence of antibiotic. Confirmation of these initial findings has come from further studies on other autolysin-defective bacterial mutants for which the general term 'tolerant' mutant has been coined.

Although autolysins clearly have a role in lytic death, their activity in this process is no longer thought to be related to the 'unbalanced growth' model mentioned above. This modified view has arisen mainly from observations showing that autolysins are not essential enzymes needed for cell wall expansion, but rather are probably involved in degradation of peptidoglycan accompanying cell separation at the end of cell division. Studies with autolysin-defective mutants support this view. For instance, autolysin-deficient mutants of rods or streptococci frequently form long chains of cells and mutant staphylococci have been described that grow as large clumps of cells, suggesting that lowered autolysin activity in each case prevents separation of daughter cells. An attractive theory relating autolysin activity to antibiotic-induced lytic death has been advanced by Tomasz. He speculates that the activity of the autolysins is 'triggered' at the end of the cell cycle by a properly timed and genetically programmed halt in peptidoglycan synthesis, the whole process permitting controlled separation of daughter cells. Antibiotic (e.g. penicillin) induced lysis is considered by Tomasz as a premature 'triggering' of terminal events in bacterial cell separation, but differing from the normal physiological process

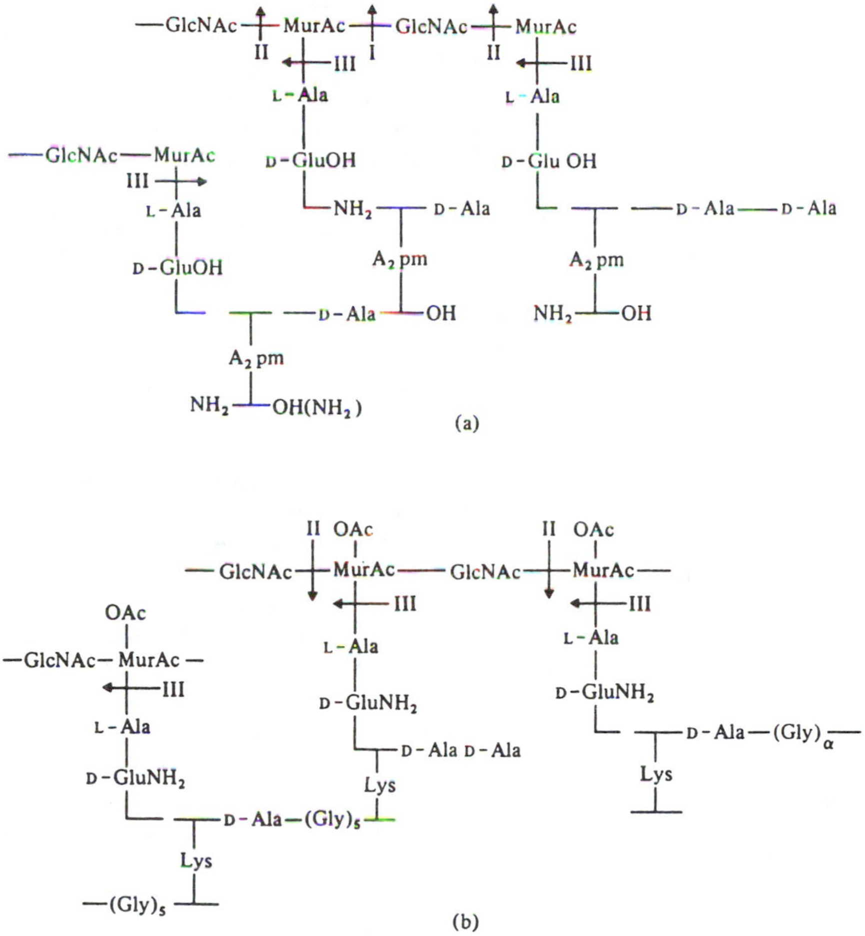

Fig. 2.33 — Bond specificities of three common types of autolytic enzymes. The arrows indicate the bonds hydrolysed by (I) *endo*-muramidase, (II) *endo*-β-*N*-acetylglucosaminidase and (III) *N*-acetylmuramyl-L-alanine amidase (amidase). (a) Shows the structure of peptidoglycans present in many bacilli and in all the Gram-negative species examined. (b) Shows the structure of a peptidoglycan with a 'bridge' peptide. The one illustrated is present in *S. aureus*. (Reproduced, with modifications, from Rogers *et al.* (1980).)

because autolytic activity is not localized, transient or properly timed. The consequences of uncontrolled autolytic activity are lysis and death.

The concept of naturally occurring autolysin inhibitors is also central to Tomasz's theory on lytic death. The activity of autolytic enzymes is proposed to be negatively controlled by one or more natural inhibitors and the bactericidal action of beta-lactams (and other inhibitors of peptidoglycan synthesis) is mediated by antibiotic-induced deregulation or 'triggering' of the autolytic system, possibly due to dissociation of autolysin-natural inhibitor complexes (Fig. 2.32). Amphipathic, membrane-associated, substances are implicated as the naturally occurring autolysin inhibitors (regulators), but little is known about the molecular basis of events during the 'triggering' process. Nor is it known why inhibition of certain essential PBPs, e.g. PBPs 1A and 1B in *E. coli*, leads to very rapid cell lysis, whereas inhibition of other essential PBPs, e.g. PBP2 of *E. coli*, does not result in rapid 'triggering' of autolytic activity.

A further important point relating to lytic death mechanisms concerns the well-known observation that beta-lactams generally do not promote lysis of non-growing bacteria. This phenomenon was first recognized in the 1940s when it was noted that starvation of nutritional auxotrophs protected against the bactericidal effect of penicillin. The exact basis of this phenomenon is still not fully understood, but has been examined to some extent in *E. coli*. When bacteria suffer from nutrient starvation, particularly deprivation of amino acids, the so-called 'stringent response' ensues. This is a regulatory system that suppresses synthesis of certain cellular macromolecules such as stable RNA species, phospholipids and peptidoglycan. The response is mediated, in a complex manner, by the nucleotide guanosine tetraphosphate (ppGpp) which is derived from guanisome pentaphosphate (pppGpp). The latter is synthesized from GTP by a ribosome associated ATP:GTP 3′ pyrophosphotransferase (the product of the *relA* gene) which is activated during amino acid deprivation. The stringent response inhibits peptidoglycan synthesis at two points: (a) an early step in the synthesis of UDP-MurNAc-pentapeptide, and (b) a late step in the polymerization of peptidoglycan catalysed by one or more of the PBPs. The combination of these events presumably prevents the unnecessary accumulation of peptidoglycan intermediates when growth is arrested by amino acid deprivation. The mechanism by which the stringent control system regulates peptidoglycan synthesis is not yet fully understood. However, preliminary evidence suggests that inhibition of peptidoglycan synthesis is a consequence of inhibition of phospholipid synthesis by ppGpp.

On the basis of these and other findings a speculative model has recently been proposed to explain why most beta-lactams are only able to promote lysis of growing *E. coli* (Fig. 2.34). Although beta-lactams are able to bind to PBPs that are not actively engaged in peptidoglycan synthesis such interactions fail to activate the 'trigger' pathway leading to activation of autolysins. In contrast, binding of beta-lactams to PBPs, particularly PBPs 1A and 1B, that are actively engaged in peptidoglycan synthesis leads to activation of autolytic enzymes and cell death. When considering this model it should be remembered that certain beta-lactams (e.g. imipenem) promote lysis of non-growing *E. coli* by interaction with PBP7 (Section 3.5.4.2f). Possibly the activity of PBP7 is not subject to stringent control and remains permanently 'active' even though net peptidoglycan synthesis may have stopped. Alternatively, PBP7 may be coupled to a different type of 'triggering' pathway from that of PBPs 1A and 1B.

3.5.5.3   Non-lytic death
Although beta-lactam antibiotics frequently cause cell lysis, they are able to kill some types of bacteria by a non-lytic process. Death without lysis usually occurs in bacteria that do not possess detectable autolytic activity. In these cases death in the absence of

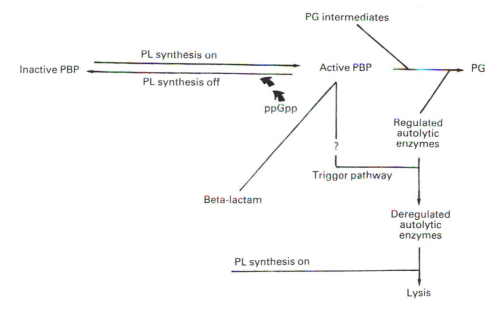

Fig. 2.34 — Model for regulation of peptidoglycan synthesis and antibiotic-induced lysis. From Ishiguro & Kusser (1988), with modifications. PG, peptidoglycan; PBP, penicillin-binding protein; ppGpp, guanosine tetraphosphate; PL, phospholipid.

lysis might result from a very limited amount of wall damage, or peptidoglycan 'nicking' which could affect the sequence of changes essential for completion of cell division. Thus although extensive wall damage and lysis do not occur, hydrolysis of even a few strategically located bonds in the peptidoglycan might result in non-lytic death by a process related to that of lytic death. Although the above mechanism may account for some types of non-lytic death, McDowell and Lemanski (1988) recently reported that sublytic autolysin activity (peptidoglycan nicking) is not responsible for penicillin-induced death of a group A streptococcus. In this case death was associated with hydrolysis and loss of RNA from the cell, changes that may arise from irreversible, penicillin-mediated, membrane damage.

3.6   Antibiotics that inhibit membrane integrity

The polymyxins (e.g. polymyxin B, Fig. 2.35) are a group of cyclic, polycationic, peptides with a fatty acid chain attached to the peptide through an amide linkage. The bactericidal activity of these compounds results from their interaction with the bacterial cytoplasmic membrane causing gross disorganization of its structure. Membranes containing the phospholipid phosphatidylethanolamine are particularly sensitive to polymyxins which explains why Gram-negative bacteria are more susceptible to polymyxins than Gram-positive organisms, because membranes of the latter generally do not contain phosphatidylethanolamine.

Polymyxins have only a minor place in medicine because they also have affinity for mammalian membranes. However, they appear to bind less readily to mamma-

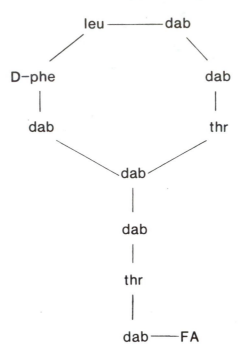

Fig. 2.35 — Generalized structure of the polymyxins. For polymyxin B the fatty acyl (FA) residue is 6-methyloctanoic acid. dab=L-diaminobutyric acid.

lian membranes than to bacterial membranes. The basis for this discrimination may relate to the presence of cholesterol in mammalian membranes.

4.   UPTAKE OF ANTIBIOTICS BY BACTERIA

4.1   Introduction

From previous sections it is obvious that many clinically useful antibiotics have target sites that are either located within the bacterial cell (e.g. inhibitors of protein and DNA synthesis), or within the cytoplasmic membrane (e.g. beta-lactam antibiotics). Therefore, in order to reach these targets, the antibiotic molecules may have to cross either one or two membranes depending upon whether the organism is Gram-negative and therefore surrounded by both an outer and cytoplasmic membrane (Figs 1.1 and 1.2, Chapter 1), or Gram-positive and therefore surrounded only by a cytoplasmic membrane (Figs 1.1 and 1.3, Chapter 1).

    Passage of antibiotics across the outer membrane usually occurs by passive diffusion or self-promoted uptake, the latter probably best regarded as a special form of passive diffusion. Passive, or simple, diffusion of antibiotics across the outer membrane occurs primarily through the water-filled pores (porins; see Chapter 1) and is influenced by the molecular size, charge and lipophilic properties of the permeating molecule. Molecules able to diffuse most rapidly through porin channels are, in general, soluble in water and have molecular weights of less than 600 to gain access to the transmembrane pores. Most porins show little chemical selectivity for permeating solutes, but can either be cation or anion selective. For example, the cation selective OmpF channel in *E. coli* favours diffusion of zwitterionic over anionic antibiotics, whereas for the anion selective PhoE channel this situation is reversed. Self-promoted uptake of antibiotics across the outer membrane of Gram-negative organisms is not well understood and is restricted to polycationic antibiotics such as the aminoglycosides and polymyxins (see below). Self-promoted uptake involves destabilization and disorganization of the outer membrane as a result of displacement of divalent cations in the outer membrane by the polycationic antibiotics. Some antibiotics, as mentioned above, may either be too large or too hydrophobic to cross the outer membrane. This phenomenon can contribute considerably to the intrinsic resistance of Gram-negative bacteria to certain antibiotics, whereby the outer membrane 'shields' intracellular targets from antibiotic action: see Chapter 5.

In contrast to the situation with the outer membrane, transfer of antibiotics across bacterial cytoplasmic membranes frequently results from active transport of the drug molecules.

Active transport involves specific carrier proteins that are coupled to an energy source. When metabolic energy is available antibiotics can be accumulated within the cell against a concentration gradient. The energy for transport may derive from ATP or the proton motive force (pmf). ATP-coupled transport is referred to as primary transport whereas pmf-dependent processes are described as secondary systems. Active transport of antibiotics into bacteria usually results from 'illicit' transport, i.e. the antibiotic bears sufficient structural resemblance to a naturally occurring molecule to be able to utilize the normal transport carrier.

Figs 2.36 and 2.37 present models depicting the routes of entry of antibiotics into Gram-negative and Gram-positive cells and the following sections consider in detail the uptake of those antibiotics whose mode of action has been detailed in earlier sections of this chapter. The antibiotics are grouped into the same major divisions previously used.

4.2   Inhibitors of nucleic acid synthesis
4.2.1   Introduction

Of those antibiotics described in Section 2, information on transport mechanisms is only available for the quinolones. Since the target (DNA gyrase) of these antibiotics is located intracellularly, they must be able to cross both outer and cytoplasmic bacterial membranes.

4.2.2   Uptake of quinolones

Most quinolones are low molecular weight (<400 daltons) hydrophilic molecules. These properties imply that the drugs cross bacterial outer membranes through porin channels. Quinolones are indeed known to penetrate the outer membrane of *E. coli* through OmpC and OmpF porins. However, these antibiotics are also able to promote their own uptake across the outer membrane by displacement of divalent cations which leads to membrane destabilization and further insertion of antibiotic molecules into the outer membrane bilayer. Therefore both porin and non-porin pathways contribute to total uptake of quinolones.

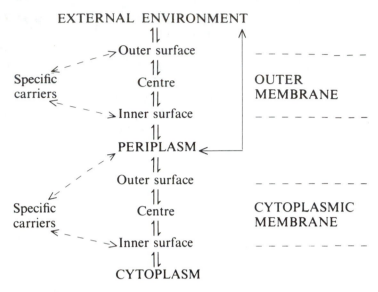

Fig. 2.36 — Model depicting the routes of entry of antibiotics across the Gram-negative bacterial cell envelope. <−>, Involvement of specific carrier proteins; ⇌, passive diffusion and partitioning; in the case of the outer membrane passage by this route usually involves 'self-promoted' transfer (see text); ↔, passive diffusion through hydrophilic pores. (Reproduced, with permission, from Chopra & Ball (1982).)

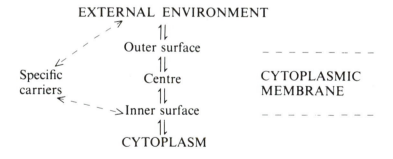

Fig. 2.37 — Model depicting the routes of entry of antibiotics across the cytoplasmic membrane of Gram-positive bacteria. <−>, involvement of specific carrier proteins; ⇌, passive diffusion and partitioning. (Reproduced, with permission, from Chopra & Ball (1982).)

The mechanism of uptake of quinolones across the bacterial cytoplasmic membrane is at present uncertain. Some evidence points towards an energy-independent passive diffusion mechanism, whereas other data suggest that an energy-dependent mechanism is responsible. However, it would be difficult to explain how passage of hydrophilic molecules like the quinolones can occur across the hydrophobic phospholipid bilayer of the cytoplasmic membrane without involvement of an energy-coupled transport process.

4.3   Inhibitors of protein synthesis
4.3.1   Introduction

Of those protein synthesis inhibitors considered in Section 3.4, information on transport is available for mupirocin, the aminoglycoside-aminocyclitol (AGAC) group, chloramphenicol and tetracyclines.

4.3.2   Mupirocin
The hydrophibic nature of this antibiotic suggests that it will not easily penetrate the outer membrane of most Gram-negative bacteria. This is consistent with the observation that mupirocin has poor activity against *E. coli*, but is about 500-fold more active against *S. aureus*. Thus, although the *E. coli* outer membrane 'shields' the inner membrane from the antibiotic, it is able to cross the cytoplasmic membrane of Gram-positive bacteria. Transport of mupirocin into *B. subtilis* and *S. aureus* is energy-independent, but temperature-dependent. These features suggest non-carrier-mediated passive diffusion across the cytoplasmic membrane, an uptake mechanism that is consistent with the hydrophobic nature of the antibiotic.

4.3.3   Aminoglycoside-aminocyclitol (AGAC) antibiotics
Since the primary site of action of aminoglycosides is the bacterial ribosome, these drugs will need to cross both outer and cytoplasmic membranes before reaching their target.

Little is known about the mechanism of transfer of the AGAC group across bacterial outer membranes. In *E. coli* some evidence points towards utilization of porins for uptake, but in *Pseudomonas aeruginosa* these antibiotics may be able to promote their own transfer across the outer membrane by causing localized distortion of the bilayer. Self-promoted uptake involves the displacement of divalent cations from lipopolysaccharide by the polycationic aminoglycosides. This interferes with cross-bridging between neighbouring lipopolysaccharide molecules which leads to outer membrane destabilization and enhancement of antibiotic uptake. However, this mechanism of aminoglycoside accumulation is not widespread amongst Gram-negative bacteria.

Uptake of AGAC antibiotics across the bacterial cytoplasmic membrane is essential for antibacterial activity and is similar in Gram-positive and Gram-negative bacteria. Aminoglycoside uptake is multiphasic with three distinct phases, one of which is energy-independent (EIP), the remainder being energy-dependent (EDPI and EDPII).

The EIP phase of uptake, occurring very rapidly, represents the initial binding of antibiotic to bacteria. Although, in Gram-negative bacteria this partially represents interaction with the outer membrane, uptake during the EIP also represents binding of drug molecules to the cytoplasmic membrane. EDPI represents a slow, but poorly characterized, energy dependent uptake of drug molecules across the cytoplasmic membrane. EDPII, associated with progressive binding of aminoglycosides to ribosomes within the cell, results in an acceleration of uptake seen towards the end of

EDPI. It is not known whether this third phase of uptake (i.e. EDPII) involves a transport carrier, nor even the exact nature of the energy source driving EDPII mediated AGAC uptake. However, some evidence shows that EDPII depends upon respiratory activity within the cytoplasmic membrane.

4.3.4   Chloramphenicol
Since the target site of this antibiotic is intracellular, the drug must therefore be able to cross bacterial outer and cytoplasmic membranes. The antibiotic crosses the outer membrane by passive diffusion through transmembrane porins and crosses the cytoplasmic membrane probably by using two (as yet unidentified) active transport systems. Studies in *E. coli* on the nature of energy coupling for chloramphenicol transport suggest the involvement of both primary and secondary transport processes for drug uptake.

4.3.5   Tetracyclines
Since tetracyclines act intracellularly they must cross both outer and cytoplasmic membranes. Although a variety of tetracycline analogues exist (Fig. 2.19), detailed studies on the transport of these antibiotics have been confined mostly to tetracycline itself. Furthermore, attention has been primarily focused upon the basis of uptake into *E. coli*.

Movement across the outer membrane involves passive diffusion through outer membrane porins with a preference for those formed by the OmpF porin. Some studies suggest that tetracycline crosses the outer membrane as a cationic chelate of magnesium which would be consistent with the utilization of OmpF pores for uptake since the OmpF channels are cation-selective.

Passage of tetracycline across the cytoplasmic membrane occurs both by energy-independent and energy-dependent (active) processes. Energy-independent uptake undoubtedly represents passive diffusion of the drug through the membrane. Much effort has been devoted towards understanding the molecular basis of active transport of tetracycline into *E. coli*. At least two active transport systems for the drug seem to occur. One transport system is ATP dependent (i.e. a primary transport process), whereas the other is coupled to the pmf (i.e. a secondary system). The nature of the membrane-located tetracycline transport systems have not yet been identified, but an earlier suggestion that they may normally function in the active transport of L-glutamate into the cell has now been discounted.

4.4   Antibiotics that inhibit peptidoglycan synthesis
4.4.1   D-cycloserine
Since the D-cycloserine target enzymes (alanine racemase and D-alanyl-D-alanine synthetase) are intracellular, the drug must be able to cross both outer and cytoplasmic bacterial membranes.

Little is known about uptake of the antibiotic across the bacterial outer membrane, but it is assumed to diffuse passively through porin channels. The nature of D-cycloserine transport across the *E. coli* cytoplasmic membrane is well defined. The antibiotic is accumulated by the D-alanine transport system which is coupled to the pmf. The ability of D-cycloserine to utilize the D-alanine transport system reflects the structural similarity between the two molecules (Fig. 2.21).

4.4.2   *Fosfomycin*
Since fosfomycin (phosphonomycin) inhibits a cytoplasmic target enzyme, the antibiotic must be able to cross bacterial outer and cytoplasmic membranes. In *E. coli* passage across the outer membrane is mediated by the glpT protein which may act as a porin both for fosfomycin entry and the naturally occurring molecule sn-glycerol-3-phosphate (Fig. 2.38). Transport across the cytoplasmic membrane can be

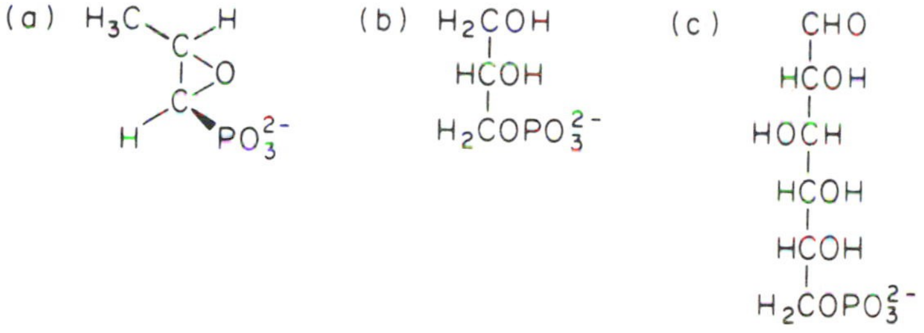

Fig. 2.38 — Structures of fosfomycin (*a*), glycerol-3-phosphate (*b*) and glucose-6-phosphate (*c*).

mediated either by the sn-glycerol-3-phosphate or hexose phosphate transport systems reflecting the structural similarity between the antibiotic and the naturally occurring molecules (Fig. 2.38). Both these transport systems are coupled to the pmf.

4.4.3   *Bacitracin A and glycopeptide antibiotics*
These antibiotics all comprise large molecules (bacitracin 1411 daltons; vancomycin, ristocetin and teicoplanin about 3300 daltons) that are too large to cross Gram-negative outer membranes. Hence these antibiotics exhibit poor antibacterial activity twards Gram-negative organisms. Their ability to inhibit targets in Gram-positive bacteria does not depend upon transport into the cell since the targets are exposed at the cell surface.

4.4.4   *Beta-lactams*
As already discussed (Section 3.5.4.2) inhibition of bacterial growth by beta-lactam antibiotics is a complex process which involves the binding of drug molecules to penicillin-binding proteins (PBPs) that are located on the surface of bacterial cytoplasmic membranes. Therefore, in Gram-negative organisms these antibiotics must cross the bacterial outer membrane to exert their inhibitory effects.

There is overwhelming evidence that the majority of beta-lactams cross the outer membrane by passive diffusion through porin channels. In *E. coli* this primarily involves the OmpF and OmpC porins. The rate of influx of beta-lactams through the porins is influenced by a number of factors that include drug hydrophobicity, size and net charge. In general, increases in hydrophobicity, size or net negative charge tend to decrease the rate of permeation of beta-lactams through porin channels. However, as emphasized by Nikaido, these parameters frequently interact with one another so that it is the gross physicochemical properties that influence the rate of permeation of beta-lactams through the porin channels.

4.5   Antibiotics that inhibit membrane integrity — polymyxins

As already noted (Section 3.6) the bactericidal activity of these compounds results
primarily from their interaction with the bacterial cytoplasmic membrane causing
gross disorganization of its structure. Therefore, in order to reach their target site in
Gram-negative organisms, polymyxins need to cross the bacterial outer membrane.
This is achieved primarily by self-promoted uptake of polymyxins across the outer
membrane whereby divalent cations are displaced leading to membrane destabilization and further insertion of antibiotic molecules into the outer membrane bilayer.

5.   CONCLUSIONS

A very large number of antibiotics (about 6000) have now been identified and this
chapter has focused upon the mode of action of the most important antibacterial
antibiotics. The molecular basis by which these compounds prevent bacterial growth
has been considered in detail, but it is beyond the scope of this book to describe their
specific clinical uses. Readers interested in this important aspect of antibiotic usage
can refer to the specific texts on the subject cited in the reference list at the end of this
chapter. However, it should be remembered that the presence of antibiotic-resistant
organisms, particularly in the hospital environment, may influence the choice of
antibiotic used for a particular therapeutic purpose. The subject of antibiotic
resistance is considered in detail in Chapter 5.

FURTHER READING

Books

(a) With an emphasis on the mode of action of antibiotics

Franklin, T. J. & Snow, G. A. (1989). *Biochemistry of Antimicrobial Action*. Fourth
    edition. Chapman & Hall, London.
Gale, E. F., Cundliffe, E., Reynolds, P. E., Richmond, M. H. & Waring, M. J.
    (1981). *The Molecular Basis of Antibiotic Action*. John Wiley & Sons, London.
Lorian, V. (1986). *Antibiotics in Laboratory Medicine*. Second edition. Williams
    and Wilkins, Baltimore.
Rogers, H. J., Perkins, H. R. & Ward, J. B. (1980). *Microbial Cell Walls and
    Membranes*. Chapman & Hall, London.

(b) With an emphasis on the clinical application of antibiotics

Garrod, L. P., Lambert, H. P. & O'Grady, F. (1981). *Antibiotic and Chemother-
    apy*. Fifth edition. Churchill Livingstone, Edinburgh.
Kuckers, A., & MckBennett, N. (1987). *The Use of Antibiotics*. Fourth edition.
    William Heinemann, London.

Review articles

Bachmann, B. J. (1987). Linkage map of Escherichia coli K-12, edition 7. In
    Escherichia coli and Salmonella typhimurium, Cellular and Molecular Biology,
    Volume 2 (ed. F. C. Neidhardt) pp. 807–876. American Society for Microbio-
    logy, Washington, DC.
Ball, P. (1986). Toxicity of sulphonamide-diaminopyrimidine combinations: impli-
    cations for future use. *Journal of Antimicrobial Chemotherapy* **17**: 694–696.

Benz, R. & Bauer, K. (1988). Permeation of hydrophilic molecules through the outer membrane of Gram-negative bacteria. *European Journal of Biochemistry* **176**:1–19.

Brisson-Noel, A., Trieu-Cuot, P. & Courvalin, P. (1988). Mechanism of action of spiramycin and other macrolides. *Journal of Antimicrobial Chemotherapy* **22** (Suppl. B): 13–23.

Brown, A. G. (1982). Beta-lactam nomenclature. *Journal of Antimicrobial Chemotherapy* **10**, 365–368.

Brown, G. M. & Williamson, J. M. (1987). Biosynthesis of folic acid, riboflavin, thiamine and pantothenic acid. In *Escherichia coli and Salmonella typhimurium, Cellular and Molecular Biology*, Volume 1 (ed. F. C. Neidhardt) pp. 521–538. American Society for Microbiology, Washington, DC.

Casewell, M. W. & Hill, R. L. R. (1987). Mupirocin ('pseudomonic acid') — a promising new topical antimicrobial agent. *Journal of Antimicrobial Chemotherapy* **19**:1–5.

Cashel, M. & Rudd, K. E. (1987). The stringent response. In *Escherichia coli and Salmonella typhimurium, Cellular and Molecular Biology*, Volume 2 (ed. F. C. Neidhart) pp. 1410–1438. American Society for Microbiology, Washington, DC.

Chopra, I. (1985). Mode of action of the tetracyclines and the nature of bacterial resistance to them. In *The Tetracyclines, Handbook of Experimental Pharmacology*, Volume 78 (ed. J. J. Hlavka & J. H. Boothe) pp. 317–392. Springer-Verlag, Berlin.

Chopra, I. (1988). Molecular mechanisms involved in the transport of antibiotics into bacteria. *Parasitology* **96**:S25–S44.

Chopra, I. (1989). Transport of antibiotics into bacteria. *Annual Reports in Medicinal Chemistry* **24**: in press.

Chopra, I. & Ball, P. R. (1982). Transport of antibiotics into bacteria. *Advances in Microbial Physiology* **23**, 183–240.

Chu, D. T. W. & Fernandes, P. B. (1989). Structure–activity relationships of the fluoroquinolones. *Antimicrobial Agents and Chemotherapy* **33**: 131–135.

Davis, B. D. (1987). Mechanism of bactericidal action of aminoglycosides. *Microbiological Reviews* **51**:341–350.

Davis, B. D. (1988). The lethal action of aminoglycosides. *Journal of Antimicrobial Chemotherapy* **22**: 1–3.

Doyle, R. J. & Koch, A. L. (1987). The functions of autolysins in the growth and division of *Bacillus subtilis*. *CRC Critical Reviews in Microbiology* **15**, 169–222.

Drlica, K. (1987). The nucleoid. In *Escherichia coli and Salmonella typhimurium, Cellular and Molecular Biology*, Volume 1 (ed. F. C. Neidhardt) pp. 91–103. American Society for Microbiology, Washington, DC.

Hancock, R. E. W. (1987). Role of porins in outer membrane permeability. *Journal of Bacteriology* **169**, 929–933.

Hancock, R. E. W. & Bell, A. (1988). Antibiotic uptake into Gram-negative bacteria. *European Journal of Clinical Microbiology and Infectious Diseases* **7**: 713–720.

Hershey, J. W. B. (1987). Protein synthesis. In *Escherichia coli and Salmonella typhimurium, Cellular and Molecular Biology*, Volume 1 (ed. F. C. Neidhardt) pp. 613–647. American Society for Microbiology, Washington, DC.

Hooper, D. C. & Wolfson, J. S. (1985). The fluroquinolones: pharmacology, clinical uses, and toxicities in humans. *Antimicrobial Agents and Chemotherapy* **28**: 716–721.

Ishiguro, E. E. & Kusser, W. (1988). Regulation of peptidoglycan biosynthesis and antibiotic-induced autolysis in nongrowing *Escherichia coli*: a preliminary model. In *Antibiotic Inhibition of Bacterial Cell Surface Assembly and Function* (eds P. Actor, L. Daneo-Moore, M. L. Higgins, M. R. J. Salton & G. D. Shockman) pp. 189–194. American Society for Microbiology, Washington, DC.

McMacken, R., Silver, S. & Georgopoulos, C. (1987). DNA replication. In *Escherichia coli and Salmonella typhimurium, Cellular and Molecular Biology*, Volume 1 (ed. F. C. Neidhardt) pp. 564–612. American Society for Microbiology, Washington, DC.

Moazed, D. & Noller, H. F. (1987). Interaction of antibiotics with functional sites in 16S ribosomal RNA. *Nature* **327**: 389–394.

Nichols, W. W. (1987). On the mechanism of translocation of dihydrostreptomycin across the bacterial cytoplasmic membrane. *Biochimica et Biophysica Acta* **895**: 11–23.

Nikaido, H. & Vaara, T. (1986). Molecular basis of bacterial outer membrane permeability. *Microbiological Reviews* **49**, 1–32.

Noller, H. F. & Nomura, M. (1987). Ribosomes. In *Escherichia coli and Salmonella typhimurium, Cellular and Molecular Biology*, Volume 2 (ed. F. C. Neidhart) pp. 104–125. American Societey for Microbiology, Washington, DC.

Noller, H. F., Stern, S., Moazed, D., Powers, T., Svensson, P. & Changchien, L-M. (1987). Studies on the architecture and function of 16S rRNA. *Cold Spring Harbor Symposia on Quantitative Biology,* Volume 52: 695–707.

Nomura, M. (1987). The role of RNA and protein in ribosome function: a review of early reconstitution studies and prospects for future studies. *Cold Spring Harbor Symposia on Quantitative Biolgy,* Volume 52: 653–658.

Park, J. T. (1987). Murein synthesis. In *Escherichia coli and Salmonella typhimurium, Cellular and Molecular Biology*, Volume 1 (ed. F. C. Neidhardt) pp. 663–671. American Society for Microbiology, Washington, DC.

Pogwizd, S. M. & Lerner, S. A. (1984). Mechanisms of action of antimicrobial agents. In *CRC Handbook of Microbiology*, Volume 6 (eds A. I. Laskin & H. A. Lechevalier) pp. 299–316. CRC Press, Boca Raton, Florida.

Reynolds, P. E. (1985). Inhibitors of bacterial cell wall synthesis. In *The Scientific Basis of Antimicrobial Chemotherapy*, 38th Symposium of the Society for General Microbiology (eds D. Greenwood & F. O'Grady) pp. 13–40. Cambridge University Press, Cambridge.

Rolinson, G. N. (1988). The influence of 6-aminopenicillanic acid on antibiotic development. *Journal of Antimicrobial Chemotherapy* **22**, 5–14.

Rosen, B. P. & Kashket, E. R. (1978). Energetics of active transport. In *Bacterial Transport* (ed. B. P. Rosen) pp. 559–620. Marcel Dekker, New York, Basel.

Russell, A. D. (1988). Design of antimicrobial chemotherapeutic agents. In *Introduction to the Principles of Drug Design* (ed. H. J. Smith) pp. 265–308. Wright, London.

Sanders, C. C. (1988). Ciprofloxacin: in vitro activity, mechanism of action and resistance. *Reviews of Infectious Diseases* **10**: 516–527.

Shockman, G. D., Daneo-Moore, L., McDowell, T. D. & Wong, W. (1981). Function and structure of the cell wall — its importance in the life and death of bacteria. In *Beta-lactam Antibiotics, Mode of Action, New Developments and Future Prospects* (eds M. R. J. Salton & G. D. Shockman) pp. 31–65. Academic Press, New York.

Smith, J. T. (1985). The 4-quinolone antibacterials. In *The Scientific Basis of Antimicrobial Chemotherapy*, 38th Symposium of the Society for General Microbiology (eds D. Greenwood & F. O'Grady) pp. 69–94. Cambridge University Press.

Spratt, B. G. (1983). Penicillin binding proteins and the future of β-lactam antibiotics. *Journal of General Microbiology* **129**, 1247–1260.

Storm, D. R., Rosenthal, K. S. & Swanson, P. E. (1977). Polymyxin and related peptide antibiotics. *Annual Review of Biochemistry* **46**, 723–763.

Tomasz, A. (1983). Mode of action of β-lactam antibiotics — a microbiologist's view. In *Antibiotics Containing the beta-Lactam Structure, Handbook of Experimental Pharmacology* Volume 67 (ed. A. L. Demain and N. A. Solomon) pp. 15–97. Springer-Verlag, Berlin.

Walker, G. C. (1987). The SOS response of *Escherichia coli*. In *Escherichia coli and Salmonella typhimurium, Cellular and Molecular Biology*, Volume 2 (ed. F. C. Neidhardt) pp 1346–1357.

Walsh, C. T. (1989). Enzymes in the D-alanine branch of bacterial cell wall peptidoglycan assembly. *Journal of Biological Chemistry* **264**: 2393–2396.

Woese, C. R., Gutell, R., Gupta, R. & Noller, H. F. (1983). Detailed analysis of the higher-order structure of 16S-like ribosomal ribonucleic acids. *Microbiological Reviews* **47**: 621–669.

Wolfson, J. S. & Hooper, D. C. (1985). The fluroquinolones: structures, mechanisms of action and resistance, and spectra of activity in vitro. *Antimicrobial Agents and Chemotherapy* **28**: 581–586.

Research papers

Casewell, M. W. & Hill, R. L. R. (1985). In vitro activity of mupirocin ('pseudomonic acid') against clinical isolates of *Staphylococcus aureus*. *Journal of Antimicrobial Chemotherapy* **15**: 523–531.

Davis, B. D., Chen, L. & Tai, P.C. (1986). Misread protein creates membrane channels: an essential step in the bactericidal action of aminoglycosides. *Proceedings of the National Academy of Sciences USA* **83**, 6164–6168.

Greenwood, D. (1988). Microbiological properties of teicoplanin. *Journal of Antimicrobial Chemotherapy* **21**, Supplement A, 1–13.

Kitano, K. & Tomasz, A. (1979). Triggering of autolytic cell wall degradation in *Escherichia coli* by beta-lactam antibiotics. *Antimicrobial Agents and Chemotherapy* **16**, 838–848.

McDowell, T. D. & Lemanski, C. L. (1988). Absence of autolytic activity (peptidoglycan nicking) in penicillin-induced nonlytic death in group A streptococcus. *Journal of Bacteriology* **170**, 1783–1788.

Phillips, I., Culebras, E., Moreno, F. & Baquero, F. (1987). Induction of the SOS response by new 4-quinolones. *Journal of Antimicrobial Chemotherapy* **20**: 631–638.

Piddock, L. J. V. & Wise, R. (1987). Induction of the SOS response in *Escherichia coli* by 4-quinolone antimicrobial agents. *FEMS Microbiology Letters* **41**: 289–294.

Takasuga, A., Adachi, H., Ishino, F., Matsuhashi, M., Ohta, T. & Matsuzawa, H. (1988). Identification of the pencillin-binding active site of penicillin-binding protein 2 of *Escherichia coli*. *Journal of Biochemistry* **104**, 822–826.

Tuomanen, E. & Schwartz, J. (1987). Penicillin-binding protein 7 and its relationship to lysis of nongrowing *Escherichia coli*. *Journal of Bacteriology* **169**: 4912–4915.

3

Antiseptics, disinfectants and preservatives: their properties, mechanisms of action and uptake into bacteria

1. INTRODUCTION

Historically, biocides have been used for many centuries. The ancient Egyptian art of mummification relied in part on the use of balsams which contained natural preservatives. The preservation of food by salting or mixing with natural spices has also been known since ancient times. Various agents (wine, vinegar, honey, mercuric chloride) found use as wound dressings. More recently, antiseptic surgery was introduced in France and Britain and disinfectant usage expanded considerably to control the spread of infection in hospitals. An important landmark was reached in 1897 when Kronig and Paul, with help from Ikeda, introduced their famous work on the dynamics of disinfection, the principles of which still form the basis of our present knowledge.

Currently, antimicrobial compounds (other than antibiotics) are used for their antiseptic, disinfectant or preservative activity. These terms were defined in Chapter 1 (Section 1) and so suffice to state here that disinfectants are normally used on inanimate objects (although it is permissible to use the term 'disinfection of the skin', for example pre-operatively), antiseptics may be applied to living tissues and preservatives are incorporated into various types of food, pharmaceutical and cosmetic products to prevent contamination or spoilage. The broad term 'biocide' is used to describe agents with these properties.

Individual infectious agents differ considerably in their response to biocides (Table 3.1). Probably the most resistant of all are 'slow viruses', known as prions. Amongst the bacteria, bacterial spores are invariably the least sensitive, followed by acid-fast bacteria, then Gram-negative organisms and finally the most sensitive, Gram-positive non-sporing, non-acid-fast bacteria such as staphylococci.

The initial reaction between an antibacterial agent and a bacterial cell involves binding to the cell surface. Changes to the outer layers may then occur to allow

Table 3.1 — Relative sensitivity[a] of microorganisms to disinfectants and other biocides

Type of microorganism	Sensitivity to biocides	Comment
Viruses	Non-enveloped more resistant than enveloped Most resistant: prions ('slow viruses')	Picornaviruses and parvoviruses may show resistance just below acid-fast bacteria
Bacteria	Non-sporing bacteria are most susceptible Acid-fast bacteria are more resistant Bacterial spores are most resistant	*Ps. aeruginosa* may show high resistance, e.g. to QACs Probably associated with waxy 'overcoat' Less so than prions
Fungi	Fungal spores may be resistant	Rather less so than acid-fast bacteria
Parasites	Coccidia may be highly resistant	Similar to bacterial spores

[a]Mechanisms of bacterial resistance to biocides are considered in Chapters 6 and 7.

agents to penetrate the cell to reach their primary site of action at the cytoplasmic membrane or within the cytoplasm. The effect at the primary target site may lead to additional, secondary, changes elsewhere in the organism. Such secondary alterations may also contribute to the bacteriostatic or bactericidal activity of the biocide. For these reasons, it may not always be easy to ascribe a mode of action to a particular biocide.

This chapter considers the properties and mechanisms of antibacterial action of a range of antiseptics, disinfectants and preservatives, and of the possible ways in which they enter bacterial cells. It is first necessary, however, to describe those factors that influence their activity, since some of these are important in assessing the mechanism of action of a particular biocide.

2.   FACTORS INFLUENCING ACTIVITY

The antimicrobial activity of biocides depends markedly on several factors, some of the most important of which will be considered briefly here. These are time of exposure, concentration, temperature, pH and the presence of organic matter.

2.1   Time of exposure

Contrary to popular advertising, the death of microorgansisms exposed to a biocide is not an instantaneous event, but takes place over a period of time (Fig. 3.1). Depending on the nature of the biocide and its concentration, a series of death curves of different shapes may be produced. Much time and effort have been spent in analysing these responses but this approach has yielded little information about killing mechanisms at the molecular level.

2.2   Concentration

As would be excpected when concentration rises (e.g. D to H, Fig. 3.2) the rate of bacterial inactivation increases. However, the effect of concentration varies from

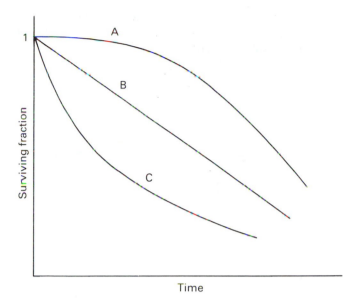

Fig. 3.1 — Different types of response of micro-organisms to a biocide. A, initial shoulder followed by exponential death; B, exponential death; C, initial exponential death followed by tailing-off.

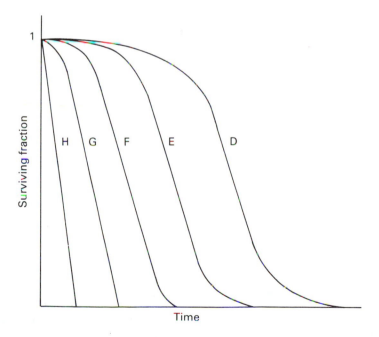

Fig. 3.2 — Effect of concentration of biocide on rates of microbial death. D, lowest concentration through intermediate concentrations (E–G) to H, highest concentration.

biocide to biocide. When the logarithm of the time needed to kill a specified number of cells is plotted against $\log_{10}$ concentration, a straight line is produced, the slope (η) of which (Fig. 3.3) is known as the concentration exponent or dilution coefficient.

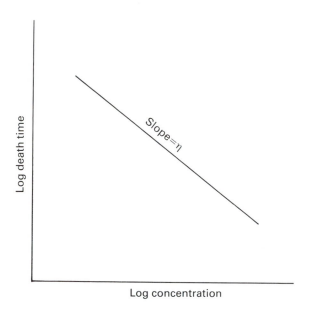

Fig. 3.3 — Plot of log concentration against log time for each concentration to bring about a specified degree of microbial inactivation: slope of line $=n$.

This is a measure of the effect of concentration (or dilution) on antibacterial activity. The value of η can also be deduced from the equation

$$C^{\eta}t = \text{constant} \tag{1}$$

or

$$C_1^{\eta}t_1 = C_2^{\eta}t_2 \tag{2}$$

in which t_1 and t_2 are the times required to kill a specified number of cells after exposure to concentrations C_1 and C_2 respectively.

Antibacterial agents with high η-values lose their activity rapidly on dilution, whereas those with low η-values retain much of their original activity. The η-value for a particular compound is probably related to its mechanism of action and accordingly biocides have been classified into three general categories, A, B and C (Table 3.2).

Table 3.2 — The possible relationship between η-values and mechanism of action of antibacterial agents

Group	Antibacterial agent[a]	Mechanism of action[a]
A ($\eta < 1$ to 2)	Hydrogen peroxide	–SH reactor
	Mercury compounds	–SH reactors
	Chlorhexidine	Membrane disrupter
	QACs	Membrane disrupter
	Formaldehyde	Interacts with protein
	Glutaraldehyde	–NH$_2$ groups and nucleic acids
	Acridines	Intercalating agents
	Iodine	–SH reactor (oxidation)
	Chlorine	–SH reactor (oxidation)
B (η 2–4)	Parabens ⎫ Sorbic acid ⎬ Benzoic acid	See Table 3.5 for specific details
C ($\eta > 4$)	Aliphatic alcohols ⎫ Phenolics ⎪ Benzyl alcohol ⎬ Phenethanol ⎭	Membrane disrupters

[a] Other reactions have also been proposed for some biocides, e.g. hydrogen peroxide, iodine and chlorine: see Sections 5 and 7.

2.3 Temperature

The antibacterial activity of most chemicals increases when the temperature is raised. This can be expressed in mathematical terms by determining the times (t_1 and t_2) necessary to kill a particular suspension at temperatures T_1 and T_2 respectively, from which the temperature coefficient (θ) can be calculated, namely:

$$\theta^{T_2 - T_1} = t_1/t_2 \tag{3}$$

θ refers to the effect of temperature per 1°C rise and nearly always has a value between 1 and 1.5. It is more usual to specify the θ^{10} value (also known as Q$_{10}$ by analogy with enzymatic reactions) which is the change in activity per 10°C rise in temperature. Examples of θ^{10} values are as follows: phenols and cresols, 3–5; formaldehyde, 1.5; aliphatic alcohols, 30–50. Antibacterial agents that are not sporicidal at ambient temperatures, e.g. phenols, become so at elevated temperatures.

2.4 pH

The activity of many antibacterial compounds is influenced quite markedly by changes in pH. Examples include phenols (Section 4.1.1.1), organic acids (Section

4.3.1.1), glutaraldehyde (Section 3.1), quaternary ammonium compounds (QACs) and chlorhexidine (Sections 4.1.1.2 and 4.1.1.3) and various halogens (Sections 5.6 and 5.7.1).

    Reasons for this change of activity are two-fold, namely:

(a) An effect on the molecule, e.g. an increase in pH increases the dissociation of organic acids, the undissociated form making the greatest contribution to killing (see Fig. 3.4). Hypochlorous acid, HOCl, and diatomic iodine (I_2) contribute

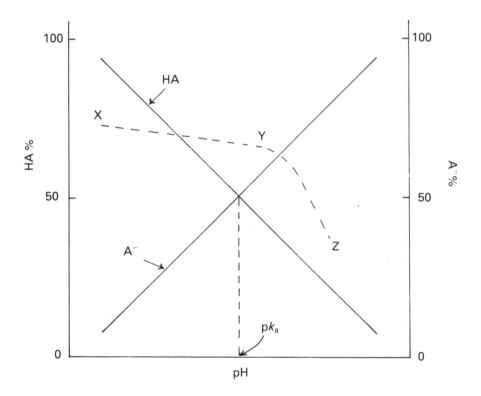

Fig. 3.4 — Relationship between pH and the ionization and bactericidal activity of an acid, HA. Bactericidal activity is shown by the dotted line XYZ, in which maximum activity is demonstrated at X with a slight decrease at Y and a considerable drop in efficacy at Z.

most to the activity of hypochlorites and iodine formulations, respectively, and occur at highest levels at acid pH.

    Glutaraldehyde combines most strongly with amino and sulphydryl groups in proteins at alkaline pH, where it is consequently most active.

(b) An alteration in the bacterial cell surface: as pH rises, the cell surface becomes more negatively charged. Cationic-type bactericides such as the quaternaries, chlorhexidine and diamidines (e.g. pentamidine, propamidine) which react with negatively charged groups thus become more effective bactericides at increased pH.

2.5   Organic matter

Organic matter may occur in several forms, especially as blood or serum, faeces, dirt, milkstone, etc. Antibacterial agents, e.g. chlorine-releasing compounds, that are highly reactive chemically thus tend to lose activity rapidly and to a considerable extent in the presence of organic matter, with which they combine strongly.

3.   AGENTS INTERACTING WITH OUTER CELLULAR COMPONENTS

Some antiseptics and disinfectants have been claimed to interact strongly with bacterial cell walls, e.g. phenols and mercury compounds, but the information available on these is sparse. Other antibacterial agents exert a significant effect on the outer layers of bacteria, although viability is not always affected. It is necessary for the reader to refer to Figs 1.2 and 1.3 in Chapter 1 for a detailed picture of the structure and chemical composition of the outer cell layers.

3.1   Glutaraldehyde

Glutaraldehyde is a a saturated 5-carbon dialdehyde that, at alkaline pH, possesses high microbicidal activity (bacteria and their spores, fungi, viruses). It interacts predominantly with amino groups in proteins and enzymes, and is used mainly as a 'chemosterilizer' of certain types of medical equipment such as endoscopes. Acid solutions are stable, but 'activated' solutions (alkalinized) are potent biocides but retain activity for only about two weeks.

Because of its interaction with amino groups, it will bind to important components in bacterial cell envelopes, e.g. proteins, peptide chains in peptidoglycan and the teichoic acids in the cell walls of Gram-positive bacteria. Evidence for these interactions is as follows:

(i)   Peptidoglycan isolated from *B. subtilis* and treated with glutaraldehyde is less sensitive than the untreated polymer to lysozyme. The aldehyde reacts with 30–50% of the ε-NH_2 groups and the two tripeptide side-chains could be joined when free groups are available (Fig. 3.5);

(ii) Ester-linked D-alanine residues in *B. subtilis* wall teichoic acids react with glutaraldehyde;

(iii) Pretreatment of wall peptidoglycan in *Staph. aureus* decreases peptidoglycan breakdown on subsequent exposure to lysotaphin, and antistaphylococcal enzyme with murein hydrolase activity.

In Gram-negative bacteria, glutaraldehyde interacts principally with outer components of the cells, notably lipoprotein.

The dialdehyde also binds strongly to the cytoplasmic membrane. Thus, glutaral-dehyde-treated mureinoplasts (which have peptidoglycan as the outer layer) exhibit a decrease in transport capacity and *B. megaterium* protoplasts and *E. coli* sphero-plasts treated with glutaraldehyde resist lysis when transferred to a medium of low

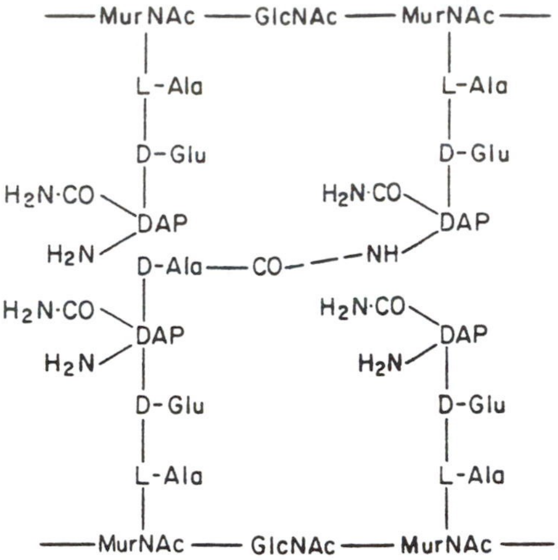

```
                 ——MurNAc——GlcNAc——MurNAc——
                      |                    |
                    L-Ala                L-Ala
                      |                    |
                    D-Glu                D-Glu
           H₂N·CO     |          H₂N·CO     |
                  ＼DAP                ＼DAP
            H₂N ／    D-Ala——CO————NH／
           H₂N·CO     |          H₂N·CO
                  ＼DAP                ＼DAP
            H₂N ／    |           H₂N ／
                    D-Glu                D-Glu
                      |                    |
                    L-Ala                L-Ala
                      |                    |
                 ——MurNAc——GlcNAc——MurNAc——
```

Fig. 3.5 — Peptide side-chains in *Bacillus subtilis* peptidoglycan showing availability of amino groups for interaction with glutaraldehyde.

osmotic pressure. Furthermore, release of certain membrane-bound enzymes is prevented by glutaraldehyde treatment. Glutaraldehyde is thus a highly reactive molecule and an effective biocide; its action on bacterial spores is considered in Chapter 4.

3.2   Permeabilizers
A permeabilizer is a chemical that increases the permeability of the outer membrane of Gram-negative bacteria. Included in this definition are ethylenediamine tetraacetic acid (EDTA), polycations, lactoferrin and transferrin.

EDTA shows significant activity against *Ps. aeruginosa* and lesser activity against other Gram-negative bacteria. The integrity of the outer leaflet of the outer membrane is maintained by hydrophobic LPS–LPS and LPS–protein interactions and the presence of divalent cations, notably Mg^{2+}, is essential for stabilizing the strong negative charges of the core oligosaccharide chain of the LPS molecules. EDTA binds these cations, thereby releasing up to about 50% of the LPS molecules, and enabling non-polar phospholipids associated with the inner membrane to be exposed at the cell surface so that hydrophobic molecules can now enter the cell. In this way, EDTA achieves a non-specific increase in cell permeability. Polycations such as polylysine ($lysine_{20}$) also induce LPS release, as do the iron-binding proteins lactoferrin and transferrin (Table 3.3).

3.3   Other agents
The enzyme lysozyme digests peptidoglycan as a result of its effect on β, 1–4 links. Hypochlorites induce lysis of Gram-positive bacteria, ostensibly by an effect on the cell wall, but have other effects on bacterial cells; in particular they act as oxidizing agents, reacting with –SH groups (Section 5.7.1). High concentrations of the anionic

Table 3.3 — Permeabilizing agents[a]

Type of agent	Specific example(s)	Mechanism(s) of action
Chelator	EDTA and similar agents	*Ps. aeruginosa*: leakage; lysis (prevented in equi-osmotic sucrose); removal of some Mg^{2+} and release of some LPS
		Resistant pseudomonads: no leakage, lysis or release of Mg^{2+} or LPS
		Coliforms: leakage; no lysis. Some release of Mg^{2+} and LPS
Polycations	Polylysine, i.e. $(lys)_{20}$	Displacement of Mg^{2+} and consequent release of some LPS
Iron-binding proteins	Lactoferrin Transferrin	Both act as chelators. Partial LPS loss.

[a] A permeabilizing agent is one that increases permeability of Gram-negative bacteria.

surfactant sodium lauryl sulphate lyse isolated outer membranes of Gram-negative bacteria, probably as a result of a potent effect on the protein components of the outer membrane, but this agent also acts on the inner membrane (Section 4.1.1.2).

4.   MEMBRANE-ACTIVE AGENTS: PROPERTIES AND MECHANISMS OF ACTION

The term 'membrane-active agent' is, rather loosely, used to describe an antimicrobial agent that damages the inner (cytoplasmic, plasma) membrane. Several such compounds are known, and include polymyxins (Chapter 2), phenols, parabens, biguanides, QACs and alcohols (see below). These differ quite markedly in chemical structure and it is therefore unlikely that they have exactly the same effect on the cytoplasmic membrane. Perturbation of homeostatic mechanisms in microorganisms can also be achieved by physical processes such as mild heat shock. Only chemically-induced damage to homeostasis will be considered here, but it must be pointed out that greater cellular damage will usually be achieved by chemicals used at elevated temperatures.

The cytoplasmic membrane (also known as the inner membrane in Gram-negative bacteria) is composed essentially of lipids and protein. Some details were given in Chapter 1 (Figs 1.2 and 1.3). A more detailed description is the Singer-Nicholson model (Fig. 3.6), in which the membrane is conceived as a fluid mosaic model in which globular proteins are embedded in a phospholipid matrix or bilayer. The membrane is semi-permeable, controls the presence of solutes into and out of the cytoplasm and is associated with several important enzymes. As such, it is a prime target for the action of many biocides. Damage to the membrane can take several forms: leakage from the cell of intracellular materials, cell lysis, dissipation of the proton-motive force and inhibition of membrane-associated enzyme activity.

4.1   Leakage of intracellular constituents
Damage to the cytoplasmic membrane is usually manifested by the release of intracellular constituents (Fig. 3.7). The first indice of membrane injury is potassium

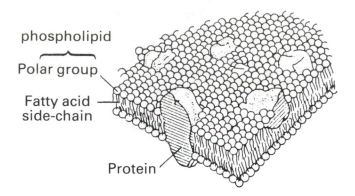

Fig. 3.6 — The proposed structure of the cytoplasmic membrane: Singer-Nicholson fluid mosaic model.

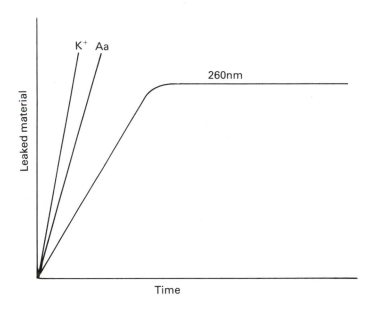

Fig. 3.7 — Rate of leakage of intracellular materials from bacteria exposed to a membrane-active agent. Aa, amino acids; 260 nm, 260 nm-absorbing material.

(K^+) leakage, followed by inorganic phosphates (Pi), pool amino acids and 260 nm-absorbing material (rather non-specific since it could indicate RNA or DNA or even, to some extent, protein material). More specific information can be obtained by examining leakage of pentoses, diphenylamine-positive material and Folin-positive material, indicative of RNA, DNA and protein respectively. Alternatively, the cells can be preloaded with a radio-active compound, e.g. $^{42}K^+$, $^{86}Rb^+$ or ^{32}P-phosphate, and the leakage from treated cells measured by liquid scintillation counting. The QAC, cetrimide, induces more rapid leakage from Gram-positive than Gram-negative bacteria, the latter being less susceptible because the outer membrane presents a barrier to the agent (see Chapter 6).

Leakage is best considered as a measure of the generalized loss of function of the cytoplasmic membrane as a permeability barrier. The rate and extent of leakage may depend on the concentration of the inhibitor and the time and temperature of exposure. Leakage may be related to bacteriostasis but not necessarily to cell death. For example, the activity of phenoxyethanol has been determined against *E. coli* at 10° and 35°C. The resulting temperature coefficient (Q_{25}) values showed a reduction in effect of 380-fold in bactericidal activity but of only 2-fold in leakage of intracellular materials. In contrast, there is a direct relationship between membrane damage and cell death in *E. coli* treated with a polymeric biguanide since Q_{10} values of about 2 were produced for both bactericidal activity and loss of intracellular substances. In studying the mechanism of action of a biocide, it is important to correlate biochemical and other changes with growth-inhibitory and lethal concentrations.

4.1.1 *Agents inducing leakage*
Several chemically unrelated biocides damage the bacterial cytoplasmic membrane, inducing leakage of intracellular constituents. They include phenolics, biguanides, quaternary ammonium compounds (QACs) and alcohols.

4.1.1.1 *Phenols and cresols*
Phenols and cresols are widely used as general disinfectants and as preservatives, but must not be employed when food may become exposed to them. The tar obtained as a by-product in the destructive distillation of coal is the source of most of the phenols (tar acids) used to produce disinfectants. Typically, coal tar contains the following fractions (in parentheses, boiling range): phenol (182°C), cresols (189–205°C), xylenols (210–230°C) and high-boiling tar acids (230–310°C).

Cresols consist of 2-(*ortho*), 3-(*meta*) and 4-(*para*) cresol, the xylenols of six isomeric dimethylphenols and ethylphenols. Cresols and xylenols are available commercially as a combined fraction (cresylic acid) and the high-boiling tar acids comprise the higher alkyl homologues of phenol, which form the basis of what are known as the Black fluids and White fluids. Examples of chemical structures are provided in Fig. 3.8. As the fractions are ascended, water solubility decreases, bactericidal activity increases but so, unfortunately, does inactivation by organic matter.

Phenol itself may also be manufactured by a synthetic process and other synthetic (non-coal tar) phenolics include 2-phenylphenol, 4-hexylresorcinol, chlorocresol (4-chloro-3-methylphenol) and chloroxylenol (4-chloro-3,5-dimethylphenol), all of which are used as antibacterial agents.

Structure–activity relationships in the phenol series demonstrate that:

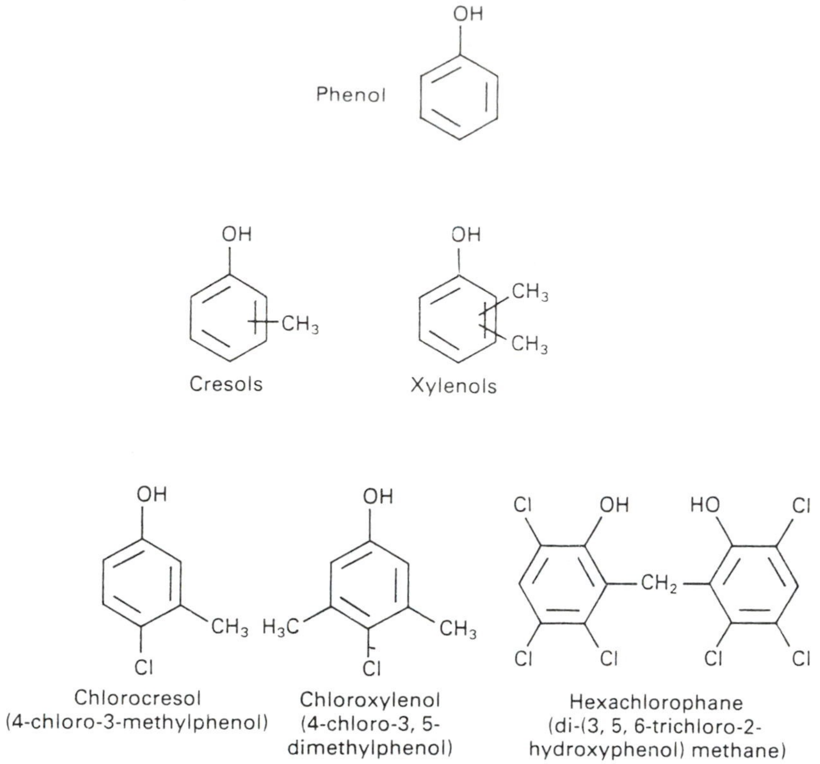

Fig. 3.8 — Some phenols and cresols.

(a) *para*(4)-Substitution of an alkyl chain of up to 6 carbon atoms in length (straight rather than branched chain substituents) increases antibacterial activity;

(b) Halogenation increases activity, and further still if this is at the *para*(4) position, and an alkyl group is introduced at the *ortho*(2) site, both in relation to the phenol group:

(c) Nitration increases activity but also increases systemic toxicity.

Phenols are predominantly membrane-active agents, but will also cause intracellular coagulation of cytoplasmic constituents. They are sometimes referred to as being merely protein precipitants, but this term masks the more subtle effects they have on bacterial cells.

Phenols, cresols and their chlorinated derivatives induce leakage of intracellular materials from bacteria. Penetration into the lipid-rich interior of the cytoplasmic membrane is an important step in the activity of 4-*n*-alkylphenols. Phenolic compounds which were at one time employed in antiseptic soaps and shampoos included hexachlorophane (Fig. 3.8) and tetrachlorosalicylanilide (TCS). These are now considered to be toxic. High (bactericidal) concentrations of these and the less toxic fentichlor induce leakage of intracellular constituents, but low concentrations have more specific effects as described in Sections 4.3.1.3 (TCS, fentichlor) and 4.1.1.1

(hexachlorophane). Phenol itself induces the release of ^{14}C-glutamate from *E. coli*, but leakage occurs without a drop in viable numbers and thus precedes death. Phenol damages the permeability barrier, permitting the rapid diffusion of low molecular weight substances from the metabolic pool, but cells may be able to recover rapidly following its removal.

4.1.1.2   *Surface-active agents (surfactants)*

Surface-active agents contain two structural regions, a hydrocarbon, water-repellant (hydrophobic) group and the other a water-attracting (hydrophilic or polar) group. Depending on the basis of the charge or absence of ionization of the hydrophilic group, surface-active agents are classified into the following four groups of compounds: cationic, anionic, amphoteric and non-ionic.

(1)   *Cationic agents.*   Primarily these are represented by the QACs (Fig. 3.9a), which are organically substituted ammonium compounds in which the nitrogen atom has a valency of 5, and four of the substituted radicals (R^1–R^4) are alkyl or heterocyclic radicals and the fifth (X^-) is a small anion. The sum of the carbon atoms in the four R groups is 10. In those QACs with potent antimicrobial activity, at least one of the R groups has a chain length in the range C_8 to C_{18}. The QACs are active against Gram-positive bacteria (but not spores) and less so against Gram-negative organisms, especially *Ps. aeruginosa*. Activity is markedly reduced in the presence of organic matter. The QACs are membrane-active agents, inducing a generalized increase in permeability (Table 3.5).

The QACs induce leakage of intracellular constituents from treated bacteria, which is indicative of membrane damage. The release of nitrogenous and phosphorus-containing substances was described by Hotchkiss in 1944, and Salton in 1951 demonstrated that the QAC cetrimide induced a more rapid rate of leakage from Gram-positive than Gram-negative cells. K^+ ions are released first, followed by PO_4^{3-} and then by 260 nm-absorbing material, indicative of larger molecular weight compounds: see Fig. 3.7.

Low, bacteriostatic, concentrations of cetrimide are claimed to have an effect on the pmf (Section 4.3.1.3). The effects of QACs on bacterial photoplasts are described in Section 4.2.1.

(2)   *Anionic agents.*   These are compounds which, in aqueous solution, dissociate into a large complex anion responsible for the surface activity and a smaller cation. Examples are the alkali-metal and metal soaps and lauryl ether sulphates (e.g. sodium lauryl (dodecyl) sulphate). Generally, they have strong detergent but weak antimicrobial properties, although high concentrations will induce lysis of Gram-negative bacteria (Section 4.2.1). Fatty acids are active against Gram-positive but not Gram-negative bacteria.

Anionic surfactants such as sodium lauryl sulphate (SLS) disrupt permeability barriers, inducing the leakage of intracellular constituents. They also cause protoplast lysis (Section 4.2.1) and produce a general denaturation of cell proteins. High concentrations (2%) of SLS dissolve cell walls of *E. coli*.

(3)   *Amphoteric (ampholytic) agents.*   Amphoteric agents are compounds of mixed anionic-cationic character, and combine the detergent properties of anionic surfactants with the bactericidal properties of cationic surfactants. Examples include dodecyl-di(aminoethyl)-glycine, a 'Tego' compound and dodecyl-β-alanine.

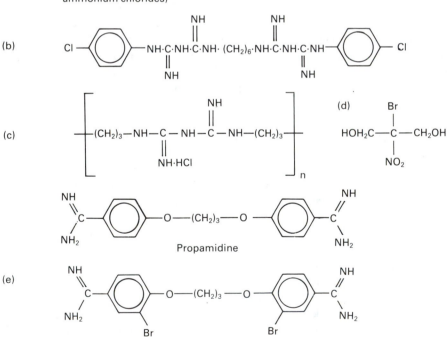

Fig. 3.9 — (a) General structure of quaternary ammonium compounds (QACs) and some examples. (b) Chlorhexidine. (c) Polyhexamethylene biguanide (PHMB). (d) Bronopol. (e) Some diamidines: propamidine, dibromopropamidine.

Table 3.4 — Membrane-active agents and permeability of *Bacillus megaterium* (strain KM) protoplasts

Antibacterial agent[a]	Protoplast inducer[b]	Protoplast permeable to	Protoplast impermeable to
None (control)	Lys Pen	NH_4^+ CH_3COO^-	Sucrose K^+ Cl^- Na^+ NO_3^-
TCC	Lys Pen	Sucrose NH_4^+ NO_3^- CH_3COO^- Cl^-	Na^+ K^+
CHA *or* CPC	Lys Pen	Sucrose NH_4^+ K^+ Na^+ CH_3COO^- Cl^- NO_3^-	None found

[a]TCC, trichlorocarbanilide; CHA, chlorhexidine diacetate; CPC, cetylpyridinium chloride.
[b]Lys, lysozyme; Pen, benzylpenicillin.

Amphoteric surfactants induce the leakage of intracellular materials from treated bacteria, but information about their precise mechanism of antibacterial action is sparse.

(4)   *Non-ionic agents.*   These consist of a hydrocarbon chain attached to a non-polar water-attracting group, which is usually a chain of ethylene oxide units, e.g. cetomacrogols and sorbitan derivatives such as the polysorbates (Tweens). Strictly speaking, they are not antibacterial agents but are important because low concentrations affect the permeability of the outer parts of the envelopes of Gram-negative cells whereas high concentrations overcome the activity of QACs, parabens and phenols.

4.1.1.3   Biguanides

Chlorhexidine (Fig. 3.9b) is the most important member of a family of N^1,N^5-substituted biguanides, and is available as dihydrochloride, diacetate (acetate) and gluconate salts. It has a broad spectrum of activity against both Gram-positive and Gram-negative bacteria, but is not sporicidal and is not lethal to acid-fast bacteria (mycobacteria) or to many viruses. Activity is reduced in the presence of serum, blood, pus and other organic matter, and, because of its cationic nature, in the presence of soaps and other anionic compounds.

Chlorhexidine is considered as being predominantly a membrane-active agent, but it has several effects on susceptible bacteria which contribute to its overall bactericidal efficacy (Sections 5.4 and 5.6; Table 3.5). The biguanide has a diphasic effect on membrane permeability (Fig. 3.10): an initial high rate of leakage of intracellular material occurs as the concentration of chlorhexidine increases, but at higher biocide concentrations, coagulation or precipitation of the cytosol occurs so that leakage is progressively decreased. It must be emphasized that there is no obvious relationship between the amount of cell constituents released and the drop in viability.

Another biguanide, polyhexamethylene biguanide (PHMB, Fig. 3.9c) with a molecular weight of approximately 3000 is active against Gram-positive and Gram-negative bacteria (*Ps. aeruginosa* and *P. vulgaris* are less sensitive) but is not sporicidal. Because of the residual positive charges on the polymer, it is precipitated

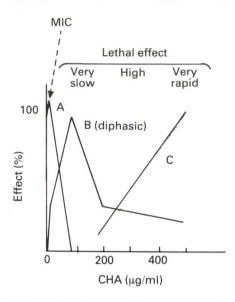

Fig. 3.10 — Effect of chlorhexidine diacetate (CHA) on *E. coli*: effects on viability, triphenyl terrazolium chloride (TTC) reduction (A), leakage of intracellular constituents (B) and intracellular coagulation and precipitation of nucleic acids and proteins (C) (based on Longworth, 1971). M IC, minimum inhibitory concentration.

from aqueous solutions by anionic compounds which include soaps and detergents based on alkyl sulphates. PHMB is a membrane-active agent which also impairs the integrity of the outer membrane of Gram-negative bacteria. A detailed consideration of its effect on susceptible bacteria is presented later (Section 4.5, and Fig. 3.21).

4.1.1.4   Alcohols

Several alcohols are rapidly bactericidal even to acid-fast bacteria. However, they are not sporicidal and usually have poor activity against viruses. Some important alcohols are as follows:

(a) Ethanol (ethyl alcohol C_2H_5OH): the presence of water is essential for its activity.
(b) Methanol (methyl alcohol, CH_3OH): this alcohol has poor activity but is believed to potentiate the sporicidal activity of hypochlorites (Chapter 7).
(c) Isopropanol (propan-2-ol, isopropyl alcohol, $(CH_3)_2CHOH$): this is a more effective bactericide then ethanol.
(d) Phenylethanol (phenylethyl alcohol, $C_6H_5.CH_2.CH_2OH$): this has selective activity against Gram-negative bacteria.
(e) Phenoxyethanol, $(C_6H_5.O.CH_2.CH_2OH)$: this alcohol possesses significant activity against *Ps. aeruginosa* but less against other Gram-negative organisms or against Gram-positive bacteria.
(f) Bronopol (2-bromo-2-nitropran-1,3-diol; Fig. 3.9d): bronopol is an aliphatic halogenonitro compound which possesses a broad antibacterial spectrum includ-

ing activity against *Ps. aeruginosa*. It is also antifungal but is not sporicidal. Its activity is reduced in the presence of 10% serum and more so by sulphydryl compounds (Section 4.4.1.2). Bronopol oxidizes thiol groups to disulphides, an action that is reversed by sulphydryl compounds (Fig. 3.19a).

Ethanol and isopropanol are membrane disrupters. Phenylethanol and phenoxyethanol also induce a generalized loss of the function of the cytoplasmic membrane, but both have other, more specific effects (see, for example, the information provided on phenoxyethanol in Section 4.3.1.3). Ethanol produces a rapid release of intracellular constituents from treated bacteria, and disorganization of the membrane probably results from penetration of the solvents into the hydrocarbon interior of the cytoplasmic membrane.

4.1.1.5   Other biocides
Other agents such as organic acids and esters may also induce leakage. They have an additional effect by dissipating the proton-motive force and will thus be considered elsewhere (Section 4.3).

4.2   Total membrane disruption: agents inducing lysis of wall-deficient forms
Despite extensive cytoplasmic membrane damage, bacterial lysis does not normally occur when bacteria are exposed to membrane-active agents. However, the use of cells without cell walls (protoplasts) or with modified cell envelopes (spheroplasts) enables a virtually direct effect of the inhibitor on the membrane so that lysis frequently results. Lysis of such wall-deficient forms is therefore indicative of gross membrane disruption by the biocide.

Protoplasts of organisms such as *B. megaterium* and *Micrococcus lysodeikticus* are produced by treatment with lysozyme in the presence of sucrose. *Staph. aureus* is much less sensitive to this enzyme, but lysostaphin is a suitable agent. Gram-negative bacteria are resistant to lysozyme but spheroplasts are produced when the cells are exposed to it in the presence of EDTA, tris buffer and sucrose. Spheroplasts of Gram-negative bacteria can also be induced by exposure in a growth medium containing sucrose to a beta-lactam that has an affinity for PBP 1B (Chapter 2). In each method of preparation of these morphological variants, sucrose (or other suitable solute) is a non-penetrating solute that is used at a concentration that roughly equalizes the internal and external osmotic pressures.

Protoplasts and spheroplasts are osmotically fragile forms, lysing when transferred from a medium of high osmotic pressure, e.g. 0.5M sucrose, to water or to a solute which readily penetrates the cytoplasmic membrane. Thus, the effects of inhibitors can be studied on the passage of ions across the membrane. For example, the membrane of *B. megaterium* protoplasts is naturally permeable to glycerol, NH_4^+ and CH_3COO^-; however, protoplasts are stable in, for example, ammonium chloride because the membrane is impermeable to Cl^-. Protoplast stability thus occurs under the following conditions:

(a) a membrane-permeable and a membrane-impermeable ion-pair;
(b) two membrane-impermeable ions.

The effects of antibacterial agents on protoplasts (or spheroplasts) suspended in sucrose or other solutes can then be used to obtain information about the type and specificity of action.

In addition, effects of a biocide on lysis of protoplasts (or spheroplasts) suspended in solutions of acetate salts (caesium, Cs; sodium, Na; lithium, Li) can be studied. The osmotically fragile forms are naturally permeable to acetate (CH_3COO^-) ions, and so biocide-induced lysis in solutions of these acetate salts provides data about membrane permeability towards the cation.

4.2.1   Nature of agents inducing major membrane disruption
Low concentrations of chlorhexidine and QACs effect lysis of spheroplasts and protoplasts suspended in sucrose, but at higher concentrations lysis is reduced because of an intracellular precipitation or coagulation (Fig. 3.11). Parallels have

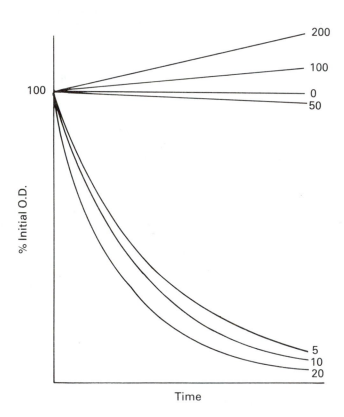

Fig. 3.11 — Lysis of protoplasts of *Bacillus megaterium* by chlorhexidine. (Figures represent μg/ml.) *Note*: at concentrations above 50 μg/ml, lysis is prevented because of intracellular precipitation.

been noted between bactericidal action against whole cells and lytic activity on protoplasts of *M. lysodeikticus* of detergents containing a dodecyl chain ($C_{12}H_{25}$) attached to a charged group. The order of activity was

$$C_{12}H_{25}-NH_3^+ > -NMe_3^+ > -SO_4^- > -SO_3^-$$

Cationic agents (QACs) react with phospholipid components (Fig. 3.6) in the cytoplasmic membrane, thereby producing distortion of the membrane and protoplast lysis under osmotic stress. Isolated membranes do not undergo disaggregation on exposure to QACs because membrane distortion is not sufficiently drastic. Anionic surfactants, in contrast, interact with the protein components (Fig. 3.6) of cytoplasmic membranes; these proteins are solubilized, so that anionic detergents will lyse protoplasts and disaggregate isolated membranes (in the absence of osmotic stress).

Alcohols also will induce protoplast lysis. Equal thermodynamic activities of alcohols produce equal degrees of lysis of *M. lysodeikticus* protoplasts, and the amount of damage that they produce is probably related to their concentrations in the lipid phase.

Useful information about the selectivity of membrane action can thus be obtained by studying the effects of biocides on protoplasts or spheroplasts suspended in various solutes (Table 3.4).

Trichlorocarbanilide induces lysis in ammonium chloride because it increases Cl^- permeability whereas tetrachlorosalicylanilide induces lysis in ammonium nitrate by increasing NO_3^- permeability (Table 3.4). However, QACs and chlorhexidine produce lysis of protoplasts suspended in various solutes because they effect a generalized, rather than specific, membrane damage. The effects and conclusions are summarized in Table 3.5.

Chlorhexidine-induced rate of lysis of spheroplasts in acetate salts is inversely proportional to the hydrated ionic radii of the cations, i.e. greatest in Cs and least in Li. These findings conform to Fick's laws of diffusion which state that the rate of diffusion of a solute per unit area in a direction perpendicular to the area is proportional to the gradient of solute concentration in that direction.

4.3   Dissipation of proton-motive force

As pointed out in Chapter 1, Mitchell's chemi-osmotic theory envisages a mechanism whereby active transport, oxidative phosphorylation and adenosine triphosphate (ATP) synthesis in chloroplasts, mitochondria and bacteria, as well as bacterial flagellar movement, can be explained. These are powered by a proton-motive force (pmf) generated by ATP hydrolysis or metabolic oxido-reductions (Fig. 3.12). The pmf is expressed as a gradient across the cytoplasmic membrane and in bacteria is demonstrated with the interior of the cell alkaline and negatively charged in relation to the external environment. Another pertinent aspect of Mitchell's theory is that the cytoplasmic membrane must be non-conducting and not readily permeable to protons and other ions.

As described in Chapter 1, the theory may be expressed mathematically as follows:

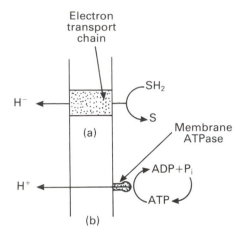

Fig. 3.12 — Mitchell's chemiosmotic theory. Generation of proton-motive force (pmf) by (a) electron transport chain, (b) hydrolysis of adenosine triphosphate (ATP). $SH_2{\rightarrow}S$: oxidation of substrate. (For further information on ATPase, see Fig. 3.20.)

$$p=\Delta\psi-Z\Delta pH$$

in which p is the pmf, ψ the membrane electrical potential, ΔpH the trans-membrane pH gradient, and Z a constant (2.303 RT/F) with a value of 61 at 37°C.

The electron transport chain is fixed in a definite direction in the membrane. In consequence, the protons generated during the oxidation of substrate ($SH_2{\rightarrow}S$, Fig. 3.12a) leading eventually to the reduction of oxygen, are transported from the interior of the cell outwards. The fact that a pmf is also generated by ATPase hydrolysis of ATP explains the existence of a pmf in anaerobic bacteria and in facultative organisms metabolizing anaerobically.

Some antibacterial agents interfere with oxidative phosphorylation by stimulating oxygen uptake whilst inhibiting phosphorylation. These are called uncouplers or uncoupling agents.

4.3.1 Agents dissipating the pmf
Several antibacterial agents are known to cause dissipation of the pmf. The properties of some of these agents were considered previously.

4.3.1.1 Acids and esters
Several acids (a few inorganic and some aromatic and aliphatic) have found use as preservatives in food and/or pharmaceutical products, whereas others, e.g. salicyclic and undecylenic, are sometimes incorporated into products used for the topical treatment of fungal skin infections. Acids used as food preservatives include acetic (ethanoic), propionic, sorbic (2,4-hexadienoic acid), dehydroacetic and benzoic (usually as the sodium salt): see Fig. 3.13.

Environmental pH is one of the major factors affecting the activity of organic

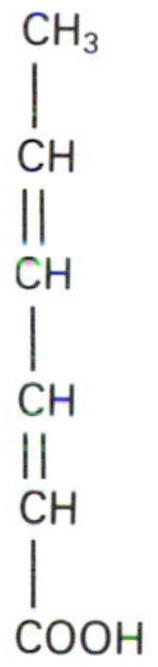

2,4-Hexadienoic acid
(Sorbic acid)

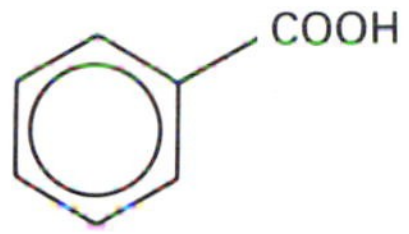

Benzoic acid

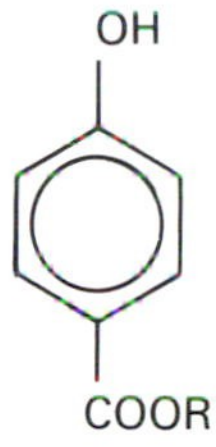

Ester of *p*-hydroxybenzoic acid
(R=methyl, ethyl, propyl, butyl, etc.)

Fig. 3.13 — Some organic acids and esters of *p*(4)-hydroxybenzoic acid.

acids. In aqueous solutions of mineral acids, but not of weaker organic acids, complete ionization occurs. The latter type will contain three components and these can be considered as being an acid of symbol HA and the ionized components A^- and H^+. The ionization constant, K_a, of the acid is represented by

$$K_a=[A^-][H^+]/[HA]$$

and the pK_a value (the pH at which 50% ionization occurs) varies with different acids, e.g. benzoic acid 4.2, sorbic acid 4.8. At pH values greater than pK_a, antibacterial activity decreases rapidly, permitting the conclusion that the undissociated moiety (HA) makes the greatest contribution to inhibitory activity (Fig. 3.4).

The most important esters of organic acids are those of *para*(4)-hydroxybenzoic acid (Fig. 3.13). These, known as the parabens, consist usually of the methyl, ethyl, propyl, butyl and sometimes benzyl esters. Their activity is less susceptible to changes in pH and they are employed as pharmaceutical, cosmetic and food preservatives.

Studies with pharmaceutical and food preservatives have demonstrated that lipophilic acids (e.g. propionic, sorbic, benzoic, 4-hydroxybenzoic) and the parabens inhibit the active uptake of some amino and oxo acids in *E. coli* and *B. subtilis*. Despite the long history of these agents as food and pharmaceutical preservatives, their exact mode of action continues to be the subject of debate. Sorbic acid affects the pmf in *E. coli* and accelerates the movement of H^+ ions from low pH media into the cytoplasm (see Fig. 3.14). Acidification of the cytoplasm to about pH 6 is sufficient to prevent growth. In the light of current knowledge, it may be rather tentatively concluded that sorbic acid dissipates pH across the membrane and

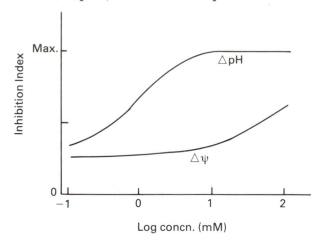

Fig. 3.14 — Effect of sorbic acid on Δ*pH and* Δψ in *E. coli* membrane vesicles. (Based on
T. Eklund, *Journal of General Microbiology*, 1985, **131**, 73–76.)

inhibits solute transport, but may also have another, as yet unidentified, target. The
membrane potential (Δψ) is reduced but to a much smaller extent than ΔpH (Fig.
3.14).

The parabens induce leakage of intracellular constituents from treated cells,
activity increasing from the methyl to the butyl ester. Their effect on bacteria is,
however, markedly concentration-dependent, because only high concentrations
affect membrane integrity in this way, low concentrations causing a selective
inhibition of pH across the membrane.

4.3.1.2   Dinitrophenol

2,4-Dinitrophenol (DNP) inhibits ATP synthesis whilst stimulating respiration, i.e.
it acts as an uncoupler of oxidative phosphorylation. DNP is a weak lipophilic acid
which 'short-circuits' the membrane, thereby causing a back-flow of protons across
the cytoplasmic membrane into the cell with the consequent collapse of Δ*p*, the pmf
(Fig. 3.15). The cellular activities powered by the pmf are inhibited. Provided

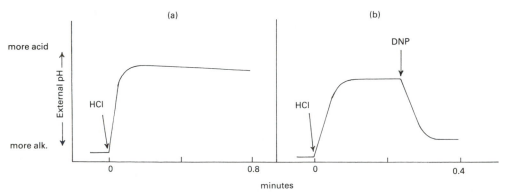

Fig. 3.15 — Effect of dinitrophenol (DNP, 5×10^{-5}M) on proton flux in the obligate anaerobe,
Clostridium perfringens. (a) Control, cells exposed only to hydrochloric acid (external pH
falls). (b) Cells exposed to hydrochloric acid and then to DNP. DNP causes an instantaneous
influx of protons (seen as a sudden *rise* in external pH) and a complete discharge of the proton
gradient. (Based on D. C. Daltrey & W. B. Hugo, *Microbios*, 1974, **11**, 131–146.)

substrate accumulation was not dependent on proton-driven active transport, cellular respiration (oxygen uptake) would continue whereas ATP synthesis, which is dependent on the pmf, would cease. Thus, the phenomenon of the uncoupling of oxidative phosphorylation can now be explained at the molecular level.

4.3.1.3   Other agents
Low concentrations of phenoxyethanol induce proton translocation in *E. coli* but higher concentrations produce gross membrane damage (Fig. 3.16). Fentichlor and

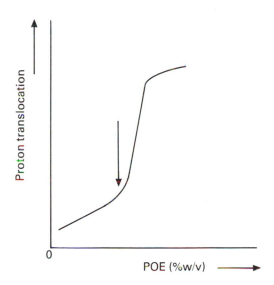

Fig. 3.16 — Rate of phenoxyethanol (POE)-induced proton translocation in *E. coli*: relationship between POE concentration and its effect on gross membrane damage. (Arrow indicates POE concentration causing gross membrane damage.) (Based on P. Gilbert, E. G. Beveridge & P. B. Crone, *Microbios*, 1977, **19**, 17–26.)

TCS inhibit energy-dependent uptake of amino acids and glucose into cellular material. TCS also discharges the membrane potential component ($\Delta\psi$) in *Strep. faecalis*. The QAC, cetrimide, has been claimed to discharge the pH component of Δp in *Staph. aureus* at the MIC level.

4.4   Inhibition of membrane enzymes
The cytoplasmic membrane is made up of phospholipids and proteins, many of which possess enzymatic properties. The membrane is rich in enzyme activity, particularly those associated with the electron transport chain that use the electrochemical potential of protons to power the complex active transport system (Section 4.3). One antibacterial agent, hexachlorophane, has a specific effect on the electron transport chain and other biocides interact with thiol groups in enzymes. Nevertheless, it is now generally accepted that enzyme inactivation is unlikely to be a primary mechanism of action since it is only one of many effects that biocides have on a bacterial cell.

4.4.1 Agents inhibiting membrane enzyme activity

Several biocides interact with and inhibit membrane enzyme activity. In some rare instances, this effect is sufficient to explain the mechanism of action of the antibacterial compound, but in others the inhibition is only one out of many inhibited sites, as pointed out above.

4.4.1.1 Hexachlorophane

The phenolic agent hexachlorophane (hexachlorophene, HCP) induces the leakage of intracellular material from *B. megaterium*. The threshold concentration of HCP for bactericidal activity is 10 μg/mg cell dry weight, yet peak leakage occurs at concentrations >50 μg/mg and cytological changes above 30 μg/mg. Furthermore, HCP is bactericidal at 0°C despite causing little leakage at this temperature. The primary effect of HCP is to inhibit the membrane-bound part of the electron transport chain (Fig. 3.17b) and the other effects noted above are thus secondary ones occurring only at high HCP concentrations (Fig. 3.17a).

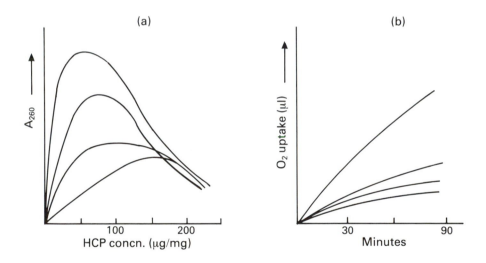

Fig. 3.17 — Mode of action of hexachlorophane (HCP) on *B. megaterium*. (a) HCP-induced leakage of 260 nm-absorbing material after (top to bottom) 300, 180, 60 and 30 minutes, respectively. (b) Effect on endogenous respiration of HCP concentrations (top to bottom) of 0, 2, 5 and 8 μg/mg, respectively. (8 μg/mg is also the minimum lethal dose.) Figures redrawn from the data of (a) H. L. Joswick *et al.*, *Journal of Bacteriology*, 1971, **109**, 492–500; (b) J. J. Frederick *et al.*, *Antimicrobial Agents and Chemotherapy*, **6**, 712–721. Note that the greatest amount of leakage (A_{260}) occurs at concentrations much higher than 8 μg/mg.

4.4.1.2 Agents interacting with thiol groups

Some inhibitors interact with the thiol groups found in enzymic and structural protein (and this thus includes interaction with cytoplasmic membrane constituents). The thiol groups derived from cysteine residues are vital for the activity of many enzymes. Reaction with, or oxidation of, these essential groups produces cell inhibition or cell inactivation, but it is possible to reverse this by adding a thiol-containing compound, such as thioglycollic acid or cysteine.

Interaction of a mercury compound with enzyme or protein thiol groups and its reversal by means of a sulphydryl (thiol containing) compound are depicted in Fig. 3.18. Other metals such as silver and copper and the element arsenic react similarly.

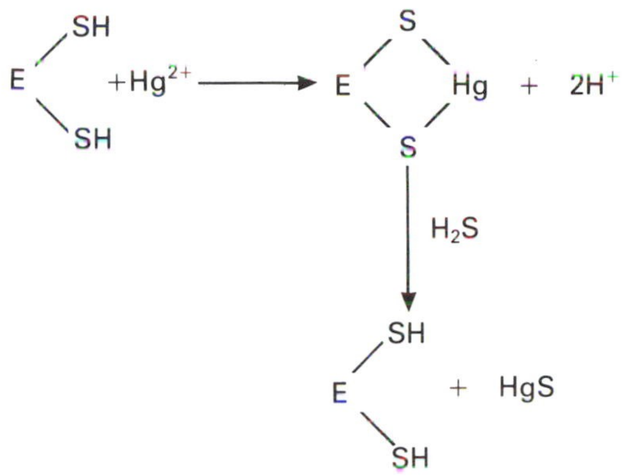

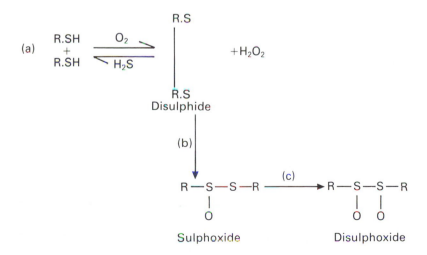

Fig. 3.18 — Effect of mercury compound on enzyme (E) –SH groups and reversal by thiol-containing compounds.

Bronopol (Section 4.1.1.4) oxidizes thiol groups to disulphides, and this action may also be reversed by sulphydryl compounds (see Fig. 3.19a).

Fig. 3.19 — Oxidation of thiol groups to (a) disulphides (and possible reversal), (b) sulphox-ides, (c) disulphoxides.

4.4.1.3   Other agents

Chlorhexidine has been claimed to be a specific inhibitor of membrane-bound adenosine triphosphatase (ATPase). Enzymes coupling the diffusion of protons back through the membrane to ATP synthesis are globular bodies protruding from the membrane surface (Fig. 3.20). The protruding knob (F_1) is a soluble protein

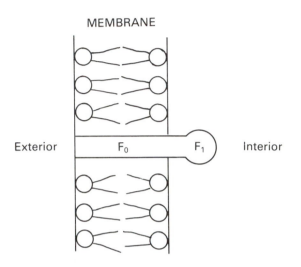

Fig. 3.20 — Adenosine triphosphatase (ATPase). F_0: membrane-bound (integral, pore-forming unit). F_1: soluble, catalytic unit. ⊃○ :phospholipid.

attached to the membrane through another set of proteins (F_0) embedded in the membrane. F_1 is readily removed, F_0 only when the membrane is destroyed. Some *E. coli* mutants have been isolated that lack ATPase activity because of a defective F_1 although F_0 is unaffected, and the permeability of the cytoplasmic membrane of these mutants to protons is greatly enhanced. N,N^1-dicyclohexylcarbodiimide (DCCD) and the antifungal compound oligomycin act at the F_0 site, but modern thought is inconsistent with the contention that membrane-bound ATPase is the primary target of chlorhexidine action, since activity is inhibited only at high biguanide concentrations.

4.5   Mechanisms of interaction with cytoplasmic membrane

Although membrane-active agents perturb homeostasis, the manner in which they interact with the membrane itself is not always clear. QACs and chlorhexidine combine with membrane phospholipids and thereby bring about disruption of the membrane. However, phenols and cresols probably interact with membrane protein. Anionic detergents, unlike cationic ones (QACs), interact with the protein moiety of the membrane which is thus completely dissolved.

The most detailed studies have involved the polymeric biguanide, PHMB. The

proposed sequence of events during its interaction with the cell envelope of *E. coli* is
as follows (see Fig. 3.21):

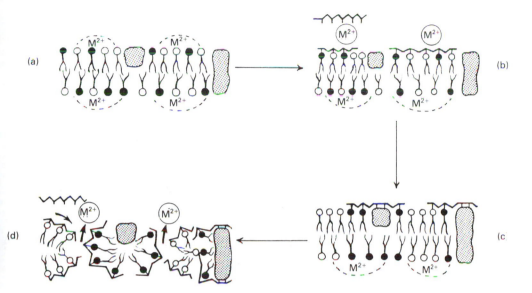

Fig. 3.21 — Proposed mechanism of action of PHMB. (Based on P. Broxton *et al.* (1984),
Journal of Applied Bacteriology, **57**, 115–124.) (A) Cytoplasmic membrane conforming to
fluid mosaic model (Singer–Nicholson) and stabilized by metallic cations. (B) Surface cations
displaced by PHMB, which binds to phospholipids causing changes in packing. (C) Phospholipid phase separation induced, with K^+ efflux and loss of enzyme function (bacteriostatic
effect). (D) Aggregation of destablized zones, complete loss of membrane function (bactericidal effect). PHMB, ⌇⌇⌇ ; M^{2+}, divalent cation; ⌇ , acidic phospholipid; ⌇ , neutral
phospholipid.

(1) There is rapid attraction towards the negatively charged bacterial cell surface
    with specific and strong adsorption to phosphate-containing compounds.
(2) The integrity of the outer membrane is impaired and PHMB is attracted towards
    the inner membrane.
(3) Binding to phospholipids occurs followed by an increase in inner membrane
    permeability involving K^+ loss and accompanied by bacteriostasis.
(4) Complete loss of membrane function, and precipitation of intracellular consti-
    tuents, leading to a bactericidal effect.

Chlorhexidine probably acts in a similar manner.

4.6 Mechanisms of action of membrane-active agents: summary
As noted above, biocides can damage the bacterial cytoplasmic membrane by
various mechanisms. A summary is provided in Table 3.5. It must be emphasized

Table 3.5 — Summary of effects of membrane-active agents

Antibacterial agent(s)	Effect(s) on bacterial cell	Mechanism of action
Phenols	Leakage: protein denaturation	Generalized membrane damage
QACs	Leakage; protoplast lysis; discharge of pH component of Δp in pmf	Generalized membrane damage
Chlorhexidine	Leakage; protoplast lysis; high concentrations interact with cytoplasmic constituents	Concentration-dependent effects: membrane integrity affected (low), protoplasm congealed (high)
Hexachloro-phane	Leakage; protoplast lysis; respiration inhibited	Inhibits membrane-bound electron transport chain
Phenoxyethanol	Leakage; low concentrations stimulate total oxygen uptake and uncouple oxidative phosphorylation; H^+ translocation	Proton-conducting uncoupler
Sorbic acid	Transport inhibition (conflicting data reported); inhibition of ΔpH across membrane	Transport inhibitor (effect on pmf); another unidentified mechanism?
Parabens	Leakage; transport inhibition; selective inhibition of ΔpH across membrane	Concentration-dependent effects: transport inhibited (low), membrane integrity affected (high)

that a distinction has often been drawn between the effects of low and high concentrations of a biocide. Low concentrations, usually associated with bacteriostasis, often produce far more subtle damage than the gross damage produced by lethal concentrations. For example, low (bacteriostatic) concentrations of chlorhexidine induce K^+ loss, whereas progressively higher concentrations increase both the extent of the membrane damage and the size of the permeable species, i.e. $Cs^+>Na^+>Li^+$ (Section 4.2.1).

5. AGENTS INTERACTING WITH CYTOPLASMIC CONSTITUENTS: PROPERTIES AND MECHANISM OF ACTION

Several biocides interact with cytoplasmic constituents. With some agents, noticeable interaction occurs only at high concentrations. For example, at high concentrations the biguanide chlorhexidine causes intracellular coagulation or precipitation of proteins and nucleic acids. Undoubtedly these effects play at least some role in the

bactericidal action of the agents. Other biocides alkylate proteins, and still others
cross-link proteins, so that it is difficult to pinpoint an exact target site in the cell.
Bearing this limitation in mind, the interaction of various antibacterial agents with
cytoplasmic components will now be considered in more detail

5.1   Alkylating agents

Alkylation is defined as the conversion

$$H-X \rightarrow R-X$$

in which R is an alkyl group. The biological activity of the alkylating agents is
indicated by reaction with nucleophilic groups.

Some vapour-phase disinfectants act as alkylating agents. Ethylene oxide
($Ch_2.CH_2.O$), propylene oxide ($CH_2.CH.O.CH_3$) and β-propiolactone are bactericidal and sporicidal, although activity may be slow and may depend on factors such as
gaseous concentration, time of exposure, temperature and especially relative
humidity.

Ethylene oxide combines with the amino, carboxyl, sulphydryl and hydroxyl
groups in bacterial protein, as depicted in Fig. 3.22. It also interacts with nucleic acids

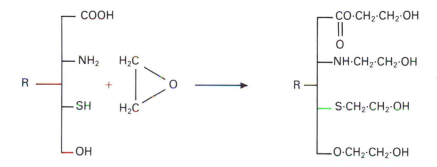

Fig. 3.22 — Interaction of ethylene oxide with protein groups.

with a principal site of interaction at N-7 of guanine moieties in DNA to produce 7-
(2'-hydroxyethyl) guanine (Fig. 3.23), the second most reactive site being at N-3 of
adenine moieties. The other alkylating agents react similarly with proteins and
DNA.

5.2   Cross-linking agents

Formaldehyde is used as a disinfectant in both the liquid (e.g. formalin) and vapour
phases. It is a microbicidal agent with lethal activity against bacteria and their spores,
fungi and many viruses. It is an extremely reactive chemical and combines with
protein, RNA and DNA, interaction with the latter probably explaining its mutage-

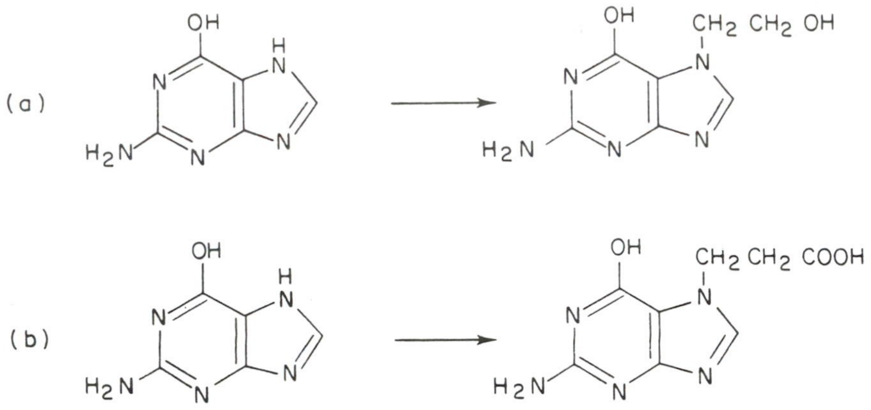

Fig. 3.23 — Interaction with guanine of (a) ethylene oxide, (b) β-propiolactone.

nic activity. It interacts with protein to give intermolecular cross-links, but also acts as an alkylating agent (see above) by virtue of its interaction with –NH$_2$, –COOH, –SH and –OH groups.

Interaction of glutaraldehyde with proteins involves a reaction between the dialdehyde and the α-amino groups of amino acids, the rate of reaction being pH-dependent and increasing considerably over the pH range 4–9.

5.3 Intercalating agents

Antibacterial dyes include the triphenylmethane group (e.g. crystal violet) and the acridines. The acridines are weakly active against Gram-positive and Gram-negative bacteria but are not sporicidal. They are more effective at alkaline pH and compete with H$^+$ ions for anionic sites on the cell surface. Activity increases with the degree of acridine ionization but this must be cationic in nature, i.e. acridine derivatives that are ionized to form anions or zwitterions are only poorly antibacterial in comparison with those that form cations.

The acridine series of antibacterial dyes illustrate how small changes in the chemical structure of the molecule greatly alter the biological activity. Acridines combine with several sites on or in the bacterial cell, the most important of which is DNA. The attachment results from intercalation of an acridine molecule between two layers of base pairs in such a way that the primary amino groups are held in ionic linkage by two phosphoric acid residues of the DNA spiral with the flat skeleton of the acridine ring (Fig. 3.24a) resting on the purine and pyrimidine molecules to which it is held by van der Waals forces (Fig. 3.24c, cf. normal DNA in Fig. 3.24b).

5.4 Other nucleic acid-binding (NAB) agents

The triphenylmethane dyes are more active against Gram-positive than Gram-negative bacteria but are not sporicidal. They react with acid groups, in particular

(a)

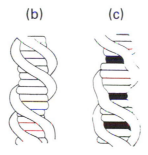

ACRIDINE
(International Union of Chemistry numbering)

2HCl

3,6, Diaminoacridine dihydrochloride

HCl

3,6-Diamino-10 methylacridinium
chloride hydrochloride

Acriflavine

HCl,H₂O

9-Aminoacridine hydrochloride
(Aminacrine hydrochloride)

H₂SO₄, 2H₂O

3,6-Diaminoacridine hemisulphate
(Proflavine)

(b)   (c)

Fig. 3.24 — (a) Chemical structure of acridines. (b) and (c): secondary structure of normal
DNA (b) and of DNA containing intercalated proflavine molecules (c).

nucleic acids, within the cell. Intercalation is not involved and the interaction is
probably of a non-specific nature.

The isethionate salts of pentamidine, propamidine and their dibromo derivatives
(Fig. 3.9e) are occasionally used as biocides. They are cationic, or more active at
alkaline than at acid pH and are considerably more effective against Gram-positive

than Gram-negative organisms. Their precise mechanism of action has not been elucidated: they are NAB agents, but inhibit protein synthesis more effectively than RNA or DNA synthesis.

Other NAB agents include the QACs and chlorhexidine, but they only act in this manner at high concentrations.

5.5   Ribosome-binding agents

Sulphydryl reagents dissociate 70S ribosomes into 30S and 50S subunits, the effect being dependent on concentration, time of contact and especially of temperature. The effect may be reversed by β-mercaptoethanol. Hydrogen peroxide also dissociates 70S ribosomes into their ribosomal units, and this efffect can be reversed by Mg^{2+} ions.

5.6   Interaction with cytoplasmic protein

Several biocides at high concentrations, e.g. chlorhexidine, QACs and phenolics, cause cytoplasmic protein coagulation. The mode of action of iodine and iodophors has, surprisingly, been little studied, but evidence to date suggests that they react with bacterial cytoplasmic protein. They will also combine with thiol groups in enzymes. Biocides already described, such as alkylating agents (Section 5.1) and cross-linking agents (Section 5.2) also combine with proteins.

The halogen iodine is bactericidal, fungicidal, sporicidal and virucidal but is highly toxic and stains materials. The activity of low, but not of high, concentrations is reduced significantly by organic matter. Iodine is far more effective at acid than at alkaline pH, the active moiety being diatomic iodine (I_2) although hypoiodous acid (HI) makes some contribution. At alkaline pH, the formation of the hypoiodide (HI^-) ion, which possesses feeble activity, and of the inactive iodate (IO_3^-), iodide (I^-) and tri-iodide (I_3^-) ions explain the decreased efficacy of iodine as the pH rises.

Iodophors (literally, iodine carriers) are compounds in which iodine is solubilized by means of an appropriate surface-active agent. They retain the germicidal action, but not the undesirable properties, of iodine, and are active over a wide pH range.

5.7   Interaction with identifiable chemical groups

Diverse types of biocides react with identifiable chemical groups within the bacterial cell. Some of these biocides have already been described, e.g. alkylating agents (Section 5.1) and cross-linking agents (Section 5.2). Other types of biocides are included here.

5.7.1   Oxidizing agents

Hypochlorites are powerful antimicrobial agents, being bactericidal, sporicidal, fungicidal and virucidal. Activity is decreased markedly by organic matter, and the hypochlorites are more active at acid than at alkaline pH because undissociated hypochlorous acid (HClO) is the active moiety. N-chloro (organic chlorine) compounds containing the =N–Cl group, e.g. chloramine-T, dichloramine-T, dichloroisocyanurates and trichloroisocyanurates, hydrolyse in water to produce an imino (=NH) group.

Oxidizing agents, such as halogens, may progressively oxidize thiol groups to disulphides (Fig. 3.19a), sulphoxides (Fig. 3.19b) or disulphoxides (Fig. 3.19c).

Whereas the first reaction may be reversible, the latter two are not. The halogens can also halogenate essential groups in proteins, such as amino groups, with the formation of halogenamines. Chlorine dioxide has been found to inhibit bacterial protein synthesis.

The most important peroxygens are hydrogen peroxide (H_2O_2) and peracetic acid (CH_3COOOH). Hydrogen peroxide (H_2O_2) is a powerful oxidizing agent, water-miscible and possessing bactericidal and sporicidal properties. Its activity results from the formation of free hydroxyl radicals ($\cdot OH$) which oxidize thiol groups in enzymes and proteins. Effects elsewhere have also been noted, however, e.g. on the bacterial cell surface and on ribosomes (Section 5.5).

Peracetic acid (CH_3COOOH) combines the active oxygen characteristics of a peroxide within an acetic acid molecule, existing with these in equilibrium. It decomposes ultimately to acetic acid and peroxide, which is further broken down to water and oxygen, and is claimed to be more powerful than hydrogen peroxide. Peracetic acid is believed to disrupt thiol groups in proteins and enzymes.

Ozone (O_3) possesses potent bactericidal and sporicidal properties, and could prove to be an important sterilizing agent. It reacts with amino acids, RNA and DNA, but its exact mechanism of action is unknown.

5.7.2 Metal derivatives
Derivatives of mercury, silver, copper and tin are used as antiseptics, disinfectants and preservatives. Inorganic mercurials such as mercuric chloride are now little used as biocides. However, organomercurials such as phenylmercuric nitrate (PMN), phenylmercuric acetate (PMA) and thiomersal (Fig. 3.25) are widely used as

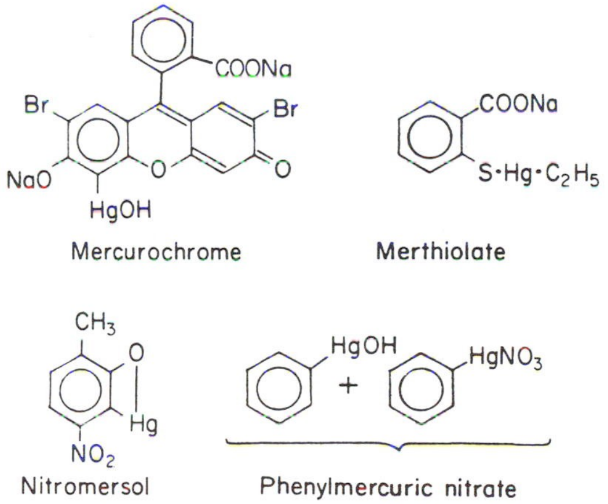

Fig. 3.25 — Organomercurials: mercurochrome, thiomersal (merthiolate), nitromersol and phenylmercuric nitrate.

preservatives in the pharmaceutical and cosmetic fields. They are bactericidal and fungicidal but not sporicidal. As described earlier (Section 4.4.1.2, Fig. 3.18) they combine strongly with –SH groups in bacterial enzymes, an action that can be reversed by the addition of a thiol-containing compound.

Silver nitrate, a somewhat astringent compound, possesses significant antibacterial activity, including *Ps. aeruginosa*, but is not sporicidal. Silver sulphadiazine is another useful compound. Ag^+ reacts with thiol groups of enzymes, presumably in a manner similar to that shown by Hg^{2+}. Copper(II) salts also combine with thiol groups in bacterial enzymes, but are used mainly as fungicides and algicides.

5.8   Conclusions

It is difficult to ascribe a single target site to many of the biocides discussed in this section. The reasons for this are two-fold: (i) several biocides are highly reactive and combine with several types of receptor molecules so that the mechanism of inactivation is often unclear; (ii) the paucity of information available for some of the biocides.

6.   UPTAKE OF BIOCIDES BY BACTERIA

Most biocides are bactericidal because of their effects on the cytoplasmic membrane and/or the innermost parts of the bacterial cell. This means that they must cross the cell wall of Gram-positive bacteria or the outer membrane of Gram-negative organisms. In contrast to antibiotics (see Chapter 2), there are no specific receptor molecules or permeases to assist biocide penetration. Most biocides enter Gram-positive bacteria readily, probably by passive diffusion and partitioning, as described for antibiotics (Fig. 2.37, Chapter 2). Such organisms are frequently more sensitive to biocides than are Gram-negative cells.

The latter organisms are more complex because of the presence of the outer membrane (see Chapter 1). The cell surface of smooth Gram-negative bacteria is hydrophilic in nature, a property that can be readily demonstrated by measuring the partitioning of cells into a water-immiscible hydrocarbon solvent. Deep rough (heptoseless) mutants, on the other hand, are much more hydrophobic. Thus, wild-type (smooth) strains are resistant to hydrophobic antibiotics and biocides whereas deep rough mutants are much more sensitive (Chapter 6). The entry of biocides into Gram-negative bacteria is not a well-researched topic. It is believed that cationic bactericides such as the QACs and chlorhexidine are able to promote their own entry by displacing divalent metal cations in the outer membrane. Nevertheless, QACs are considerably more effective against deep rough mutants than wild-type strains of *E. coli* whereas chlorhexidine shows almost equal activity against both. It has recently been demonstrated that ^{14}C-chlorhexidine is rapidly bound (maximum within 30 seconds) to wild-type and envelope mutants of *E. coli* and *Ps. aeruginosa* (which is much less sensitive than *E. coli* to the biguanide) whereas loss of cell viability is a much slower event. The slow rate of kill could result from slow passage of the biocide across the outer membrane to inner membrane targets. There is little evidence to date that OmpC and OmpF porins are utilized by biocides. Hydrophobic-type biocides (phenolics and higher esters of *p*-hydroxybenzoic acid) utilize the hydrophobic lipid bilayer pathway but information about their mechanism of penetration across the outer membrane is sparse.

Many of the biocides described in this chapter affect the cytoplasmic membrane in various ways (Tables 3.5 and 3.6). Damage to the membrane is followed by penetration into the cytoplasm where further injury to nucleic acids and/or proteins may take place. Other biocides are not considered to be membrane-active, but the manner in which they cross the membrane is unknown.

7. MECHANISMS OF ACTION: GENERAL CONCLUSIONS

Many of the biocides described in this chapter are potent antibacterial agents with an effect that often embraces more than one target site. This is exemplified in Fig. 3.26 and in Table 3.6, the latter summarizing the responses elicited at different biocide concentrations. The effect on different target sites contrasts with the situation for antibiotics which often have a specifically-characterized target site and specific uptake systems for delivery to the target (Chapter 2). Furthermore, biocides are usually toxic to mammalian cells and lack the selectively toxic properties associated with antibiotics used as chemotherapeutic agents (Chapter 2). For this reason, these

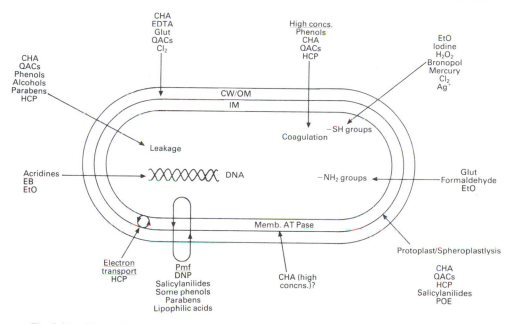

Fig. 3.26 — Target sites and effects of biocides. *Note*: many biocides have more than one target site. The figure should be read in conjunction with Table 3.6 which summarizes concentration-dependent effects. EDTA, ethylenediamine tetraacetic acid; Glut, glutaraldehyde; CHA, chlorhexidine diacetate (or gluconate); QACs, quaternary ammonium compounds; HCP, hexachlorophane; Cl_2, chlorine-releasing agents (e.g. hypochlorites); POE, phenoxyethanol; DNP, dinitrophenol; EB, ethidium bromide; EtO, ethylene oxide. CW, cell wall (Gram-positive); OM, outer membrane (Gram-negative); IM, inner (or cytoplasmic) membrane; pmf, proton motive force.

Table 3.6 — Mechanisms of action of biocides: a summary

Site of action[b]	1	2	3	4	5	6	7	8	9	10	11	12	13	14	15	16	17	18
1. Cell wall/outer membrane								?						?	?			
Lysis													L					
C ross-linking									L									
Increased permeability (Gram-negative)					L	L										L		
2. Cytoplasmic membrane					?													
General membrane permeability (leakage)	L		L		L									I	L			L
Lysis (of protoplasts/spheroplasts)					I					H					I			
Membrane potentials	L									L					L[c]			L
Electron transport chain										L								
ATPase					H													
Enzymes with thiol groups								L	L		L	L	L	L		L		
3. Cytoplasm																		
Alkylation				L			L	L	L									
Cross-linking								L	L									
Intercalation		L																
Coagulation				H					I	H				H	H	H		
Thiol groups				L			L		L			L	L					
Amino groups				L			L		L					L				
Ribosomes										L		L						

Key to headings:
1=Acids (organic), 2=Acridines, 3=Alcohols, 4=β-Propiolactone, 5=Chlorhexidine, 6=EDTA, 7=Ethylene oxide, 8=Formaldehyde, 9=Glutaraldehyde, 10=Hexachlorophane, 11=Hydrogen peroxide, 12=Hypochlorites, 13=Iodine and iodophors, 14=Mercury compounds, 15=Phenols, 16=QACs, 17=Silver salts, 18=TCS.
[a]Activity is usually concentration-dependent: L denotes activity elicited at low, H at high, concentrations; I, intermediate concentration; ?, unclear whether effect occurs.
[b]See also appropriate section of text.
[c]Some phenolics: see Section 4.3.1.

biocides are employed as antiseptics, disinfectants and preservatives and are not used for the *in vivo* treatment of infections.

FURTHER READING

General works on antisepsis, disinfection and preservation

Block, S. S. (1990). *Disinfection, Sterilization and Preservation*, 4th edition, Lea & Febiger, Philadelphia.

Branen, A. L. & Davidson, J. M. (1983). *Antimicrobials in Foods*. Marcel Dekker, New York.

Gardner, J. F. & Peel, M. M. (1986). *Introduction to Sterilization and Disinfection*. Churchill Livingstone, Edinburgh.

Hugo, W. B. (1971). *Inhibition and Destruction of the Microbial Cell*. Academic Press, London.

Kabara, J. J. (1984). *Cosmetic and Drug Preservation: Principles and Practice*. Marcel Dekker, New York.

Linton, A. H., Hugo, W. B. & Russell, A. D. (1987). *Disinfection in Veterinary and Farm Animal Practice*. Blackwell Scientific Publications, Oxford.

Lueck, E. (1980). *Antimicrobial Food Additives*. Springer-Verlag, New York.

Payne, K. R. (1988). *Industrial Biocides*. Critical Reports on Applied Chemistry, Vol. 23. John Wiley & Sons, Chichester.

Russell, A. D., Hugo, W. B. and Ayliffe, G. A. J. (1982). *Principles and Practice of Disinfection, Preservation and Sterilization*. Blackwell Scientific Publications, Oxford.

General works on mechanisms of action

Albert, A. (1979). *Selective Toxicity*, 5th edition. Methuen & Co., London.

Freese, E. & Levin, B. C. (1978). Action mechanism of preservatives and antiseptics. *Developments in Industrial Microbiology*, **19**, 207–227.

Gould, G. W. (1988). Interference with homeostasis-food. *FEMS Symposium*, No. 44, pp. 220–228. Bath University Press, Bath.

Hugo, W. B. (1982). Disinfection mechanisms. In *Principles and Practice of Disinfection, Preservation and Sterilization* (Eds A. D. Russell, W. B. Hugo and G. A. J. Ayliffe) pp. 147–174. Blackwell Scientific Publications, Oxford.

Russell, A. D. & Hugo, W. B. (1988). Perturbation of homeostatic mechanisms in bacteria by pharmaceuticals. *FEMS Symposium*, No. 44, pp. 206–219. Bath University Press, Bath.

Salton, M. R. J. (1968). Lytic agents, cell permeability and monolayer penetrability. *Journal of General Physiology* **52**, 227S–252S.

Mechanisms of action: selected papers

Broxton, P., Woodcock, P. M., Heatley, F. & Gilbert, P. (1984). Interaction of some polyhexamethylene biguanides and membrane phospholipids in *Escherichia coli*. *Journal of Applied Bacteriolgy* **57**, 115–124.

Chopra, I., Johnson, S. C. & Bennett, P. M. (1987) Inhibition of *Providencia stuarti* cell envelope enzymes by chlorhexidine. Journal of Antimicrobial Chemotherapy **19**, 743–751.

Eklund, P. (1985). The effect of sorbic acid and esters of p-hydroxybenzoic acid on the protonmotive force in *Escherichia coli* membrane vesicles. *Journal of General Microbiology* **313**, 73–76.

Lambert, P. A. & Hammond, S. M. (1973). Potassium fluxes. First indications of membrane damage in micro-organisms. *Biochemical and Biophysical Research Communications* **54**, 796–799.

Salmond, C. V., Kroll, R. G. & Booth, I. R. (1984). The effect of food preservatives on pH homeostasis in *Escherichia coli*. *Journal of General Microbiology* **130**, 2845–2850.

Sofos, J. N., Pierson, M. D., Blocher, J. C. & Busta, F. F. (1986). Mode of action of sorbic acid on bacterial cells and spores. *International Journal of Food Microbiology* **3**, 1–17.

4

Sporistatic and sporicidal agents: their properties and mechanisms of action

1. INTRODUCTION

The bacterial spore is a complex entity consisting of one or two spore coats, a cortex and an inner spore core (protoplast), with an exosporium present in some types (see Chapter 1).

In this chapter, we shall consider how some chemicals, including antibiotics, destroy spores or inhibit their development. To encompass the topic adequately, it is necessary to describe the complex processes leading, first, to the development of a spore and then to the production of a vegetative cell.

2. SPORULATION

Sporulation is a multiphase process leading to the production of a spore from a vegetative cell (summarized in Table 4.1 and Fig. 4.1). The process involves the production of a refractile cell which is resistant to many forms of harmful treatments, both chemical and physical.

2.1 Stages in sporulation

There are seven stages (I–VII) in sporulation and Stage 0 represents the end of logarithmic growth of the vegetative cell culture. There appears to be a link between the induction of sporulation and a specific stage in the DNA replication cycle. The amount and rate of sporulation in starting cultures depends on DNA replication, and the successful termination of existing rounds of DNA replication is essential for sporulation to occur.

In the pre-septation stage (Stage I), the nuclear material in *Bacillus* spp. is present as an axial filament, although this is rarely observed in clostridia. Stage I terminates when a septum starts to form asymmetrically in the mother cell, resulting in the synthesis of the forespore membrane and the compartmentalization of DNA in Stage II.

Table 4.1 — Summary of stages in the sporulation process[a]

Stage	Characteristics
0	Vegetative cell
I	Pre-septation: DNA in axial filament form. Extra-cellular products (including amylase, proteases and antibiotics) appear
II	Septation: separation of chromosomes resulting in asymmetric cell formation.
III	Engulfment of forespore: membrane of developing spore becomes completely detached from that of mother cell to give the spore protoplast. Appearance of characteristic enzymes.
IV	Cortex formation begins to be laid down between the two membranes of the protoplast. Refractility begins to develop, commencement of peptidoglycan synthesis (see text in present chapter and in Chapter 7).
V	Synthesis of spore coats. DPA deposition, uptake of Ca^{2+}. Development of resistance to organic solvents (octanol, chloroform).
VI	Spore maturation: coat material becomes more dense, increase in refractility, development of heat resistance.
VII	Lysis of the mother cell, and liberation of the mature spore.

[a]This should be read in conjunction with Fig. 4.1. Additional information appears in the text.

The forespore protoplast is engulfed in Stage III, the result being the existence of the forespore as a discrete cell, bounded by two forespore membranes (see Chapter 7), the former later becoming the cytoplasmic membrane of the germinated spore.

Cortex synthesis takes place in Stage IV. During this phase, peptidoglycan is laid down between the two membranes, possibly in two phases. The first phase involves the synthesis of vegetative cell-type polymer and the second the formation of spore-specific peptidoglycan. In conditional cortex-less mutants of *B. sphaericus*, the spore cortex cannot be detected unless the medium contains diaminopimelic acid (see Chapter 7).

Synthesis of the spore coats takes place in Stage V, although deposition of at least part of these layers occurs during earlier stages. In addition, dipicolinic acid (DPA) accumulates and there is an uptake of calcium.

Stage VI is termed spore maturation. Here, the coat material becomes more dense in appearance, spore refractility increases and heat resistance develops. In addition, dehydration occurs and the spore shows resistance to ionizing and ultraviolet radiation. Liberation of the spore takes place in Stage VII.

Resistance to chemical agents is considered more fully in Chapter 7.

2.2   Commitment to sporulation

Commitment, a specific term, may be defined as 'the point of no return', i.e. the events associated with the developing system cannot be reversed. In contrast, initiation is a different term since it implies the commencement of the sporulation process but not necessarily that the process is committed to forming a mature spore.

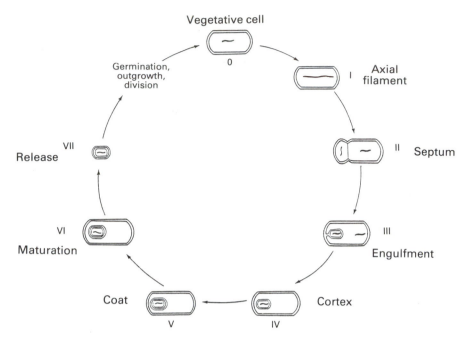

Fig. 4.1 — Stages in the sporulation process. 0, vegetative cell; I, axial filament formation (pre-
septation); II, formation of septum; III, engulfment (encystment, envelopment) of forespore;
IV, cortex formation; V, coat formation; VI, maturation (development of refractility and heat
resistance); VII, release of forespore.

Early sporulation events can be overcome and growth resumed if the sporulating
culture is diluted into fresh medium, whereas later the cells are committed to
continue the sporulation process.

3.   GERMINATION

Activation is a treatment resulting in a spore which is poised for germination but
which still retains most spore properties (e.g. heat resistance, lack of stainability,
refractility). It is thus responsible for the breaking of dormancy in spores but is
reversible (Fig. 4.2). The most widely used procedure is heat activation in which
spores are exposed to a sublethal heat treatment; it must, however, be pointed out
that not all types of bacterial spores require heat activation for the breaking of
dormancy to take place, since many types undergo germination rapidly when placed
in an appropraite germination medium.

Germination itself is an irreversible process and is defined as a change of
activated spores from a dormant to a metabolically active state within a short period
of time (Fig. 4.2). The first biochemical step in germination is termed a biological
trigger reaction. This initiation process can be induced by metabolic or non-
metabolic means, although it is now generally believed that the trigger reaction is
allosteric in nature rather than metabolic, because the inducer does not need to be

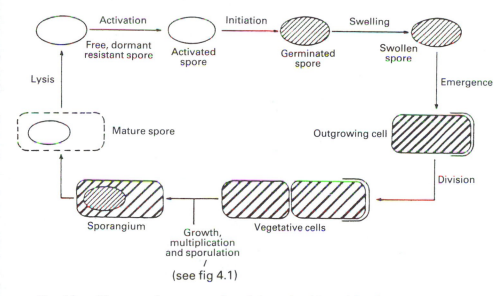

Fig. 4.2 — Diagrammatic representation of the cycle of bacterial endospore formation, germination and outgrowth. Reprinted with permission from G. W. Gould (1984).

metabolized to induce germination. The most widely studied nutrient and non-nutrient germinants are L-alanine and calcium dipicolinate (CaDPA), respectively.

Initiation of germination is followed rapidly by various degradative changes in the spore, leading within a short period of time to outgrowth (Section 4). An early event is loss of heat resistance with a decrease in optical density a late marker. Intermediate events are changes in stainability, a decrease in refractility so that phase-bright spores take on the appearance of phase-dark forms (Fig. 4.3), a decrease in dry weight and the release of DPA.

Inhibition and control of spore germination are important considerations in many fields, including food preservation. Chemical antibacterial agents that act as germination inhibitors, as well as those possibly having an effect on the trigger mechanism, are considered in Section 5.3.

4.   OUTGROWTH

Outgrowth is defined as the development of a vegetative cell from a germinated spore. It takes place in a synchronous and orderly manner when germination is carried out in a medium that supports vegetative growth. After germination, germinated spores become swollen and shed their coats to allow the young, vegetative cells to emerge, elongate and divide. There is a sequential alteration in cell structure, with an initial swelling followed by emergence from the spore coat, elongation of the emergent organism and, finally, cell division. During outgrowth, RNA synthesis occurs soon after the termination of the germination phase and is

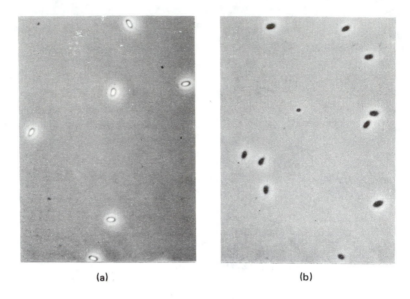

(a)   (b)

Fig. 4.3 — (a) Phase-bright spores. (b) Phase-dark germinated spores.

closely followed in *Bacillus* spp. by the onset of protein synthesis, and then DNA synthesis which occurs later. Dormant and newly-germinated spores possess little or no functional mRNA. Spores do, however, contain a DNA-dependent RNA polymerase which is responsible for synthesizing the mRNAs necessary for transcription of early functions during outgrowth.

Cell wall synthesis commences after RNA and protein synthesis but before DNA synthesis and coincides with swelling of the germinated spore.

5.   MECHANISMS OF ACTION OF SPORISTATIC AND SPORICIDAL AGENTS

Antibacterial agents that can be considered in this context include chemotherapeutic drugs, food and pharmaceutical preservatives, and antiseptics and disinfectants.

5.1   Effects on sporulation

β-lactam antibiotics inhibit the sporulation septation stage. There are, in fact, two periods of enhanced binding of these drugs during sporulation. The first increase in binding corresponds to the period of spore septum formation and the second to spore cortex formation. There are also two periods of peptidoglycan synthesis during the sporulation process with differences occurring in the structure of the peptidoglycan present in the cortex and the germ cell wall. The cortical peptidoglycan contains a muramic lactam, a unique spore constituent (Fig. 1.17 in Chapter 1). The two peaks of penicillin binding to sporulating cultures could either be due to the appearance of new penicillin-binding proteins (PBPs) that are specific to the spore itself or to changes in the amounts of PBPs that are present in vegetative cells of the organism. The latter is believed to be the correct interpretation.

Other antibiotics also inhibit septation (Fig. 4.4). These include D-cycloserine (a

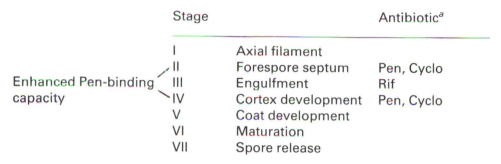

	Stage		Antibiotic[a]
	I	Axial filament	
	II	Forespore septum	Pen, Cyclo
Enhanced Pen-binding	III	Engulfment	Rif
capacity	IV	Cortex development	Pen, Cyclo
	V	Coat development	
	VI	Maturation	
	VII	Spore release	

Fig. 4.4 — Effect of antibiotics on the sporulation process. Pen, benzylpenicillin; Cyclo, D-cycloserine; Rif, rifampicin. "Other antibiotics also inhibit the septation stage (see text).

specific inhibitor of peptidoglycan synthesis in vegetative cells: see Chapter 2) and chloramphenicol, an inhibitor of protein synthesis (see Chapter 2). The latter also affects the morphology of spores during their formation, since the spores are rounder and smaller, and inhibits the incorporation of amino acids into the protein fraction of sporangia.

Rifampicin is an antibiotic that binds strongly to DNA-dependent RNA polymerase and acts as an inhibitor of RNA synthesis (Chapter 2). Rifampicin blocks spore development at stage III, the encystment (engulfment) stage (Fig. 4.4).

Effects of biocides on sporulation have not been widely studied. In contrast, effects on mature spores are fairly well, but by no means fully, documented (Section 5.2).

5.2   Effects on mature spores

The antibiotics mentioned in Section 5.1 are not sporicidal, even at high concentrations, but this is hardly surprising since they are inhibitors of specific biosynthetic reactions and the spore is virtually metabolically inert. On the other hand, some bactericidal agents, e.g. certain aldehydes, alkylating agents, halogens and oxidizing agents may be sporicidal. In order to define the basis by which these agents act, certain questions need to be addressed: whether (a) intact spores are lysed, (b) spore permeability is increased/decreased, (c) surface layers/cortex/core are affected, (d) mutant and coat-less forms are more or equally sensitive than parent cells.

Answers to the above questions, together with knowledge about the mechanism of action of bactericides against non-sporing bacteria (Chapter 3) suggest the following mechanisms of sporicidal action (see also Table 4.2):

(i) Glutaraldehyde: interaction at acid and alkaline pH occurs to a considerable extent with the spore surface, but it is believed that at alkaline pH the aldehyde is better able to penetrate into the spore.

Table 4.2 — Mechanisms of sporicidal action

Sporicidal agent	Site or mechanism of action	Comment
Alkali	Inner spore coat	
Chlorine compounds	Cortex	Effect on coats also
Ethylene oxide	Alkylation of core protein and DNA	
Glutaraldehyde	Cortex	Effect on coats also
Hydrogen peroxide	Spore core?	Effect on coats also
Lysozyme	Cortex	β,1–4 links in peptidoglycan
Nitrous acid	Cortex	At muramic acid residues

(ii) Formaldehyde: this mono-aldehyde probably penetrates into the spore where it combines with RNA, DNA and amino groups in protein.

(iii) Alkylating agents: ethylene oxide and β-propiolactone probably kill spores by combining with specific groups in proteins and by alkylation of guanine in DNA (Figs 3.22 and 3.23 in Chapter 3).

(iv) Chlorine-releasing agents: hypochlorites induce DPA leakage, suggesting an increase in spore permeability and a site of action on the cortex. The cortex controls the water content of the core and hence the heat resistance of spores; pretreatment of spores with sublethal concentrations of chlorine increases their sensitivity to moist heat, a finding that supports the contention of an action of hypochlorites on the cortex.

(v) Hydrogen peroxide: its target site remains a matter for conjecture, with some evidence suggesting the outer spore layers and other evidence the spore core. Copper (Cu^{2+}) ions potentiate the sporicidal action of peroxide and are bound to the core, providing a tentative conclusion that the core may be the major site of peroxide action.

5.3 Effects on germination

Several inhibitors prevent spore germination. They include phenols and cresols, parabens, alcohols, glutaraldehyde and formaldehyde. An example of the effect of phenol is presented in Fig. 4.5(a). It is noticeable that amongst these agents only glutaraldehyde and formaldehyde are sporicidal. The effects of inhibitors of spore germination may be reversible, as demonstrated for phenol in Fig. 4.5(b). Thus, there appears to be a fairly loose binding to a site or sites on the spore surface, since mere washing is sufficient to dislodge this antibacterial agent (also cresols, parabens, alcohols and low formaldehyde concentrations). As might be expected from a powerful cross-linking agent, however, the effects of glutaraldehyde on spore germination are not readily reversible. A summary of inhibitors of germination is provided in Table 4.3 and Fig. 4.6.

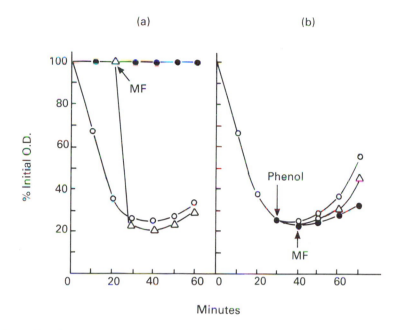

Fig. 4.5 — Reversibility by membrane filtration (MF) of the germination-inhibitory effect of 0.15% w/v phenol on *B. subtilis* spores. (a) Phenol added at zero time; (b) phenol added at 30 min; O———O, control (phenol absent); ●———●, phenol treatment without filtration; △———△, phenol treatment followed by filtration, 10 or 20 min later. The initial decrease in optical density represents germination, the subsequent increase denotes outgrowth, which is followed (not shown here) by vegetative cell multiplication.

As pointed out in Section 3, initiation of germination is followed by rapid degradative changes. Thus, antibiotics that inhibit specific biosynthetic processes are without effect on germination but will, however, inhibit an appropriate stage of outgrowth (Section 5.4).

5.3.1 *Inhibition of the trigger reaction*
Some antibacterial agents inhibit the L-alanine-induced trigger reaction. Four possible mechanisms of inhibition are envisaged in the light of current knowledge (Fig. 4.7): (a) inhibition of uptake of L-alanine by competition for binding sites on the spore, (b) prevention of passive diffusion of L-alanine into the spore, (c) sealing of the spore surface, (d) a later, unexplained, inhibition of the L-alanine-stimulated trigger effect. Glutaraldehyde has been shown to achieve (c), whereas (a) appears to be unaffected. Mechanism (b) might occur as a consequence of (c). Sorbic acid is believed to inhibit the trigger reaction, albeit by an unknown mechanism.

5.4 Effects on outgrowth
As previously stated (Section 4), outgrowth is the development of a vegetative cell from a germinated spore. During outgrowth, several biosynthetic processes are stimulated and it is, therefore, not surprising that various antibiotics are inhibitory

Table 4.3 — Inhibitors of spore germination or outgrowth[a]

Commitment to germination[b]	Germination	Outgrowth[c]
Alcohols?	Phenols	Nisin
Sorbate?	Cresols	QACs
Glutaraldehyde	Parabens	Chlorhexidine
Chlorocresol?	Alcohols	Ethylene oxide
	Thioglycollate[d]	Chlorine compounds
	Glutaraldehyde	Glutaraldehyde
	Hg^{2+}	PMN
	Formaldehyde	Tylosin
		Subtilin

[a]An antibacterial agent may act at more than one stage.
[b]It is, as yet, unclear as to whether, or how, these agents act.
[c]QACs . . . quaternary ammonium compounds, PMN . . . phenylmercuric nitrate.
[d]Thioglycollate, a constituent of some culture media, may have an adverse effect on some types of spores.

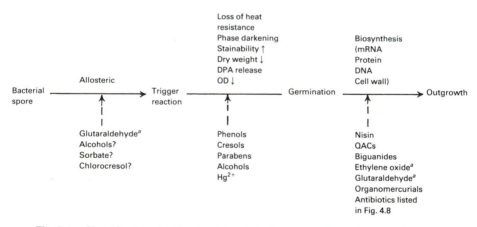

Fig. 4.6 — Sites of action of antibacterial agents during germination and outgrowth. *Note:* some agents, e.g. glutaraldehyde, can act at more than one stage. [a]Denotes sporicidal agent when used at high concentrations. ↑, increase; ↓, decrease; OD, optical density.

during these stages. Thus, β-lactams inhibit a late stage involving synthesis of vegetative cell-type peptidoglycan, whereas the earlier stages of mRNA, protein and DNA syntheses are inhibited by, respectively, actinomycin D, chloramphenicol or tetracycline, and mitomycin C (Fig. 4.8).

Some disinfectant-type compounds are also effective during outgrowth. These include the following (Fig. 4.6):

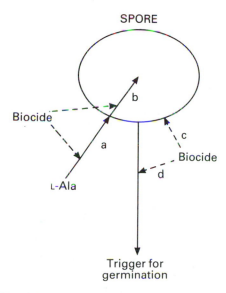

Fig. 4.7 — Possible mechanisms of inhibition of the trigger reaction. See text for comments.

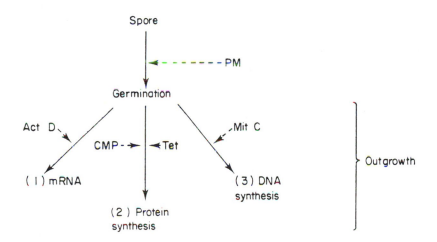

Fig. 4.8 — Effect of chemotherapeutic agents on germination and outgrowth. Act D, actinomycin D; CMP, chloramphenicol; Mit C, mitomycin C; PM, polymyxin; Tet, tetracycline.

(a) QACs, which are sporistatic and not sporicidal. They are bound strongly to spores but do not inhibit germination.

(b) Parabens, which inhibit outgrowth only at concentrations higher than those active at the germination stage.

(c) Chlorine, which prevents outgrowth at moderate, but germination only at high, concentrations.
(d) Ethylene oxide, sublethal concentrations of which inhibit outgrowth, but not germination.
(e) Organomercury preservatives, such as phenylmercuric nitrate, which are sporistatic agents.
(f) Nisin, tylosin and subtilin, which have been considered for use as food preservatives.

Nisin is produced by *Streptococcus lactis* and contrary to early findings, it is now known that it is not firmly adsorbed by spores and that it is not sporicidal although it is inhibitory, probably by virtue of its effect on outgrowth. Subtilin has a similar action, and tylosin also is inhibitory and not sporicidal. Their possible usefulness as preservatives thus resides in their ability to inhibit rather than destroy spores. Tylosin inhibits protein synthesis in non-sporulating bacteria and might have a similar effect during outgrowth. The antibacterial action of nisin is restricted to its action on outgrowing spores, because the growth of vegetative cells of many *Bacillus* spp. is unaffected by much higher nisin concentrations.

From the above, it is clear that disinfectants and preservatives are generally inhibitors of either germination or outgrowth. Where an agent inhibits both processes, it is likely that wide concentration differences are necessary for the duality of action. What has yet to be properly examined, however, is the reason for the different effects. Why, for example, should some inhibitors but not others prevent the degradative changes that are a feature of germination? Is their effect linked to the type and degree of binding to the spore? Are some, but not other, disinfectants capable of preventing the binding of L-alanine associated with the trigger reaction of germination? Answers to such questions would be illuminating.

6.   SPECIFIC SPORICIDAL AGENTS

As previously noted, some bactericidal agents are also effective sporicides. These include glutaraldehyde, formaldehyde, hydrogen peroxide, ethylene oxide, β-propiolactone, chlorine, iodine and ozone. Their sporicidal activity will be considered briefly.

6.1   Glutaraldehyde

Glutaraldehyde is sporicidal at high concentrations. As pointed out previously, glutaraldehyde is considerably more effective at alkaline than at acid pH, but stability is lost at higher pH comparatively rapidly. Novel formulations have attempted to optimise both stability and sporicidal properties.

6.2   Formaldehyde

Formaldehyde (methanal) has long been considered as a sporicidal agent. Some recent findings have cast doubt on this belief, since it has been possible by appropriate thermal treatments to revive formaldehyde-treated spores, i.e. to resuscitate them from what would have been inactivation.

6.3 Hydrogen peroxide
Low concentrations (6% w/v, 20 vols) are only slowly sporicidal. Temperature exerts a marked effect on sporicidal activity (θ^{10} or $Q_{10}=2-3$). Spore lysis induced by peroxide increases in the presence of Ca^{2+} and Co^{2+}. Cu^{2+} ions promote decomposition with an increase in oxidizing properties and in sporicidal activity. Activation of peroxide to hydroxyl radicals ($\cdot OH$) is necessary for sporicidal action which is probably why a combination of H_2O_2 and ultraviolet radiation is synergistic.

6.4 Ethylene oxide
This epoxide is a gaseous sporicide. Its action is slow but can be accelerated by a rise in temperature. The most important factor governing its activity is relative humidity, although this is a complex relationship depending both on the water content of the organism and on the atmosphere surrounding spores (the 'micro-environment') rather than the overall humidity.

6.5 β-Propiolactone (BPL)
BPL in both liquid and vapour phases is sporicidal under suitable conditions. Relative humidity is the most important factor influencing the activity of BPL vapour, although again the moisture content and location of water in the spore are of paramount importance.

6.6 Chlorine-releasing agents
Freshly prepared hypochlorite solutions have a very rapid sporicidal action, which may be potentiated in the presence of sodium hydroxide, notwithstanding the fact that hypochlorites are more effective at acid than at alkaline pH. The action of sodium hydroxide might be related to its effect on the spore coating rendering the spores more permeable to hypochlorite.

6.7 Iodine and iodophors
Iodine, in aqueous or alcoholic solution, and iodophors are effective sporicides. The concentration of free iodine (I_2) in iodine solutions and in iodophors determines sporicidal activity. The reasons for sporicidal activity are unknown but may be associated with binding of iodine to protein within the cell.

6.8 Peracetic acid
Peracetic acid has sporicidal activity. Furthermore, it has the advantage of eventually breaking down to innocuous decomposition products, oxygen and acetic acid. Its effects against obligate anaerobes are, in fact, potentiated by one of these (oxygen). Although its mechanism of sporicidal action is unknown, peracetic acid might disrupt sulphydryl (–SH) and disulphide (S–S) bonds.

6.9 Ozone
Ozone is sporicidal, and because it is converted ultimately to oxygen there are no toxic residues. Ozone probably kills by interacting with amino acids, RNA and DNA, but the exact mechanism is unknown.

7. CONCLUSIONS

Comparatively few antibacterial compounds show sporicidal activity although all are sporistatic, inhibiting germination and/or outgrowth. Studies on mechanisms of action demonstrate that the cortex, spore membranes and spore protoplast are major target sites. Nevertheless, much less information is available about the manner of inactivation of spores than of non-sporulating bacteria. There is considerable scope for further investigations leading to improved knowledge of modes of sporicidal action, since this is one approach to the ultimate development of better sporicides.

FURTHER READING

General works on sporicidal and sporistatic agents

Cook, F. K. & Pierson, M. D. (1983). Inhibition of bacterial spores by antimicrobials. *Food Technology* **37** (11), 114–126.

Gould, G. W. (1984). Injury and repair mechanisms in bacterial spores. In *The Revival of Injured Microbes* (eds M. H. E. Andrew and A. D. Russell) Society for Applied Bacteriology Symposium Series No. 12, pp. 199–220. Academic Press, London.

Hurst, A. & Gould, G. W. (1983). *The Bacterial Spore,* volume 2, Academic Press, London.

Russell, A. D. (1982). *The Destruction of Bacterial Spores.* Academic Press, London.

Russell, A. D. (1983). Mechanisms of action of chemical sporicidal and sporistatic agents. *International Journal of Pharmaceutics* **16,** 127–140.

Russell, A. D. (1990). Chemical sporicidal agents. *Clinical Microbiology Reviews* (in press).

Russell, A. D. (1990). Chemical sporicidal and sporistatic agents. In *Disinfection, Sterilization and Preservation* (ed. S. S. Block), 4th edition. Lea & Febiger, Philadelphia.

Russell, A. D., Dancer, B. N. & Power, E. G. M. (1990). Effects of chemical agents on bacterial sporulation, germination and outgrowth. *Society for Applied Bacteriology Technical Series.* Blackwell Scientific Publications, Oxford (in press).

Waites, W. M. (1985). Inactivation of spores with chemical agents. In *Fundamental and Applied Aspects of Bacterial Spores* (eds G. J. Dring, D. J. Ellar and G. W. Gould) pp. 383–396. Academic Press, London.

Sporicidal and sporistatic agents: selected papers

Bloomfield, S. F. & Uso, E. E. (1985). The antibacterial properties of sodium hypochlorite and sodium dichloroisocyanurate as hospital disinfectants. *Journal of Hospital Infection* **6,** 20–30.

Dadd, A. H. & Rumbelow, J. E. (1986). Germination of spores of *Bacillus subtilis* var. *niger* following exposure to gaseous ethylene oxide. *Journal of Applied Bacteriology* **60,** 425–433.

Foegeding, P. M. & Busta, F. F. (1983). Hypochlorite injury of *Clostridium botulinum* spores alters germination responses. *Applied and Environmental Microbiology* **45,** 1360–1368.

Gorman, S. P., Scott, E. M. & Hutchinson, E. P. (1984). Interaction of the *Bacillus subtilis* spore protoplast, cortex, ion-exchange and coatless forms with glutaraldehyde. *Journal of Applied Bacteriology* **56** 95–102.

Gorman, S. P., Scott, E. M. & Russell, A. D. (1980). Antimicrobial activity, uses and mechanism of action of glutaraldehyde. *Journal of Applied Bacteriology* **48,** 161–190.

Gorman, S. P., Hutchinson, E. P., Scott, E. M. & McDermott, L. M. (1983). Death, injury and revival of chemically treated *Bacillus subtilis* spores. *Journal of Applied Bacteriology* **54,** 91–99.

Russell, A. D., Jones, B. D. & Milburn, P. (1985). Reversal of the inhibition of bacterial spore germination and outgrowth by antibacterial agents. *International Journal of Pharmaceutics* **25,** 105–112.

Sofos, J. N., Pierson, M. D., Blocher, J. C. & Busta, F. F. (1986). Mode of action of sorbic acid on bacterial cells and spores. *International Journal of Food Microbiology* **3,** 1–17.

Stewart, G. S. A. B., Johnstone, K., Hagelberg, E. & Ellar, D. J. (1981). Commitment of bacterial spores to germinate. A measure of the trigger reaction. *Biochem. J.* **198,** 101–106.

5

Genetic and biochemical basis of resistance to chemotherapeutic antibiotics

1. INTRODUCTION

1.1 The distinction between intrinsic and acquired resistance

Antibiotics have been widely available for the treatment of bacterial infections for over forty years. However, even during the initial period surrounding the commercial development of penicillin, it was realized that certain bacteria were not killed by the antibiotic, i.e. that antibiotic-resistant bacteria existed. Today, two broad categories of antibiotic resistance are recognized: intrinsic (or intrinsic insusceptibility) and acquired. These categories also apply to biocides (see Chapters 6 and 7). The term instrinsic is used to imply that inherent features of the cell are responsible for preventing antibiotic action and to distinguish this situation from acquired resistance, which occurs when resistant strains emerge from previously sensitive bacterial populations, usually after exposure to the agent concerned. Intrinsic resistance is usually expressed by chromosomal genes, whereas acquired resistance may result from mutations in chromosomal agents, or by acquisition of plasmids and transposons. In the context of clinical microbiology, acquired antibiotic resistance results essentially from the selective pressure exerted on bacteria during the administration of antibiotics for chemotherapy.

Both types of resistance can complicate the treatment of infections. For instance many 'opportunistic' infections are caused by intrinsically resistant bacteria and the emergence and spread of acquired antibiotic resistance within bacteria of medical importance has had a profound impact on clinical practice within the last forty years, often imposing constraints on the options available for the treatment of infections. This chapter is devoted primarily to the fundamental nature of antibiotic resistance, i.e. its genetic and biochemical basis. Chapter 8 considers more fully the practical problems posed, in particular, by acquired antibiotic resistance and some of the ways by which resistance can be counteracted.

1.2   Genetic determinants of antibiotic resistance

Antibiotic resistance can be determined by genes that reside in the host cell chromosome, on plasmids or on transposons. The genetic basis of these mechanisms is outlined below, but it is beyond the scope of this book to deal with these aspects in detail. More comprehensive treatments of the topics can be found by consulting 'Further Reading' at the end of this chapter.

1.2.1   Resistance determined by chromosomal genes

It is well established that resistance to certain antibiotics can be acquired by chromosomal mutations. Chromosomal mutations, i.e. changes in the base sequence of DNA, can be divided into two broad categories: microlesions, in which a single base pair has been altered, and macrolesions, in which more extensive changes have occurred. Both categories of mutations can be further subdivided.

Microlesions comprise transition, transversion or frameshift mutations (Fig. 5.1). Transition mutations involve base pair changes in which one purine is substi-

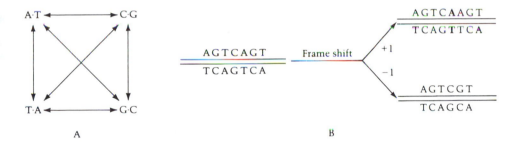

Fig. 5.1 — Classes of microlesion mutations. A, base pair mutations. Horizontal and vertical lines indicate transversions; diagonal lines indicate transitions. B, frameshift mutations illustrated by possible changes in a length of double-stranded DNA. (Reproduced, with permission, from Ingraham *et al.* (1983) (for reference see 'Further Reading', Chapter 1).

tuted for another purine, and consequently one pyrimidine for another pyrimidine. Transversions involve substitution of a purine for a pyrimidine and vice versa, whereas addition or loss of one or two base pairs comprises a frameshift mutation. Macrolesions involve deletions, duplications, inversions and translocations (insertions) (Table 5.1). In principle, each type of chromosomal mutation might directly or indirectly confer antibiotic resistance on the cell. However, in the vast majority of cases, the precise molecular basis of the mutational events leading to antibiotic resistance is unknown. Exceptions concern chromosomal mutations to trimethoprim and nalidixic acid resistance in *E. coli* which involve transition, transversion or insertion mutations that have been precisely determined (see Sections 2.1.2 and 2.2.2).

Not all chromosomally-specified antibiotic resistance is due to mutation. For instance, the intrinsic resistance of the majority of Gram-negative bacteria to

Table 5.1 — Macrolesions of DNA

Type	Molecular change[a]	
Deletion	abcdefghi	abc–ghi[b]
Duplication	abcdefghi	abcdef–defghi
Inversions	abcdefghi	abc–fed–ghi
Translocations (insertions)	abcdefghi	uvw–def–xyz

[a] Letters are meant to indicate genes on double-stranded DNA.
[b] The dash (–) indicates improper junction as in abc–ghi.
(Reproduced, with permission, from Ingraham *et al.* (1983) (for reference see 'Further Reading', Chapter 1).)

hydrophobic antibiotics (e.g. fusidic acid) is due to the expression of normal, resident, genes involved in the synthesis and assembly of lipopolysaccharide in the outer membrane, the macromolecule comprising an exclusion barrier to the penetration of hydrophobic compounds. Another example concerns the chromosomally encoded beta-lactamases in Gram-negative bacteria that confer resistance to beta-lacatam antibiotics by hydrolysis of the beta-lactam ring.

1.2.2 Resistance determined by plasmids

It is well known that plasmids, i.e. extrachromosomal genetic elements that replicate independently of the chromosome, frequently carry genes that confer antibiotic resistance. Plasmid determined antibiotic resistance is more common than chromosomal resistance in clinically important bacteria. The reasons for this are complex, but include the following: (a) In the absence of antibiotic selection pressure, the majority of cells in a particular population need not maintain plasmids, thereby reducing the biochemical stress on the cell that would otherwise be required for replication and expression of plasmid DNA. Therefore, it is not necessarily essential for every member of a particular species to maintain a particular resistance plasmid. Provided that certain organisms maintain such plasmids, selective pressure following exposure to an antibiotic will ensure the plasmid-carrying (resistant) progeny will survive and replicate. (b) Genes encoded by plasmids are intrinsically more mobile than chromosomal genes because plasmids can be transferred both within and between certain species. Thus plasmids can be acquired from other bacteria in addition to inheritance from mother cells. In naturally occurring systems, plasmid transfer occurs either by conjugation or transduction. Conjugation is a process requiring cell-to-cell contact whereby DNA is transferred from a donor bacterium to a recipient. Many Gram-negative bacteria and some Gram-positive bacteria are able to conjugate. The ability to conjugate is normally encoded by conjugative plasmids, many of which also carry antibiotic resistance genes. Although some resistance plasmids are non-conjugative, they may often be transferred (mobilized) to a recipient if they co-inhabit a cell with a conjugative plasmid. Transduction involves the transfer of genes by bacteriophage particles and plays an important role in the natural transmission of antibiotic resistance plasmids amongst strains of *S. aureus* and of *Strep. pyogenes*. Since the process depends on donors and recipients possessing common, surface-located, bacteriophage receptors, transduction is generally limited to related species and is not effective as a means of plasmid transfer across species boundaries. (c) Plasmids are frequent vectors of transposons (see Section 1.2.3 below).

1.2.3 Resistance determined by transposons

Transposons are mobile DNA sequences capable of transferring (transposing) themselves from one DNA molecule (the donor) to another (the recipient). Unlike plasmids, transposons are not able to replicate independently and must be maintained within a functional replicon (e.g. plasmid or chromosome). Transposons contain at their ends short regions that in any particular transposon are almost identical. These regions, or *repeats*, as they are termed, can lie in the same direction with respect to each other (*direct repeats*), or more commonly, in the opposite direction (*inverted repeats*). The terminal repeats are believed to serve as recognition sequences for transposition enzymes (or transposases) in their role of fusing the ends of the transposon with the recipient DNA. The central, or *core*, regions of transposons lying between the repeated ends, frequently carry antibiotic resistance genes (Table 5.2), in addition to genes necessary for the process of transposition itself.

Transposition does not involve the normal host mechanism for recombining homologous DNA molecules, i.e. the process is *recA* independent. For some elements (like Tn3) the process of transposition is replicative and involves cointegration or fusion of donor and recipient replicons, which are coupled by two similarly oriented copies of the transposon. The cointegrate is subsequently resolved by transposition encoded resolvase protein (Fig. 5.2). Although certain so-called composite (or class 1 transposons), e.g. Tn5 and *Tn*10 transpose by a replicative process to give stable cointegrates (Fig. 5.2a), movement of these elements more usually involves a conservative, non-replicative mechanism that can result in destruction of the donor replicon following movement of the transposon (Fig. 5.2b).

The existence of transposons that confer antibiotic resistance accounts for the emergence of multiply-resistant bacteria. Since transposons do not require extensive DNA homology to insert into the recipient molecule, it is possible for bacteria to acquire several different resistance genes by a series of transposon insertions in resident plasmids.

1.3 Biochemical mechanisms of antibiotic resistance

A variety of biochemical mechanisms for antibiotic resistance have been described, the most important of which are summarized in Table 5.3. However, it should be noted at the outset that resistance to a particular antibiotic can result from the combined expression of several of the listed mechanisms. For instance, the efficacy of a beta-lactam antibiotic against a Gram-negative organism will be determined by the diffusion rate of the antibiotic across the outer membrane, its affinity for and resistance towards any periplasmic beta-lactamase that may be present, and finally

Table 5.2 — Properties of some antibiotic resistance transposons

Transposon	Size (kilobase pairs)	Resistance encoded
Found in Gram-negative bacteria		
Tn*1*	5.0	Ampicillin
Tn*2*	5.0	Ampicillin
Tn*3*	5.0	Ampicillin
Tn*5*	5.1	Kanamycin
Tn*7*	14.0	Streptomycin, trimethoprim
Tn*9*	2.7	Chloramphenicol
Tn*10*	9.3	Tetracycline
Tn*21*	19.0	Streptomycin, sulphonamides, (mercury)[a]
Tn*1721*	11.2	Tetracyline
Found in staphylococci		
Tn*551*	5.3	MLS group[b]
Tn*552*	6.1	Penicillin
Tn*554*[c]	6.7	MLS group, spectinomycin
Tn*4001*	4.7	Gentamicin, trimethoprim, kanamycin
Tn*4002*	6.7	Penicillin
Tn*4003*	3.6	Trimethoprim
Tn*4201*	6.6	Penicillin
Tn*4291*	7.5	Methicillin
Found in streptococci		
Tn*916*[d]	*16.4*	Tetracycline

[a] Resistance to mercury is described in Chapter 6.
[b] MLS group = macrolides, lincosamides and streptogramins.
[c] Tn*554* is unusual among transposons in that it does not possess inverted or direct repeat sequences at its termini.
[d] Tn*916* is a conjugative transposon (see Clewell *et al.* (1988) for further details).

its affinity for target penicillin binding proteins (PBPs) located in the cytoplasmic membrane. Consequently, beta-lactam resistance may evolve by affecting one or more of these parameters.

The sections that follow discuss the basis of bacterial resistance to the antibiotics described in Chapter 2. As before, the antibiotics are grouped into four classes, i.e. as inhibitors of nucleic acid, protein and peptidoglycan synthesis and of membrane integrity. Resistance mechanisms responsible for acquired resistance are considered separately from those conferring intrinsic resistance.

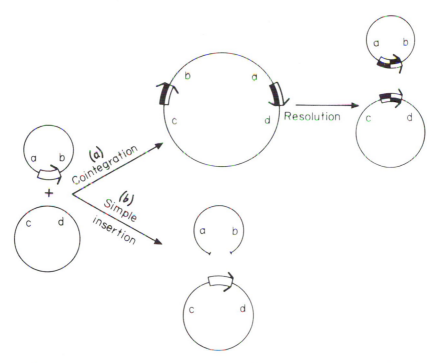

Fig. 5.2 — Replicative and conservative transposition. The transposable element is indicated by the box. The donor replicon is lettered ab and the target replicon cd. Replicative transposition is shown to involve fusion of the replicons to give a cointegrate. This can be resolved by site-specific recombination between the duplicated copies of the transposable element. The outcome of conservative transposition is simple insertion of the element into the target replicon; the donor replicon may be destroyed or undergo other fates. (Reproduced, with permission, from Wilkins (1988).)

2.   ACQUIRED RESISTANCE TO INHIBITORS OF NUCLEIC ACID SYNTHESIS

2.1   Compounds that interrupt nucleotide metabolism

2.1.1   Sulphonamides

Both chromosomal and plasmid-mediated resistance to sulphonamides has been described.

Chromosomal resistance can result from two mechanisms. The first involves hyperproduction of *p*-amino-benzoic acid (PABA) that overcomes the metabolic block imposed by the inhibition of dihydropteroate synthetase (DHPS). Resistance of this type was observed in certain organisms (e.g. *Staph. aureus*) soon after the introduction of sulphonamides for therapeutic purposes. Although resistance probably results from chromosomal mutation, the nature of the change responsible for PABA hyperproduction has not been examined. A second type of chromosomal reistance involves mutation of DHPS (e.g. in *Strep. pneumoniae*) to produce an altered enzyme for which sulphonamides have a lower affinity than the wild-type enzyme.

Table 5.3 — Mechanisms of antibiotic resistance

Mechanism	Examples
1. Alteration (antibiotic inactivation)	Acquired resistance to aminoglycosides, beta-lactams and chloramphenicol. Intrinsic resistance to beta-lactams.
2. Target site in the cell is insensitive to the inhibitor but still able to perform its normal physiological function	Acquired resistance to aminoglycosides, beta-lactams, macrolides, quinolones, rifampicin and trimethoprim. Intrinsic resistance to trimethoprim.
3. Decreased antibiotic accumulation	
(a) Impaired uptake	Intrinsic and acquired resistance to many antibiotics.
(b) Enhanced efflux	Acquired resistance to tetracycline.
4. By-pass of antibiotic-sensitive step by duplication of the target site, the second version being insusceptible to drug action	Acquired resistance to methicillin, sulphonamides and trimethoprim.
5. Overproduction of target so that higher antibiotic concentrations are needed to inhibit bacterial growth	Acquired resistance to trimethoprim
6. Absence of an enzyme/metabolic pathway	Intrinsic resistance to some antibiotics in certain species.

Plasmid mediated resistance to sulphonamides involves a by-pass of the drug-sensitive step by duplication of the respective target enzyme, the second (plasmid-encoded) version conferring resistance. Two different types (I and II) of plasmid-encoded sulphonamide resistant DHPS enzymes have been found in Gram-negative bacteria. These enzymes bind sulphonamides about 10000-fold less efficiently than the chromosomally encoded (sensitive) enyme, but resistance is achieved without sacrificing the efficiency with which natural substrate is bound. The structural genes for the type I and II enzymes have recently been sequenced, thereby permitting deduction of amino acid sequences in the respective polypeptides. The type I polypeptide comprises 279 and type II 271 amino acids. However, even though the enzymes have similar sizes, their deduced amino acid sequences only show about 50% similarlity. This suggests that the genes encoding these enzymes have different evolutionary histories.

2.1.2   2,4-diaminopyrimidines

Chromosomal-, plasmid- and transposon-encoded resistances to the 2,4-diamono-pyrimidine antibiotic trimethoprim have been reported in various bacterial species.

Chromosomal mutations have been reported in *E. coli* that cause overproduction of dihydrofolate reductase (DHFR). This leads to trimethoprim resistance because a higher inhibitor concentration is needed inside the cell to decrease the residual enzyme activity to a level below that required to sustain tetrahydrofolic acid synthesis. Furthermore, mutation to enzyme overproduction can act in concert with other mutations rendering the DHFR less susceptible to inhibition by trimethoprim. A clinical *E. coli* isolate of this type, resistant to more than 1000 μg trimethoprim/ml, was recently examined in detail. Various mutations were defined in the chromosomal DHFR gene (three transitions, four transversions and one nucleotide addition) that collectively lead to more efficient transcription and translation of the enzymes. A further transversion occurred within the coding region of the gene that resulted in substitution of glycine for tryptophan at amino acid position 30 in the enzyme. This change causes about a 3-fold increase in resistance of the enzyme to inhibition by trimethoprim.

Plasmid- and transposon-mediated resistance to trimethoprim has been found in a variety of Gram-positive and Gram-negative bacteria. Resistance involves a by-pass of the antibiotic-sensitive step by duplication of the chromosomally encoded target DHFR enzyme, the plasmid, or transposon, encoded version conferring resistance. Ten different trimethoprim resistant bacterial DHFR enzymes have been identified. These enzymes contain altered active sites which render them resistant to trimethoprim.

2.2   Resistance to compounds that inhibit enzymic processes in nucleic acid synthesis

2.2.1   Inhibitors of RNA polymerase

As discussed in Chapter 2, rifampicin inhibits RNA synthesis in bacteria by inhibiting DNA-dependent RNA polymerase.

The existence of rifampicin-resistant chromosomal mutants has been known for some time. Investigations in *E. coli* show that the antibiotic does not bind to the enzyme from resistant cells. In *E. coli* the RNA polymerase contains four polypeptide chains and rifampicin resistance is associated with changes in one of the these, the β-subunit.

2.2.2   Inhibitors of DNA gyrase

As discussed in Chapter 2 the quinolone antibiotics inhibit bacterial DNA gyrase.

Resistance to quinolones has been reported both in Gram-negative and Gram-positive bacteria and appears to be associated with mutations in chromosomal genes. However, since little is known of the molecular basis of resistance in Gram-positive bacteria, discussion of resistance mechanisms is restricted to Gram-negative species.

In *E. coli nor*A or *gyr*A (formerly *nal*A) mutations produce changes in the A subunit of DNA gyrase and render organisms resistant to nalidixic acid, but not the newer quinolones such as ciprofloxacin, norfloxacin and ofloxacin. However, mutations in *gyr*B confer resistance to both nalidixic acid and some of the newer quinolones. Four *gyr*A and two *gyr*B mutations have recently been studied in detail. DNA fragments containing the mutant *gyr* genes were cloned and sequenced to reveal the nature of the spontaneous mutations.

The *gyr*A mutants were all point mutations, resulting either from transitions or transversions. These mutations were near each other and clustered at the amino-terminal end of the gyrA protein subunit in a region close to the DNA binding site of the subunit. Exactly how the mutations confer resistance to nalidixic acid is unknown, but they probably result in conformational changes in DNA gyrase following association of the A and B subunits to form the functional enzyme. The conformational changes may lead to a decrease in quinolone binding to the gyrase enzyme.

The two *gyr*B mutants resulted from transitions. Both mutations affect the electical charge of the *gyr*B product which indicates that drug-gyrase interactions are probably influenced by electric charge. Thus resistance may result from decreased binding of quinolones to the DNA gyrase B subunit as a result of electrostatic repulsion.

Two other types of chromosomal mutation to 4-quinolone resistance have been reported in *E. coli*. *Nor*B mutants (mapping at about 34 minutes) show low-level resistance to some quinolones and other unrelated antibiotics as a consequence of decreased OmpF porin content and *nor*C mutants (mapping at about 8 minutes) are less susceptible to certain quinolones (e.g. norfloxacin and ciprofloxacin), but hypersusceptible to others. *Nor*C mutants are altered in both OmpF porin content and lipopolysaccharide structure. However, *nor*B mutations do not map in the OmpF structural gene, but appear to affect a locus that regulates OmpF production. Mutations that produce similar phenotypes to *nor*B and *nor*C have also been identified in other members of the Enterobacteriaceae, e.g. *Klebsiella*, *Enterobacter* and *Serratia*.

3. ACQUIRED RESISTANCE TO ANTIBIOTIC INHIBITORS OF PROTEIN SYNTHESIS

3.1 Mupirocin

As discussed in Chapter 2 mupirocin prevents incorporation of iso-leucine into growing polypeptide chains. It has proved useful in the therapy of staphylococcal skin infections, but recently highly resistant staphylococcal strains have emerged, e.g. after treatment with mupirocin of patients with eczema. The biochemical basis of resistance is unknown, but appears to be plasmid-mediated.

3.2 Aminoglycoside-aminocyclitol (AGAC) group

Acquired resistance to these antibiotics can arise by mechanisms 1, 2 and 3a described in Table 5.3.

The most widespread mechanism of resistance involves modification of the antibiotics by bacterial enzymes that are either plasmid or transposon encoded (Table 5.2). These are three classes of enzyme that modify AGAC antibiotics: acetyltransferases (abbreviated AAC), adenylyltransferases (AAD) and phospho-transferases (APH) (Fig. 5.3 and Table 5.4). AAC use acetylCoA as a cofactor,

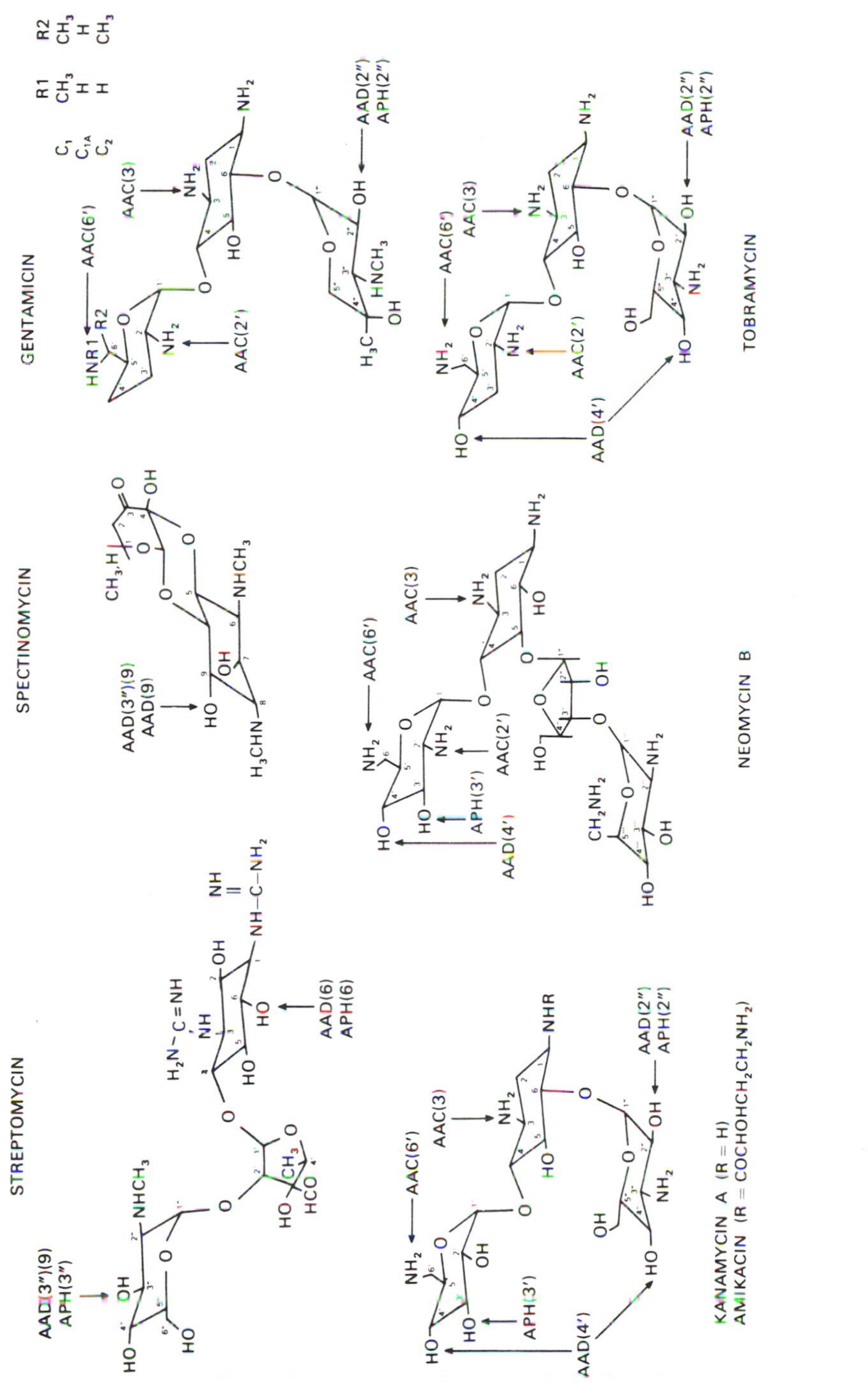

Fig. 5.3 — Enzymic modification of aminoglycoside-aninocyclitol antibiotics. The sites of acetylation (AAC), phosphorylation (APH) and adenylylation (AAD) are indicated by arrows.

Table 5.4 — Aminoglycoside-modifying enzymes

Enzyme	Modification of									Organisms where found
	Strepto-mycin	Spectino-mycin	Neo-mycin B and C	Kana-mycin A	Amikacin	Tobra-mycin	Genta-micin C sissomicin	Netil-micin	Apra-mycin	
APH(3″)	+	–	0	0	0	0	0	0	0	Gram-negative and Gram-positive organisms
APH(6)	+	0	0	0	0	0	0	0	0	Pseudomonas
APH(3′)	0	0	+	+	Variable	0	0	0	0	Gram-negative and Gram-positive organisms
APH(2″)	0	0	0	+	±	+	+	±	0	Gram-positive organisms
AAD(3″)(9)	+	+	0	0	0	0	0	0	0	Gram-negative organisms
AAD(6)	+	0	0	0	0	0	0	0	0	Staphylococci
AAD(9)	–	+	0	0	0	0	0	0	0	Staphylococci
AAD(4′)(4″)	0	0	+	+	+	+	0	0	0	Staphylococci
AAD(2″)	0	0	0	+	Variable	+	+	+	0	Gram-negative organisms
AAC(3)I	0	0	–	–	–	±	+	±	–	Gram-negative organisms
AAC(3)II	0	0	–	±	–	+	+	±	–	Gram-negative organisms
AAC(3)III	0	0	+	+	–	+	+	+	–	Gram-negative organisms
AAC(3)IV	0	0	+	+	–	+	+	+	+	Gram-negative organisms
AAC(2′)	0	0	+	0	0	+	+	+	0	Providencia
AAC(6′)I	0	0	+	+	+	+	Variable^a	+	0	Gram-negative organisms
AAC(6′)II	0	0	+	+	+	+	Variable^a	+	0	Moraxella
AAC(6′)III	0	0	+	+	±	+	Variable^a	+	0	Pseudomonas
AAC(6′)IV	0	0	±	+	+	+	Variable^a	+	0	Gram-positive organisms

Symbols: + modified; – not modified; ± poorly modified; 0 substituent necessary for modification absent
^{a} Gentamicin C_1 0, gentamicins C_{1A} and C_2 and sissomicin +
Reproduced, with permission, from Phillips & Shannon (1984).

whereas in the phosphorylation and nucleotidylation reactions ATP is the cofactor. The enzymes have been further divided into sub-types (Table 5.4) on the basis of the sites they modify in the antibiotics. For example AAC(6′) enzymes acetylate the 6′-amino group on aminohexose I of susceptible antibiotics (Fig. 5.3).

Unlike other drug resistance mechanisms involving enzymatic inactivation (see for example, beta-lactamases: Section 4.5.3), only small amounts of AGAC antibiotics are modified. This has led to the hypothesis that resistance is achieved by modification of the antibiotic during the process of transport into the cell so that resistance to a particular AGAC antibiotic is dicated by competition between the rates of drug uptake and drug modification. If accumulation occurs at a greater rate than modification, active drug will reach the ribosomes and protein synthesis will cease. However, if the rate of drug modification exceeds that of transport, modified drug is accumulated but does not inhibit protein synthesis, and the organism is resistant. The ability to modify a particular AGAC molecule will depend upon the amount of modifying enzyme per cell, and its catalytic efficiency.

AGAC resistance can also be expressed by mechanisms 2 and 3a (Table 5.3). For instance, mutations in the *rps*L gene (formerly known as *str*A) of *E. coli* K-12 lead to high-level resistance to streptomycin by altering the nature of ribosomal protein S12 and preventing the antibiotic from binding to its target. Similar types of chromosomal mutation occur in other bacterial species, e.g. clinical isolates of *S. aureus*. Resistance due to mechanism 3a (i.e. impaired uptake) has been reported both in laboratory strains with mutations affecting the coupling of energy to membrane transport processes, and in clinical isolates.

3.3   Chloramphenicol

Acquired resistance to chloramphenicol is frequently due to inactivation of the drug, a phenomenon first observed in *E. coli*. Inactivation is mediated by plasmid- or transposon-encoded chloramphenicol acetyl transferases (CATs) that convert the drug to 3-acetoxychloramphenicol followed by conversion to 1,3-diacetoxychloramphenicol, the final inactivation product (Fig. 5.4). The acetoxy derivatives are antibiotically inactive because they fail to bind to the ribosomal target. Several types of plasmid-encoded CATs are found that have been characterized with respect to catalytic properties, electrophoretic mobility and reactivity to antisera. The enzymes are tetramers of identical subunits, the monomeric polypeptides having molecular weights in the range 23–25 kDa. The type I enzyme has been most studied and the complete amino acid sequence of its subunits is known. A histidine residue at position 193 (Fig. 5.5) plays a critical role in the catalytic modification of chloramphenicol and is likely to be located at the active site of the enzyme. The type III enzyme also contains a region sharing homology with the segment running between amino acids 190 and 200 in the type I enzyme, the catalytic histidine residue being located at residue 188 in the case of the type III molecule (Fig. 5.5). Other CATs (Fig. 5.5) also contain histidine at their active sites.

Although the majority of plasmids conferring chloramphenicol resistance in *E. coli* encode CATs, at least one example of a plasmid-encoded non-enzymic resistance mechanism has been described. This type of resistance, encoded by plasmid R26, appears to result from impaired uptake (i.e. mechanism 3a — Table 5.3).

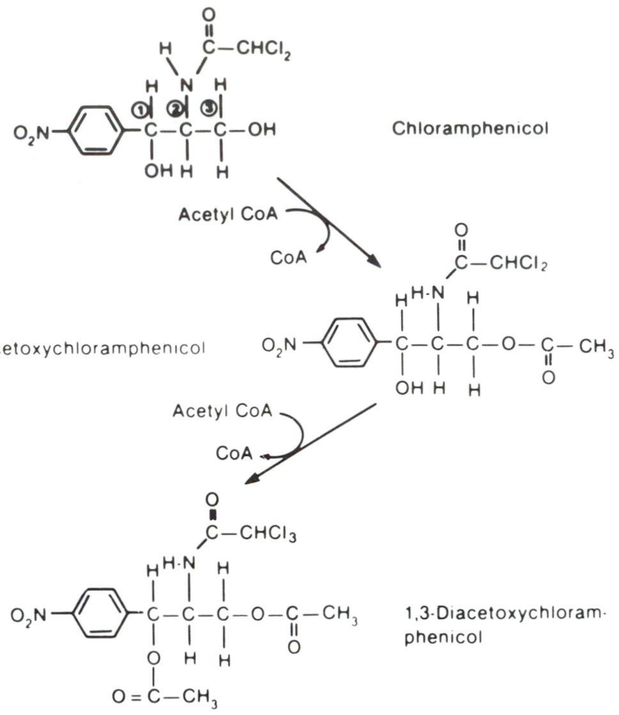

Fig. 5.4 — Modification of chloramphenicol by acetyl transferase.

Recently, attempts have been made to clarify the molecular basis of this type of chloramphenicol resistance. The R26 *cml* gene responsible for non-enzymatic resistance has been sequenced and the *cml* gene product identified as a relatively hydrophobic protein of molecular weight 33.8 K. In view of its hydrophobicity this protein may be membrane-associated and in this location prevents net influx of chloramphenicol into the cell. However, the precise molecular basis of this resistance mechanism is unknown.

In Gram-negative bacteria low-level resistance to chloramphenicol can arise by mutational loss of outer membrane porins through which the drug normally diffuses to reach the periplasm. Finally, strains resistant to chloramphenicol by virtue of general mechanism 2 (Table 5.3) have also been described. Although such strains possess drug-resistant ribosomes and/or altered ribosomal proteins, a direct causal relationship that alteration of a given protein renders ribosomes resistant to chloramphenicol has not been established.

3.4 Fusidic acid
As noted in Chapter 2, fusidic acid is a steroid antibiotic that prevents bacterial protein synthesis by inhibiting functions associated with translocation factor protein (G factor or EFG).

Gram-negative bacteria are intrinsically resistant to fusidic acid by virtue of poor

Primary structures of polypeptides

Enzyme type	1				5				10				15				20		190				195				200 → C-terminus
	Met	Glu	Lys	Lys	Ile																						
I (Tn9)	Thr	Gly	Tyr	Thr	Thr	Val	Asp	Ile	Ser	Gln	Trp	His	Arg	Lys	Glu	---	Gln	Val	His	His	Ala	Val	Cys	Asp	Gly	Phe	His ---
II	Met	Asn	Phe	Thr	Arg	Ile	Asp	Leu	Asn	Thr	Trp	Asn											not determined				
III	Met	Asn	Tyr	Thr	Lys	Phe	Asp	Val	Lys	Asn	Trp	Val	Arg	Arg	Glu	---	Gln	Val	His	His	Ala	Val	Cys	Asp	Gly	Phe	His ---
C (pC221)[a]	[Met]	Thr	Phe	Asn	Ile	Ile	Lys	Glu	Asn	Trp	Asp	Arg	Lys	Glu		---	Gln	Val	His	His	Ala	Val	Cys	Asp	Gly	Tyr	His ---
(pC194)	Met	Asn	Phe	Asn	Lys	Ile	Asp	Leu	Asp	Asn	Trp	Lys	Arg	Lys	Glu	---	Gln	Val	His	His	Ser	Val	Cys	Asp	Gly	Tyr	His ---
B. pumilus	Met	Thr	Phe	Asn	Ile	Ile	Lys	Leu	Glu	Asn	Trp	Asp	Arg	Arg	Lys	Glu	Gln	Val	His	His	Ala	Val	Cys	Asp	Gly	Tyr	His ---

Fig. 5.5 — Amino acid sequences surrounding the active site histidine residues (marked with an arrow) in various bacterial chloramphenicol acetyltransferases. The type C enzyme determined by plasmid pC221 is synthesized with an N-terminal methionine residue, but this is removed from the protein after translation. (Reproduced, with permission, from Shaw (1984).)

antibiotic penetration across the outer membrane (Section 6.3.2). However, acquired reistance to fusidic acid does occur in these organisms (e.g. the Enterobacteriaceae, see below) further elevating the level of resistance. Acquired resistance also occurs in Gram-positive bacteria that do not express intrinsic resistance to the antibiotic.

Acquired resistance results either from chromosomal mutations or possession of plasmids. Chromosomal mutants invariably have a modified G factor which has decreased affinity for the drug. In *S. aureus*, plasmid-mediated resistance to fusidic acid may involve decreased uptake of antibiotic across the cytoplasmic membrane (i.e. mechanism 3a, Table 5.3), but the molecular basis of resistance is unknown. The mechanism of plasmid-determined resistance to fusidic acid in the Enterobacteriaceae is also not fully understood and indeed is somewhat puzzling. Many plasmids confer resistance to fusidic acid, but the determinant in plasmid R100 has been studied in most detail. Surprisingly, the gene encoding resistance to fusidic acid also encodes a type I CAT. Firm evidence has been obtained that the CAT itself confers fusidic acid resistance and that a separate *fus* product is not translated from an initiation codon internal to the *cat* message. However, fusidic acid is not inactivated or modified by the enzyme, which appears to have a binding domain that sequestors a variety of aromatic compounds that are not necessarily closely related structurally.

3.5   Macrolides, lincosamides and streptogramins (MLS group)

3.5.1   Common mechanism of resistance

As noted in Chapter 2, MLS antibiotics arrest protein synthesis by binding to the 50S ribosomal subunit. Resistance mechanisms specific to individual members of the MLS antibiotics occur (see below), but in addition, resistance to all these antibiotics can be conferred by a single mechanism involving mono or dimethylation of an adenine residue in 23S rRNA. Determination of the site of methylation indicates that an analogous residue, corresponding to position 2058 of the *E. coli* rRNA, is modified by different rRNA methylases both in Gram-positive and Gram-negative bacteria. Methylation prevents the drugs from binding to the 50S ribosomal subunit probably as a consequence of a conformational change in the 23S rRNA.

Genes specifying MLS resistance by rRNA methylation are carried by plasmids and transposons. The methylase ecoded by the *S. aureus* plasmid pE194 has been studied in detail. It is a 29 kDa polypeptide which depends upon *S*-adenosylmethionine for its activity. The enzyme methylates free 23S rRNA and isolated 50S ribosomal subunits, but not intact 70S ribosomes. Therefore access to the methylation site in 23S rRNA is blocked when the 50S ribosomal subunit interacts with the 30S subunit.

3.5.2   Mechanisms of resistance to individual MLS antibiotics

3.5.2.1   *Macrolides*

Three different chromosomal mutations in *E. coli* that affect ribosomal proteins can confer resistance to the macrolides. Mutants designated *ery*A show an alteration in protein L4 which leads to loss of macrolide binding by ribosomes. The *ery*A locus is therefore probably the structural gene for protein L4. The second type of mutant, designated *ery*B, confers a change in protein L22, but the *ery*B locus does not correspond to the structural gene for L22. The third class of mutation, *eryC*, has been reported to affect maturation of ribosomal RNA and a 30S ribsomal subunit protein. Therefore the mechanisms of macrolide resistance conferred by *ery*B and C mutations are presently unclear.

Plasmid-mediated mechanisms of resistance to 14-membered macrolides (e.g. erythromycin and oleandomycin) that correspond to general mechanisms 1 and 3 (Table 5.3) have also been described. Inactivation of erythromycin and oleandomycin is widespread in enterobacteria highly resistant to these antibiotics and results from hydrolysis of the lactone ring in the antibiotics by plasmid-encoded esterases (Fig. 5.6). Inactivation is restricted specifically to 14-membered macrolides. The

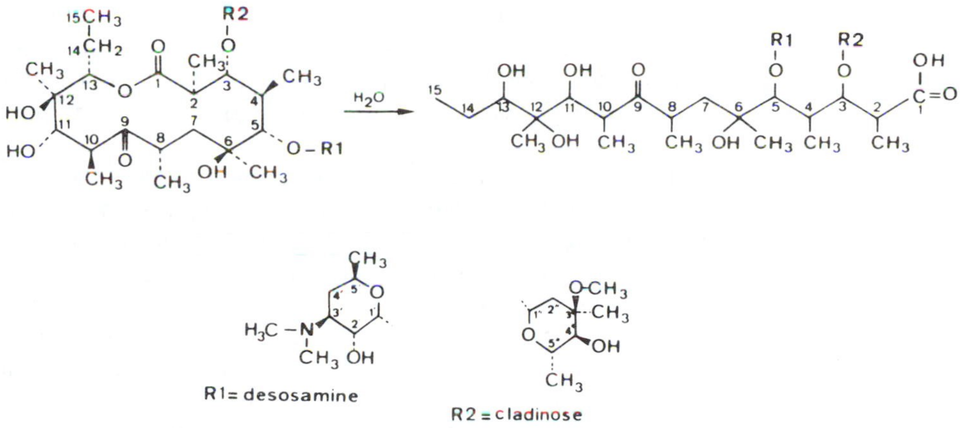

Fig. 5.6 — Enzymatic hydrolysis of erythromycin.

nucleotide sequences of two plasmid genes, *ere*A and *ere*B encoding esterases types I and II have recently been determined. Although both genes occur in clinical isolates of *E. coli*, the corresponding proteins are different. The type I esterases contains 349 amino acid residues and type II 419 amino acids. Furthermore, comparison of the amino acid sequences indicates that the proteins are unrelated.

Plasmid-mediated inactivation of erythromycin has also recently been detected in streptococci and staphylococci. However, the genes mediating resistance in these Gram-positive organisms are not homologous with either *ere*A or *ere*B.

Certain *S. epidermidis* strains express low-level resistance to erythromycin and oleandomycin which results from decreased uptake of antibiotics across the cytoplasmic membrane. However, the molecular basis of this plasmid-mediated resistance mechanism is unknown.

3.5.2.2   *Lincosamides*

Plasmid-mediated inactivation of lincosamides occurs in a variety of resistant staphyloccocal species. Inactivation results from enzymic nucleotidylation at positon 4 of the antibiotics (Fig. 5.7). Two closely related enzymes are responsible for nucleotidylation each containing 161 amino acid residues and showing 91% homology with each other.

3.5.2.3   Streptogramins

Resistance to streptogramin antibiotics in *S. aureus* can result from inactivation by plasmid-encoded enzymes. Streptogramin A is inactivated by an *O*-acetyltransferase and streptogramin B by a hydrolase.

3.6   Acquired resistance to tetracyclines

3.6.1   *Resistance from expression of plasmid or transposon encoded efflux systems*

Bacterial resistance to the tetracyclines has been recognized for many years. In many cases resistance is plasmid- or transposon-mediated and early studies demonstrated that resistance in *E. coli* and other species was associated with decreased accumulation of antibiotic thereby preventing access to the ribosome, the target of tetracycline action.

Initially, decreased tetracycline accumulation was explained solely by reduced antibiotic influx, with no apparent evidence for efflux. Since it was known that tetracycline uptake into sensitive bacteria exhibits dependence on magnesium, theories were advanced that plasmid-encoded products conferring tetracycline resistance chelated cations involved in tetracycline transport. Thus resistance was assumed to arise by a decrease in the free metal ion concentration in the membrane that prevented entry of tetracycline. However, such theories are no longer tenable and there is now little doubt that resistance associated with decreased antibiotic accumulation results from energy-dependent (active) tetracycline efflux.

Detailed studies have established the existence in both Gram-positive and Gram-negative species of several plasmid- or transposon-encoded membrane-located resistance proteins that comprise a group of tetracycline efflux proteins (Table 5.5). The energetics of tetracycline efflux mediated by the Tn*10*-encoded resistance protein have been studied in detail. This work has primarily involved the use of inverted membrane vesicles from *E. coli* into which tetracycline is transported under the action of the resistance protein that normally promotes drug efflux from the cell. Efflux is dependent on the proton-motive force (pmf: see Chapters 1 and 3) and driven principally by the pH gradient. This predicts an electrically neutral proton/tetracycline antiport system with expulsion of a cationic form of tetracycline (Fig. 5.8). The cationic tetracycline species that is expelled from the cell has not been positively identified. However, since tetracycline forms positively charged metal chelates these could comprise the cationic tetracycline form that is expelled from the cell. The known magnesium dependence of efflux is consistent with the view that magnesium-tetracycline chelates might be involved.

The studies described above concerning tetracycline efflux in *E. coli*, together with information on the nature of tetracycline transport into the cell (see Chapter 2) have produced a general model for tetracycline influx and efflux in this organism (Fig. 5.9).

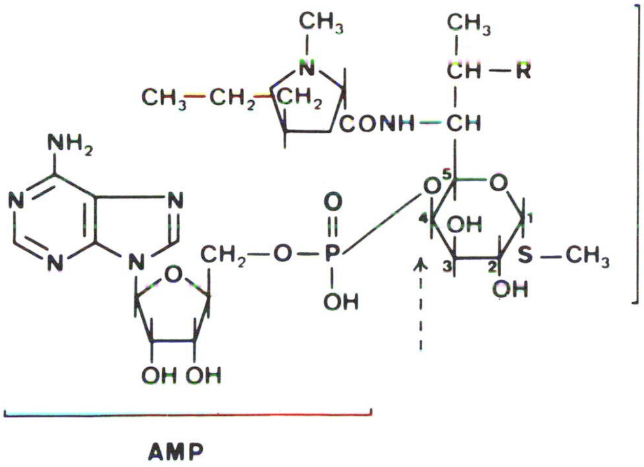

Fig. 5.7 — Structures of lincosamides inactivated by enzymic nucleotidylation at position 4 of the molecules.

Table 5.5 — Membrane-located proteins encoded by different tetracycline resistance determinants

Determinant	Protein molecular weight (k)		Amino acid residues
	SDS PAGE	DNA sequence	
Tn1721	34	42	399
Tn10	36	43	401
pBR322	34	42	396
pAB124	32	?	?
pTHT15		50	458
pT181		35	295

3.6.2   Resistance from expression of plasmid or transposon encoded ribosomal protection factors

Recently, two types of ribosomal protection factors have been described, tetM and tetO, both of which are plasmid or transposon encoded. The tetM resistance system occurs naturally in certain streptococci and *Ureaplasma urealyticum*, whereas tetO has been described in *Campylobacter jejuni*. The precise mechanism by which these protein products protect ribosomes from the action of tetracyclines is unclear. However, the tetM and tetO proteins show considerable amino acid sequence homology over the first 100 amino acid residues to known translational elongation

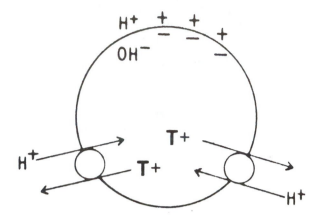

Fig. 5.8 — Diagrammatic representation of tetracycline (T^+) efflux mediated by a membrane-located electroneutral antiport system. The electrochemical proton gradient with the polarity indicated at the top can be established either by electrogenic extrusion of protons catalysed by the respiratory chain (aerobic conditions), or (under anaerobic conditions) by extrusion of protons through the membrane bound ATPase (not shown) by degradation of ATP produced, for example, by fermentation of glucose. The antiport system results in the simultaneous translocation of a cationic tetracycline species (T^+) and a proton (H^+) in opposite directions. The pH gradient is the force which drives the extrusion of T^+ from the cell.

factors, including *E. coli* EF-Tu. Therefore, tetM and tetO may act as alternative elongation factors able to bind, or sequester, tetracycline and in so doing prevent direct binding of tetracycline to ribosomes.

3.6.3 *Plasmid-mediated detoxification of tetracycline*
Recently, a plasmid-located tetracycline resistance gene has been identified which confers resistance in *E. coli* only when the cells are grown aerobically. Although the mechanism of resistance has yet to be fully established, the resistance determinant encodes a cytoplasmic 44 kDa protein that may detoxify tetracycline by an oxidative reaction.

3.6.4 *Other acquired mechanisms of tetracycline resistance*
Chromosomal mutations in *E. coli* leading to loss of the outer membrane porin OmpF, through which the antibiotic normally diffuses, confer low-level resistance to tetracycline (and other unrelated compounds). Chromosomal mutations affecting ribosomal proteins or transport of the antibiotic across the cytoplasmic membrane have also been reported.

4. ACQUIRED RESISTANCE TO ANTIBIOTICS THAT INHIBIT PEPTIDOGLYCAN SYNTHESIS

4.1 D-cycloserine
As noted in Chapter 2, D-cycloserine is transported across the bacterial cytoplasmic membrane by the D-alanine transport system. In *E. coli* this transport system is

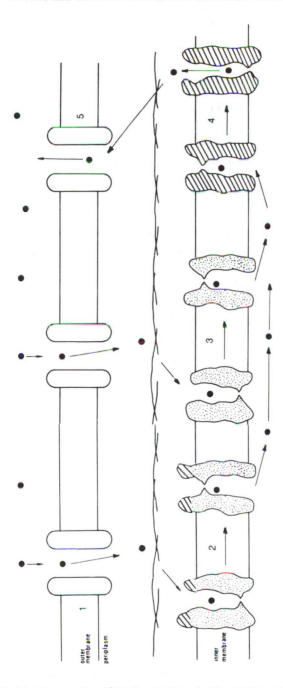

Fig. 5.9 — Model of tetracycline (●) influx (1–3) and efflux (4,5) in *E. coli*. 1,5, Passive diffusion through outer membrane porins; 2,3, energy dependent transport across the cytoplas-mic membrane mediated either by an ATP-dependent, osmotic-shock sensitive system (2), or by an osmotic shock-insensitive, protonmotive force-dependent system (3). 4, Protonmotive force-dependent efflux mediated by a tetracycline resistance protein functioning as a homomul-timer. (Reproduced, with permission, from Chopra (1986).)

encoded by the chromosomal gene *cyc*A which is involved in accumulation of D-alanine, D-glycine and D-serine as well as D-cycloserine. Mutations in *cyc*A confer resistance to cycloserine as well as defects in the transport of the other molecules.

In streptococci, transport mutants analogous to those in *E. coli* have been isolated as well as resistant mutants which produce more of the target enzymes inhibited by D-cycloserine. Mutants with up to five times more synthetase or eight time more racemase than normal can occur. The enzymes in these mutants are identical to those of the parent strain except in quantity.

4.2   Fosfomycin
As described in Chapter 2, fosfomycin acts at the level of phosphoenolpyruvate: UDP-*N*-acetylglucosamine enoylpyruvil transferase in the biosynthesis of peptidoglycan.

Resistance to the antibiotic has been reported in several types of Gram-negative bacteria and occurs principally by general mechanisms 1 and 3a (Table 5.3). Mechanisms attributable to type 3a were identified some years ago and involve chromosomal mutations in the hexose-6-phosphate or L-glycerophosphate uptake systems by which fosfomycin is transported into susceptible bacteria.

More recently, another resistance mechanism (Fo-r) was identified which confers about a 2000-fold increase in resistance and involves fosfomycin modification. The Fo-r genetic determinant is common to a variety of plasmids and, at least in one case, this determinant is also known to be located in a transposon termed *Tn*2921. Fosfomycin is modified intracellularly to produce a derivative lacking antibiotic activity. The chemical nature of the modification is not yet known, but the modifying enzyme has been identified as a cytoplasmic polypeptide with a molecular weight of about 16 K having a sulphydryl group at its active centre.

4.3   Bacitracin
As noted in Chapter 2, bacitracin forms a complex with the membrane-bound pyrophosphate form of the lipid carrier molecule involved in transferring disaccharide-pentapeptide units to the nascent peptidoglycan chain.

Gram-negative bacteria are intrinsically resistant to bacitracin (Section 6.4.1) so that discussion of acquired resistance to this antibiotic is only relevant for Gram-positive organisms. Bacitracin-resistant mutants of *S. aureus* have been isolated in the laboratory, but the mutations appear to revert at high frequency because resistance is readily lost upon removal of the selective pressure. Clinical isolates of Gram-positive bacteria resistant to bacitracin have not been reported which may reflect the unstable nature of resistance mentioned above.

4.4   Glycopeptide antibiotics
As noted in Chapter 2, glycopeptide antibiotics interfere with glycan unit insertion by combining directly with peptidoglycan, in particular to the acyl-D-alanyl-D-alanine terminus of peptidoglycan precursors.

Gram-negative bacteria are intrinsically resistant to glycopeptides (Section 6.4.1) so that discussion of acquired resistance to this group of antibiotics only concerns Gram-positive bacteria. Bacteria resistant to glycopeptides as a result of changes in the target site have never been reported. This arises because the acyl-D-alanyl-D-alanine group in peptidoglycan appears to be absolutely essential for transpeptidation to occur and therefore mutation to resistance inolving changes in these amino acids would prevent synthesis of a normal, rigid peptidoglycan, i.e. the mutation would be lethal.

Despite the comments made above, clinical isolates of enterococci resistant to glycopeptides have recently been described. Although the molecular basis of resistance has not yet been fully established, it involves the synthesis of a 39 kD membrane protein which may prevent glycopeptides from reaching their target site in the peptidoglycan region. Genetically, resistance may be mediated by a conjugative transposon.

4.5 Beta-lactam antibiotics

4.5.1 Introduction
Acquired resistance to beta-lactam antibiotics can arise by three different mechanisms: (1) in Gram-negative organisms through reduction in permeability of the outer membrane to the antibiotic, (2) by synthesis of beta-lactamases, and (3) by modification of one or more PBPs. These mechanisms, either separately or jointly, account for acquired resistance to beta-lactams.

4.5.2 Decreased beta-lactam accumulation by virtue of outer membrane changes
It has been known for many years that changes in the Gram-negative outer membrane may affect the influx rate of beta-lactams and thereby affect the resistance level. In particular, mutational loss of porins (e.g. OmpF and OmpC), through which many beta-lactams normally diffuse, provides low levels of beta-lactam resistance.

4.5.3 Beta-lactamase synthesis
Beta-lactamases hydrolyse the cyclic amide bond in beta-lactam molecules (e.g. see Fig. 5.10) thereby rendering the drugs unable to bind to bacterial PBPs. In the case of

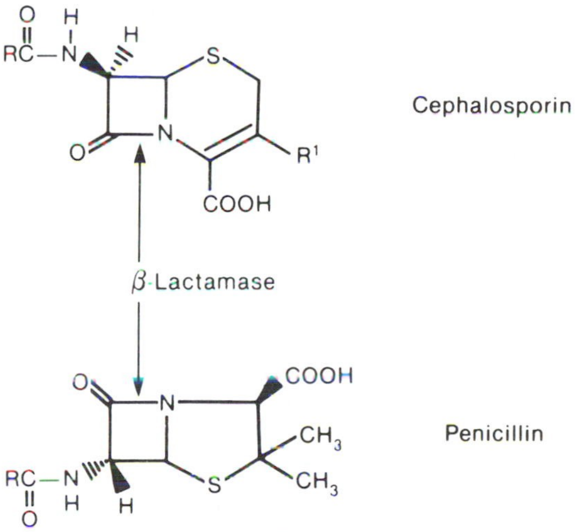

Fig. 5.10 — Interaction of cephalosporins and penicillins with β-lactamases.

Gram-negative bacteria the enzymes are synthesized within the cell and are then secreted into the periplasmic region. Resistance results from the strategic location of beta-lactamases between the antibiotic penetration barrier (the outer membrane) and the antibiotic targets (PBPs) located in the cytoplasmic membrane whereby the beta-lactamases can sequentially destroy antibiotic molecules as they enter the periplasm. Therefore, in Gram-negative bacteria resistance due to beta-lactamase production is predominantly a single-cell phenomenon. In contrast, beta-lactamases produced by Gram-positive bacteria are mainly excreted from the cell so that resistance is a population phenomenon, i.e. the excreted enzyme spreads into the external environment and can reduce the level of beta-lactam to a concentration that permits growth of both enzyme-producing and non-enzyme producing bacteria.

The majority of beta-lactamases inactivate beta-lactams by forming an acyl enzyme intermediate with an amino acid residue in the active centre of the enzyme. Eventually, a hydrolysed (penicilloic acid type) beta-lactam is released, the reaction scheme conforming to that shown in Fig. 2.31 (Chapter 2). Amino acid residues involved in the catalytic reaction include serine, histidine, tryptophan and arginine. Enzymes containing serine at their active sites have been particularly well studied, e.g. in the plasmid-encoded Temoniera (TEM) beta-lactamases the active-site serine is located at residue 45 (Fig. 5.11). The chromosomally encoded ampicillin hydrolysing (*amp*) C beta-lactamase of *E. coli* is also a 'serine enzyme', but in this case the active-site serine is located at residue 80 in the molecule (Fig. 5.11).

Enzyme

E. coli RTEM   −Arg −Phe −Pro −Met− Met −Ser −Thr −Phe −Lys − Val   Leu
                          40   41   42   43   44   45   46   47   48   49   50

E. coli ampC   −Leu − Phe− Glu − Leu − Gly − Ser − Val − Ser − Lys − Thr − Phe
                          75   76   77   78   79   80   81   82   83   84   85

Fig. 5.11 — Regions of *Escherichia coli* RTEM and *amp*C β-lactamases surrounding the active site serines. The residues are numbered from the N-terminus of each protein, the active site serines being located at residues 45 (RTEM) and 80 (*amp*C).

Bacterial beta-lactamases are extremely heterogeneous with respect to both structure and substrate profiles. Over the years, many classification schemes have been proposed for these enzymes and each requires revision as new information becomes available. The general classification scheme of Bush (Table 5.6), published in 1989, is the most suitable at present.

Many bacterial beta-lactamases are plasmid or transposon-encoded, but several Gram-negative enterobacteria and *Pseudomonas* species contain chromosomal genes encoding Group 1 beta-lactamases. In some species (e.g. *E. coli*) enzyme is produced at a low-level and is not inducible, whereas in others, e.g. *Citrobacter freundii*, *Enterobacter cloacae* and *Ps. aeruginosa*, enzyme production is normally low, but can be induced to levels several hundred times higher after exposure of bacteria to a beta-lactam. Furthermore, mutations can occur in the regulatory genes controlling expression of these normally inducible beta-lactamases to produce resistant organisms synthesizing high levels of beta-lactamase constitutively. Such mutations, which lead to enhanced expression of chromosomal beta-lactamases, are of considerable clinical importance since they have been responsible for the rapid

Table 5.6 — General classification scheme for bacterial β-lactamases

Group	Subtitle	Preferred substrates[a]	Inhibited by CA[b]	Inhibited by EDTA	Representative enzyme(s)
1	CEP-N	Cephalosporins[B]	No	No	Chromosomal enzymes from Gram-negative bacteria
2a	PEN-Y	Penicillins[A]	Yes	No	Gram-positive penicillinases
2b	BDS-Y	Cephalosporins[B], penicillins[A]	Yes	No	TEM-1, TEM-2
2b'	EBS-Y	Cephalosporins[B], penicillins[A], cefotaxime[B]	Yes	No	TEM-3, TEM-5
2c	CAR-Y	Penicillins[A], carbenicillin[A]	Yes	No	PSE-1, PSE-3, PSE-4
2d	CLX-Y	Penicillins[A], cloxacillin[A]	Yes[c]	No	OXA-1, PSE-2
2e	CEP-Y	Cephalosporins[B]	Yes	No	Proteus vulgaris
3	MET-N	Variable	No	Yes	Bacillus cereus II, Pseudomonas maltophilia L1
4	PEN-N	Penicillins[A]	No	?[d]	Pseudomonas cepacia

[a] In relation to the beta-lactam classification scheme illustrated in Fig. 2.25 (Chapter 2) the preferred substrates are classified as penams (A) and cephems (B).
[b] 10 μM clavulanic acid.
[c] Inhibition by clavulanic acid may occur at higher concentrations for some members of the group.
[d] Variable.
Reproduced, with permission, from Bush (1989).

development of bacterial resistance during therapy to a number of the newer beta-lactams, until recently regarded as beta-lactamase stable antibiotics.

Apart from beta-lactam destruction, another role in resistance for beta-lactamases has been suggested for some Gram-negative bacteria. In this theory, certain beta-lactamases are envisaged as protecting the cell against beta-lactams by binding, rather than hydrolysing the antibiotic molecules so that drug molecules become 'trapped' within the periplasm and hence fail to bind adequately to the PBPs. The enzymes thought to be responsible for this novel mechanism of resistance are the type 1 beta-lactameses, i.e. primarily the chromosomally-encoded cephalosporinases found in *Ps. aeruginosa* and several members of the Enterobacteriaceae (Table 5.6). Expression of these enzymes results in simultaneous resistance to a number of beta-lactams (e.g. broad-spectrum penicillins, new monobactams and cephamycins) that are not good substrates for the enzymes. Such data have led to the hypothesis that resistance to drugs which are poor substrates for beta-lactamases is mediated by the enzymes via a non-hydrolytic barrier mechanism. Although a poor substrate, the drug is nevertheless thought to be rapidly bound by the enzyme and even without hydrolysis the drug is 'trapped' in a long-lived, biologically inactive complex with the enzyme. However, other authors have objected to this concept of 'trapping' as a resistance mechanism. For instance, it has recently been calculated that if trapping of beta-lactams is responsible for resistance to cefsulodin and latamoxef in *Ps. aeruginosa*, 40% of the dry mass of the cell would need to be synthesized as beta-lactamase.

4.5.4   Alterations in the nature or expression of PBPs that lead to resistance

(a)   *Mutations in target PBPs rendering them insensitive to beta-lactams, but still able to perform peptidoglycan synthesis*

Since beta-lactam antibiotics bind covalently to the active sites of target PBPs, it would seem, at first thought, that a mutation affecting binding of the inhibitor (and thus conferring resistance) might also affect binding of the natural peptidoglycan substrate. However, other regions in PBPs are involved in initial, non-covalent, interactions with substrate and inhibitors prior to covalent linkage. Since these secondary sites are frequently different for inhibitor and substrate, mutation to resistance can occur without totally abolishing PBP activity.

Laboratory mutants of *E. coli* resistant to mecillinam were the first organisms to be described that displayed this resistance mechanism. Acquisition of resistance was accompanied by a decrease in the affinity of PBP2 for mecillinam and other beta-lactams with specificity for the PBP. Numerous examples of this type of resistance mechanism have now been described, both in Gram-negative and Gram-positive organisms. When resistance of this type occurs in clinical isolates it often adversely affects the use of beta-lactam antibiotics for chemotherapy. A recent example involving *Streptococcus pneumoniae* illustrates this type of resistance mechanism in a clinically important pathogen.

Resistance to penicillin in *Strep. pneumoniae* is due entirely to alterations in its PBPs, the mutant (altered) forms of the PBPs having decreased affinity for penicillin. Recently, Spratt and co-workers examined the extent to which the structure of PBP2b in a resistant strain of *Strep. pneumoniae* differed from that of penicillin-sensitive strains. The altered form of PBP2b, with decreased affinity for penicillin, contained multiple amino acid changes within the transpeptidase domain of the enzyme. This shows that the emergence of PBPs with decreased affinity for beta-lactam antibiotics is not achieved by single amino acid changes, but requires multiple substitutions. The amino acid changes do not occur in the immediate vicinity of the active-site serine residue (position 192), but are restricted primarily to seven consecutive residues (positions 232 to 238) predicted to form a loop at the bottom of the penicillin-binding site. The alterations in residues 232 to 238 in the PBP2b from resistant organisms are likely to be responsible for its ability to discriminate between the binding of normal substrate and penicillin.

(b)   *By-pass of beta-lactam susceptible PBP by duplication of target enzyme, the second version being insusceptible to antibiotic*

The most important example of this type of resistance mechanism concerns beta-lactam resistance in clinical *S. aureus* isolates mediated by the *mec* determinant. Resistance results from the synthesis of a unique PBP (Mol. wt. 74 000) designated PBP2′ or PBP2a that has a low affinity for beta-lactam antibiotics. PBP2 is the only functional PBP at concentrations of beta-lactams sufficient to inhibit the normal complement of PBPs in sensitive cells. The *mec* determinant confers resistance to all beta-lactam antibiotics, including beta-lactamase resistant compounds such as meth-icillin. The *mec* determinant is contained within a transposon designated Tn*4291* (Table 5.2).

5.   ACQUIRED RESISTANCE TO ANTIBIOTICS THAT INHIBIT MEMBRANE INTEGRITY — POLYMYXIN

Plasmid-determined resistance to polymyxin has not been described, but chromoso-mal mutants of *Ps. aeruginosa* resistant to polymyxin (and the divalent ion chelator EDTA: see Chapter 6) have been isolated. Resistance is associated with an increase in the content of an outer membrane protein (H1) which apparently decreases the requirement for divalent cations in the outer membrane. Since the initial binding of polymyxin to sensitive cells depends upon displacement of divalent cations from the outer membrane, it is suggested that protein H1 replaces cations at sites in the outer membrane which would otherwise be susceptible to the antibiotic.

6.   INTRINSIC ANTIBIOTIC RESISTANCE

6.1   Introduction

The distinction between intrinsic and acquired antibiotic resistance has already been made in the general introduction to this chapter. As stated, 'instrinsic resistance' is that resistance common to the majority of isolated strains. Genetically it is associated with chromosomal determinants — the 'normal' genetic constituents of the cell. In the following sections information on the genetic and biochemical basis of intrinsic resistance mechanisms is presented. The mechanisms are discussed in the context of the general types of resistance mechanisms outlined in Table 5.3. Further sections consider the nature of outer membranes in the Enterobacteriaceae and *Ps. aerugi-nosa* in the context of intrinsic resistance mechanisms.

6.2   Intrinsic resistance to inhibitors of nucleic acid synthesis

6.2.1   Sulphonamides and 2,4-diaminopyrimidines

Resistance mechanisms corresponding to general mechanisms 2, 3a and 6 (Table 5.3) can be responsible for intrinsic resistance to these inhibitors of tetrahydrofolic acid synthesis.

Ps. aeruginosa is intrinsically resistant to both types of antibiotic by virtue of a permeability barrier to the compounds. This probably results from the unusual nature of the outer membrane in this organism (see also Section 6.7). Intrinsic resistance to trimethoprim in several organisms is associated with an insensitive DHFR. This form of resistance is found in Neisseria spp. Clostridium spp, Bacteroides, Caulobacter and Nocardia restricta. The DHFR enzymes from these organisms are 40 to 2000-fold less susceptible to trimethoprim than the enzyme from E. coli. Intrinsic resistance to sulphonamides and trimethoprim is a characteristic of folate auxotrophs, e.g. Strep. faecium and Lactobacillus species. These organisms are able to take up and utilize preformed folic acid derivatives from the environment and hence are resistant to the antibiotics.

6.2.2   Inhibitors of RNA polymerase

Intrinsic resistance to rifamycins is displayed by most Gram-negative bacteria (Haemophilus, Neisseria and Legionella spp. are exceptions) and most species of mycobacteria. In intrinsically resistant organisms, decreased uptake of antibiotics (i.e. general mechanism 3a) is responsible for resistance since DNA-dependent RNA polymerases isolated from E. coli, S. typhimurium or M. intracellulare are as sensitive to inhibition by rifamycins as enzymes isolated from Gram-positive bacteria. The cellular components responsible for decreased permeability are unknown in M. intracellulare, but resistance in the enteric organisms mentioned is due to the presence of lipopolysaccharide in the outer membrane which prevents these hydrophobic antibiotics from crossing the outer membrane bilayer.

6.3   Intrinsic resistance to inhibitors of protein synthesis

6.3.1   Aminoglycoside-aminocyclitol (AGAC) group

Bacterial species regarded as intrinsically resistant to the AGAC group of antibiotics are listed in Table 5.7. Resistance results principally from impaired uptake (mechanism 3a, Table 5.3), either from poor outer membrane penetration (in Gram-negatives) or from inherent aspects of membrane energy coupling that affect AGAC transport across the cytoplasmic membrane. As mentioned in Chapter 2, the EDPII phase of AGAC transport is partially respiration dependent. Organisms growing primarily by fermentation (e.g. Streptococcus spp.) have limited electron transport and hence display intrinsic low-level resistance to AGAC antibiotics. Strictly anaerobic organisms (e.g. Bacteroides and Clostridium spp.) also display resistance to AGAC antibiotics because uptake by EDPII is impaired.

6.3.2   Fusidic acid

Gram-negative organisms (apart from Bacteroides spp.) are intrinsically resistant to fusidic acid. This results from failure of the hydrophobic antibiotic to cross bacterial outer membranes.

Table 5.7 — Bacterial species intrinsically resistant to AGAC group antibiotics. (Based on Godfrey & Bryan, 1984)

Pseudomonas cepacia
Pseudomonas maltophilia
Pseudomonas acidovorans
Flavobacterium spp.
Achromobacter xylosoxidans
Streptococcus spp.
Bacteriodes spp.
Clostridium spp.
Legionella pneumophila
Mycoplasma spp.
Pseudomonas stutzeri

6.3.3 Chloramphenicol

Most organisms, in the absence of acquired resistance mechanisms, are susceptible to chloramphenicol. However, there are some exceptions. *Pseudomonas* spp. show a varied response to chloramphenicol with *Ps. aeruginosa* and *Ps. putida* generally regarded as intrinsically resistant. The mechanism of resistance is poor penetration across the outer membrane, i.e. general resistance mechanism 3a (Table 5.3). It is not known whether decreased uptake into the cell accounts for intrinsic resistance in other organisms, e.g. certain *Flavobacteria*, *Proteus* spp. and *Nocardia asteroides* that display chloramphenicol-resistant phenotypes.

6.3.4 Macrolides, lincosamides and streptogramins (MLS) group

Gram-negative bacteria are generally resistant to these hydrophobic antibiotics because the compounds fail to penetrate the outer membrane.

6.3.5 Tetracyclines

Ps. aeruginosa displays intrinsic resistance to tetracycline, the antibiotic penetrating the outer membrane poorly.

6.4 Intrinsic resistance to antibiotics that inhibit peptidoglycan synthesis

6.4.1 Bacitracin and glycopeptide antibiotics

In general, Gram-negative bacteria are intrinsically resistant to bacitracin, vancomycin, ristocetin and teicoplanin. This situation arises because these polar molecules are too large to diffuse through outer membrane porins.

6.4.2 Beta-lactam antibiotics

It has been known for many years that certain beta-lactam antibiotics, e.g. benzyl-penicillin, inhibit Gram-positive bacteria more readily than most Gram-negative bacteria. To a major extent this difference is due to the presence of the Gram-negative outer membrane which confers an intrinsic permeation barrier to some of the beta-lactams. Limitations of space prevent discussion of intrinsic resistance to individual beta-lactams. However, in general, intrinsic resistance is expressed towards beta-lactams that are either hydrophobic or have multiple negative charges. These physicochemical properties are not compatible with rapid penetration across the outer membrane.

6.5 Intrinsic resistance to antibiotics that inhibit membrane integrity — polymyxins

As mentioned in Chapter 2, polymyxins are generally more active against Gram-negative organisms than Gram-positive ones. Therefore, Gram-positive organisms display some degree of intrinsic resistance to these antibiotics. As already mentioned (Chapter 2) the antibacterial activity of polymyxins is related to the nature of membrane phospholipids, and the absence of phosphatidylethanolamine in membranes from Gram-positive bacteria may account for their insusceptibility to these antibiotics.

6.6 The Gram-negative outer membrane as an exclusion barrier to antibiotics

As noted above, many examples of intrinsic antibiotic resistance in Gram-negative bacteria are attributable to exclusion of the agents from intracellular targets because of poor uptake across the outer membrane. High molecular weight and/or hydrophobic properties are two principal reasons for the failure of antibiotics to gain access across the outer membrane. Molecules of size greater than about 600 Da are unable to enter the channels (porins) formed by the Omp proteins and exclusion of hydrophobic antibiotics is attributed to the absence of phospholipid from the outer leaflet of the outer membrane so that membrane regions into which hydrophobic antibiotics could partition are not exposed to the environment. In place of phospholipid, the outer leaflet of the outer membrane contains lipopolysaccharide (LPS) which hinders partitioning of hydrophobic antibiotics. This probably arises because the fatty acyl region of LPS is markedly more rigid than that of phospholipids due to strong interaction between LPS molecules.

6.7 The *Ps. aeruginosa* outer membrane as an exclusion barrier to antibiotics

Ps. aeruginosa is generally resistant to hydrophobic antibiotics for the same reason as other Gram-negative organisms, i.e. the presence of LPS in the outer leaflet of the outer membrane. However, it has been known for many years that *Ps. aeruginosa* also displays intrinsic resistance to a number of small, hydrophilic, antibiotics (e.g. tetracycline and some beta-lactams) which are able to cross the outer membranes of other Gram-negative bacteria to reach their targets. The *Ps. aeruginosa* outer membranes was therefore suspected of exhibiting low permeability to small hydrophilic molecules as well as to hydrophobic agents.

Proof that the permeability of the *Ps. aeruginosa* outer membrane to small hydrophilic antibiotics and other solutes is markedly reduced compared with *E. coli* was obtained at the beginning of the 1980s (Table 5.8). However, until very recently, the basis of this impermeability was obscure. One explanation for the difference between *Ps. aeruginosa* and other Gram-negative bacteria could be the presence in *Ps. aeruginosa* of porins with a smaller channel diameter than other organisms. *Ps. aeruginosa* contains an abundant outer membrane protein, designated OmpF, which has been reported to form porin channels in liposome re-constitution experiments.

Table 5.8 — Comparison of outer membrane permeability to hydrophilic solutes and
        antibiotics in *Escherichia coli* and *Pseudomonas aeruginosa*

Compound	Permeability coefficient (nm/s)[a]	
	E. coli	*Ps. aeruginosa*
Glucose-6-phosphate	202	0.3 – 1.20
p-Nitrophenyl-phosphate	243	1.57– 3.68
Cephaloridine	500	9.7 –11.7
Cephacetrile	800	5.3 – 9.7

[a] The permeability coefficient $= \dfrac{V}{A(C_o - C_p)}$

where the diffusion rate of the substrate across the outer membrane (determined by Fick's law) is V, A is the area of the membrane, and C_o, C_p the substrate concentrations in the outside medium and in the periplasm respectively.
(Reproduced, with permission, from Chopra (1984).)

Surprisingly, the pores formed *in vitro* by the *Ps. aeruginosa* OmpF protein appear to have a large exclusion limit, allowing diffusion of molecules with molecular weights of 2000–3000 daltons. In contrast, the exclusion limit for the *E. coli* OmpF and OmpC pores is about 800 daltons. However, using intact cells of *Ps. aeruginosa*, the exclusion limit of the outer membrane is now known to be much smaller than that predicted from the *in vitro* studies. Therefore, the quantity of OmpF protein and the size of the pores it apparently forms, are at variance with other data on the permeability of intact cells to antibiotics and other molecules.

A possible explanation for this confusing situation is now available. The role of OmpF as a porin has been questioned on the basis that mutational loss of the protein does not affect outer membrane permeability of antibiotics such as beta-lactams, the previous liposome experiments may have been flawed and the amino acid sequence of the *Ps. aeruginosa* OmpF protein shows greater homology with the *E. coli* outer membrane structural protein OmpA, rather than *E. coli* porins. Therefore in some respects, the behaviour of *Ps. aeruginosa* resembles that of porin-deficient mutants of enteric bacteria such as *E. coli*. Possibly, uptake across the outer membrane of essential molecules required for growth of *Ps. aeruginosa* is mediated more specifically than in other Gram-negative bacteria and therefore *Ps. aeruginosa* has been able to dispense with, and is naturally deficient in, general diffusion porins through which small hydrophilic antibiotics might pass.

7.   RELATIVE IMPORTANCE OF VARIOUS RESISTANCE MECHANISMS
   AND THE ORIGINS OF ANTIBIOTIC RESISTANCE DETERMINANTS

In the clinical setting, antibiotic-resistant bacteria often emerge following heavy selective pressure with antibiotics used as chemotherapeutic agents. Thus, intrinsically resistant strains, those with chromosomal mutations and those that have

ids or transposons can multiply and threaten particular therapeutic
dition to multiplication within a particular patient, such strains may
from patient to patient through normal routes of bacterial

ortunistic' infections are caused by intrinsically resistant bacteria.
For example, *Ps. aeruginosa* is particulary troublesome in patients who are already
debilitated by burns, cancer, cystic fibrosis or major surgery. Nevertheless, acquired
antibiotic resistance usually poses the greatest threat to successful chemotherapy
because of its variable and largely unpredictable nature.

Acquired resistance resulting from chromosomal mutations is responsible for
resistance to certain antibiotics in clinical isolates and infections caused by such
organisms can indeed be life-threatening (for example see the work of Quinn and co-
workers cited at the end of this chapter). However, mutation of chromosomal genes
is not usually the easiest, or simplest, way for pathogens to acquire antibiotic
resistance. Several examples are discussed to illustrate this point.

As noted in Chapter 2, many antibiotics have specific targets within bacteria.
Mutations in the target can lead to expression of antibiotic resistance provided that
the normal physiological functions of the target are not disrupted by the muta-
tions(s). However, multiple mutations may be required before the target exhibits
resistance to the antibiotic concerned, e.g. decreased binding of beta-lactams to
PBPs in resistant strains of *Strep. pneumoniae* apparently requires many amino acid
changes in the PBPs. In other cases even through mutation to resistance occurs (for
instance it may be demonstrable in the laboratory) does not necessarily mean that
such mutations confer resistance *in vivo*, or indeed ever arise in patients undergoing
therapy. For instance, chromosomal mutations that confer resistance to fusidic acid
are readily isolated in *S. aureus* under laboratory conditions, yet such mutations are
not responsible for resistance to the antibiotic in clinical isolates of the organisms,
probably because chromosomal mutation to resistance decreases the virulence of the
pathogen. Finally, it is virtually impossible for chromosomal mutations to occur that
directly affect rRNA structure (and hence confer resistance to the many antibiotic
inhibitors of protein synthesis that bind to rRNA), because rRNA synthesis is
governed by identical structural genes that are present in several operons that have
been duplicated around the chromosome.

From the foregoing it will be evident that chromosomal mutations alone cannot
account for the rapid emergence and spread of antibiotic resistance amongst
pathogenic bacteria. Indeed, it is now well recognized that acquisition of resistance
determinants on plasmids and transposons is particularly important in the evolution
of antibiotic-resistant bacteria. In evolutionary terms, acquisition of plasmid- or
transposon-located resistance genes offers one major advantage over resistance
based on chromosomal mutation: acquisition of a resistance determinant by a
recipient cell provides it with pre-evolved genes refined to express resistance at high
level. Furthermore, resistance determinants contained in transposons can become
established in diverse bacterial species in which the original plasmid vectors themselves may be unable to replicate in. Inducibility is another phenomenon frequently
exhibited by pre-evolved resistance determinants, i.e. enzyme or other gene product
levels increase following exposure of bacteria to antibiotics specifically inactivated by
the determinant. Although we have not considered induction of resistance in detail

in this book, believing it to be beyond the scope of our text, the ability to 'switch on' resistance only when the need arises (i.e. when the cell is threatened by an antibiotic) is clearly another example of the refined nature of many pre-evolved resistance determinants. Readers wishing to learn more about the nature of induction as applied to resistance systems should consult the review articles cited at the end of this chapter, in particular the review by Foster.

The occurrence of plasmid- and transposon-located resistance determinants in clinical isolates poses the question of the origin of the determinants. Some determinants have probably arisen over a long period by a series of sequential mutations in existing bacterial chromosomal genes followed by insertion into plasmids and transposons. This scheme probably applies to the evolution of beta-lactamases in Gram-negative enteric species (Fig. 5.12). The evidence is as follows. Proteins that interact with penicillins (i.e. beta-lactamases and PBPs) appear to be members of a large family of evolutionary related proteins because they possess, along their amino acid sequences, several conserved regions that consist of strict identities or highly homologous residues. In particular, the tetrad Ser*-X-X-Lys (with Ser* representing the active-site serine) is common to beta-lactamases and PBPs (see Section 3.5.4.2i, Chapter 2 and Fig. 5.11, this chapter). Since PBPs were presumably present before beta-lactamases, it is assumed that the latter evolved from PBPs by a series of sequential mutations eventually giving rise to one or more effective chromosomal resistance genes (Fig. 5.12). It seems probable that these genes have become mobilized by various means into transposons, and for that reason transferable onto plasmids (Fig. 5.12). Further mutation of plasmid-bound genes can gives rise to enzymes with specific beta-lactam substrate profiles.

Other resistance determinants are likely to have originated by different mechanisms. Soil microorganisms that produce antibiotics, or share the same ecological niche as the antibiotic producers, are likely to be the source of many resistance determinants on the basis that resistance has evolved in soil organisms to protect the antibiotic producers from self-destruction, or to permit survival of co-inhabitants. The argument is illustrated by considering the basis of erythromycin resistance in *Streptomyces erythraeus* and *S. aureus*. The former organism, which produces erythromycin, protects itself from its own product by methylation of its 23S rRNA. A similar mechanism is responsible for plasmid-mediated resistance to erythromycin (and other members of the MLS group of antibiotics) in *S. aureus* (see Section 3.5.1), suggesting a common evolutionary origin for the genes encoding the methylases. Broadly similar conclusions have been made by comparing the nature of 3'-aminoglycoside phosphotransferases (APH 3') from neomycin-producing *Streptomyces fradiae*, staphylococci and streptococci.

8.   CONCLUSIONS

The diversity of mechanisms used by bacteria to evade the action of antibiotics and the rapidity with which bacteria acquire resistance is depressing from the viewpoint of achieving successful therapy. Nevertheless, studies on the gentic and biochemical basis of antibiotic resistance have themselves suggested ways to circumvent it. This topic is considered further in Chapter 8.

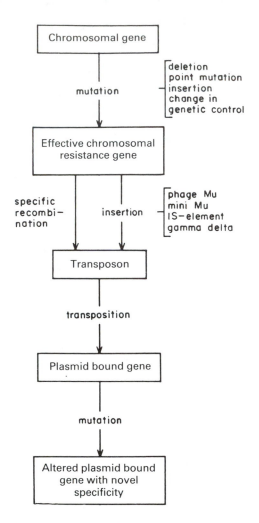

Fig. 5.12 — A scheme for the possible evolution of genes mediating resistance to beta-lactam antibiotics. The chromosomal gene at the top depicts a gene encoding a PBP, subsequent genes represent those encoding beta-lactamases. See text for further details. (Reproduced, with permission, from Korfmann *et al.* (1986).

FURTHER READING

Review articles

Arthur, M., Brisson-Noel, A. & Courvalin, P. (1987). Origin and evolution of genes specifying resistance to macrolide, lincosamide and streptogramin antibiotics: data and hypotheses. *Journal of Antimicrobial Chemotherapy* **20**, 783–802.

Bryan, L. E. (1988). General mechanisms of resistance to antibiotics. *Journal of Antimicrobial Chemotherapy* **22**, Supplement A, 1–15.

Bush, K. (1989). Characterization of beta-lactamases. *Antimicrobial Agents and Chemotherapy* **33**, 259–263.

Chopra, I. (1984). Antibiotic resistance resulting from decreased drug accumulation. *British Medical Bulletin* **40**, 11–17.

Chopra, I. (1985). Mode of action of the tetracyclines and the nature of bacterial resistance to them. In *The Tetracyclines, Handbook of Experimental Pharamacology*, Volume 78 (eds J. J. Hlavka & J. H. Boothe) pp. 317–392. Springer-Verlag, Berlin.

Chopra, I. (1986). Genetic and biochemical basis of tetracycline resistance. *Journal of Antimicrobial Chemotherapy* **18**, Supplement C, 51–56.

Chopra, I. (1988). Mechanisms of resistance to antibiotics and other chemotherapeutic agents. *Journal of Applied Bacteriology Symposium Supplement 1988*, **65**, 149S–166S.

Clewell, D. B., Senghas, E., Jones, J. M., Flannagan, S. E., Yamamoto, M. & Gawron-Burke, C. (1988). Transposition in *Streptococcus*: structural and genetic properties of the conjugative transposon Tn*916*. In *Transposition*, 43rd Symposium of the Society for General Microbiology (eds A. J. Kingman, K. F. Chater & S. M. Kingsman) pp. 43–58. Cambridge University Press.

Foster, T. J. (1983). Plasmid-determined resistance to antimicrobial drugs and toxic metal ions in bacteria. *Microbiological Reviews* **47**, 361–409.

Ghuysen, J-M. (1988). Bacterial active-site serine penicillin–interactive proteins and domains: mechanism, structure and evolution. *Reviews of Infectious Diseases* **10**, 726–732.

Godfrey, A. J. & Bryan, L. E. (1984). Intrinsic resistance and whole cell factors contributing to antibiotic resistance. In *Antimicrobial Drug Resistance* (ed. L. E. Bryan) pp. 113–145. Academic Press, New York.

Hackbarth, C. J. & Chambers, H. F. (1989). Methicillin-resistant staphylococci: genetics and mechanisms of resistance. *Antimicrobial Agents and Chemotherapy* **33**, 991–994.

Hancock, R. E. W. (1986). Intrinsic resistance of *Pseudomonas aeruginosa*. *Journal of Antimicrobial Chemotherapy* **18**, 653–656.

Hancock, R. E. W. & Nicas, T. I. (1984). Resistance to antibacterial agents acting on cell membranes. In *Antimicrobial Drug Resistance* (ed. L. E. Bryan) pp. 147–177. Academic Press, New York.

Huovinen, P. (1987). Trimethoprim resistance. *Antimicrobial Agents and Chemotherapy* **31**, 1451–1456.

Korfmann, G., Kliebe, C. & Wiedemann, B. (1986). β-lactam antibiotics and selection of resistance: speculation on the evolution of R plasmids. *Journal of Antimicrobial Chemotherapy* **18**, Supplement C, 113–121.

Levy, S. B. (1984). Resistance to the tetracyclines. In *Antimicrobial Drug Resistance* (ed. L. E. Bryan) pp. 191–240. Academic Press, New York.

Lyon, B. R. & Skurray, R. (1987). Antimicrobial resistance of *Staphylococcus aureus*. *Microbiological Reviews* **51**, 88–134.

Murphy, E. (1988). Transposable elements in *Staphylococcus*. In *Transposition*, 43rd Symposium of the Society for General Microbiology (eds A. J. Kingsman, K. F. Chater & S. M. Kingsman) pp. 59–89. Cambridge University Press.

Nikaido, H. (1988). Bacterial resistance to antibiotics as a function of outer membrane permeability. *Journal of Antimicrobial Chemotherapy* **22**, Supplement A, 17–22.

Phillips, I. & Shannon, K. (1984). Aminoglycoside resistance. *British Medical Bulletin* **40**, 28–35.

Piddock, L. J. V. & Wise, R. (1989). Mechanisms of resistance to quinolones and clinical perspectives. *Journal of Antimicrobial Chemotherapy* **23**, 475–483.

Powell, M. (1988). Antimicrobial drug resistance in *Haemophilus influenzae*. *Journal of Medical Microbiology* **27**, 81–87.

Reynolds, P. E. (1984). Resistance of the antibiotic target site. *British Medical Bulletin* **40**, 3–10.

Sanders, C. C., (1988). Ciprofloxacin: in vitro activity, mechanism of action, and resistance. *Reviews of Infectious Diseases* **10**, 516–527.

Saunders, J. R. (1984). Genetics and evolution of antibiotic resistance. *British Medical Bulletin* **40**, 54–60.

Shaw, W. V. (1984). Bacterial resistance to chloramphenicol. *British Medical Bulletin* **40**, 36–41.

Smith, J. T. & Amyes, S. G. B. (1984). Bacterial resistance to antifolate chemo-therapeutic agents mediated by plasmids. *British Medical Bulletin* **40**, 42–46.

Thompson, R. (1986). R plasmid transfer. *Journal of Antimicrobial Chemotherapy* **18**, Supplement C, 13–23.

Trieu-Cuot, P. & Courvalin, P. (1986). Evolution and transfer of aminoglycoside resistance genes under natural conditions. *Journal of Antimicrobial Chemother-apy* **18**, Supplement C, 93–102.

Wilkins, B. M. (1988). Organization and plasticity of enterobacterial genomes. *Journal of Applied Bacteriology Symposium Supplement 1988*, **65,** 51S–69S.

Research papers

Dowson, C. G., Hutchinson, A. & Spratt, B. G. (1989). Extensive re-modelling of the transpeptidase domain of penicillin-binding protein 2B of a penicillin-resistant South African isolate of *Streptococcus pneumoniae*. *Molecular Micro-biology* **3**, 95–102.

Flensburg, J. & Sköld, O. (1987). Massive overproduction of dihydrofolate reduc-tase in bacteria as a response to the use of trimethoprim. *European Journal of Biochemistry* **162**, 473–476.

Hewinson, R. G., Cartwright, S. J., Slack, P. E., Whipp, R. D., Woodward, M. J. & Nichols, W. W. (1989). Permeability to cefsulodin of the outer membrane of *Pseudomonas aeruginosa* and discrimination between beta-lactamase-mediated trapping and hydrolysis as mechanisms of resistance. *European Journal of Biochemistry* **179**, 667–675.

Medeiros, A. A., O'Brien, T. F., Rosenberg, E. Y. & Nikaido, H. (1987). Loss of OmpC porin in a strain of *Salmonella typhimurium* causes increased resistance to cephalosporins during therapy. *Journal of Infectious Diseases* **156**, 751–757.

Noble, W. C., Rahman, M., Cookson, B. & Phillips, I. (1988). Transferable mupirocin-resistance. *Journal of Antimicrobial Chemotherapy* **22**, 771–772.

Quinn, J. P., DiVincenzo, C. A., Lucks, D. A., Luskin, R. L., Shatzer, K. L. & Lerner, S. A. (1988). Serious infections due to penicillin-resistant strains of viridans streptococci with altered penicillin-binding proteins. *Journal of Infec-tious Diseases* **157**, 764–769.

Sanchez-Pescador, R., Brown, J. T., Roberts, M. & Urdea, M. S. (1988). Homology of the TetM with translational elongation factors: implications for potential modes of tetM conferred tetracycline resistance. *Nucleic Acids Research* **16**, 1218.

Shlaes, D. M., Bouvet, A., Devine, C., Shlaes, J. H., Al-Obeid, A. & Williamson, R. (1989). Inducible, transferable resistance to vancomycin in *Enterococcus faecalis* A256. *Antimicrobial Agents and Chemotherapy* **33**: 198–203.

Speer, B. S. & Salyers, A. A. (1988). Characterization of a novel tetracycline resistance that functions only in aerobically grown *Escherichia coli*. *Journal of Bacteriology* **170**, 1423–1429.

Trees, D. L. & Iandolo, J. J. (1988). Identification of a *Staphylococcus aureus* transposon (Tn*4291*) that carries the methicillin resistance genes(s). *Journal of Bacteriology* **170**, 149–154.

Wylie, B. A., Amyes, S. G. B., Young, H-K. & Koornhof, H. J. (1988). Identification of a novel plasmid-encoded dihydrofolate reductase mediating high-level resistance to trimethoprim. *Journal of Antimicrobial Chemotherapy* **22**, 429–435.

Yamagishi, J., Yoshida, H., Yamayoshi, M. & Nakamura, S. (1986). Nalidixic acid-resistant mutations of the *gyr*B gene of *Escherichia coli*. *Molecular and General Genetics* **204**, 367–373.

Yoshida, H., Kojima, T., Yamagishi, J. & Nakamura, S. (1988). Quinolone-resistant mutations of the *gyr*A gene of *Escherichia coli*. *Molecular and General Genetics* **211**, 1–7.

6

Genetic and biochemical basis of resistance to antiseptics, disinfectants and preservatives

1. INTRODUCTION

Antimicrobial activity and mechanisms of action of various types of antiseptics, disinfectants and preservatives were considered in Chapter 3. This chapter discusses ways in which non-sporing bacteria survive exposure to chemicals employed as biocides.

The term 'resistance' is a well-defined concept when applied to antibiotic resistance (Chapter 5). When applied to antiseptics, disinfectants and preservatives, however, the term is less clearly defined, and is often used to describe a bacterial strain that is not susceptible to a concentration of antibacterial agent used in practice. It is also used to denote a strain that is not killed or inhibited by a concentration that kills or inhibits the majority of strains of that organism.

Some authors prefer to restrict the terms 'resistance' and 'resistant' to instances where the genetic and biochemical basis for resistance is known, and recommend the alternative terms of 'tolerance' and 'tolerate' where the basis of insusceptibility has not been established. Although there is some merit in these proposals, we believe that two sets of terminology would be confusing. Consequently, as with antibiotics, 'resistance' and 'resistant' have been used throughout this chapter and Chapter 7 to denote insusceptibility of bacteria and spores to biocides.

Two major mechanisms of resistance will be considered: intrinsic and acquired. Possible means of counteracting biocide resistance will be discussed in Chapter 8.

1.1 Distinction between intrinsic and acquired resistance

In general, the mechanisms of bacterial resistance to antiseptics, disinfectants and preservatives are poorly understood when compared to knowledge on antibiotic resistance mechanisms (Chapter 5). However, as for antibiotics, resistance mechanisms can be considered either as natural (innate, intrinsic) or acquired. Specific examples within each group will be discussed where relevant. As with antibiotics, intrinsic resistance is usually expressed by chromosomal genes, whereas acquired resistance results from genetic changes in a cell and arises either by mutations in chromosomal genes or by the acquisition of genetic material from another cell.

Apart from a few specific instances, such as acquired resistance to some metals (Section 3.1.1) and cationic agents (Section 3.1.2), the intrinsic mechanism of biocide resistance has been more widely studied. Usually, the latter has involved examining ways whereby the cell excludes entry of a biocide, although inactivation of a biocide by deployment of a constitutive enzyme is another possible intrinsic resistance mechanism.

Acquired resistance to biocides arises either as a consequence of chromosomal gene mutation, usually — but not invariably — following exposure to a particular biocide, or by the acquisition of plasmids and transposons. The possibility exists, but has yet to be shown conclusively, that acquired biocide resistance occurs from selective pressures exerted by the widespread usage, particularly in hospitals, of antiseptics and disinfectants. If this is so, then an analogous situation to the chemotherapeutic use of antibiotics (see Chapter 8) would ensue.

2.   INTRINSIC BIOCIDE RESISTANCE

2.1   Introduction

Intrinsic resistance to biocides is often found with Gram-negative bacteria, and is associated with the composition and structure of the outer layers of these cells. An initial stage in the action of biocides involves their binding to the surface layers of bacteria (Chapter 3). This is followed by passage across the cell wall or outer membrane to the cytoplasmic membrane or deeper into the cell, wherever the target site resides. In Gram-positive bacteria, no specific receptor molecules or permeases exist to assist biocide penetration and the *Bacillus megaterium* cell wall is for example permeable to molecules with molecular weights up to 30 000 daltons. Thus, most biocides appear to enter Gram-positive bacteria readily and such organisms are generally more sensitive to these agents than are Gram-negative cells (Table 6.1). The outer membrane of Gram-negative bacteria limits the intracellular entry of many biocides. Some organisms survive biocide treatment by producing a glycocalyx. Both of these aspects will be considered here, as will the intrinsic resistance of mycobacteria. Gram-positive bacteria, e.g. staphylococci can *express* resistance to some biocides when grown in broth containing glycerol. The consequent increase in wall lipid acting as a barrier to biocide penetration is analogous to the *intrinsic* resistance presented by the outer membrane of Gram-negative bacteria.

2.2   Role of the outer membrane of Gram-negative bacteria

The outer membrane of Gram-negative bacteria plays an important role in conferring resistance to many biocides (and antibiotics: see Chapter 5). The structure of the outer membrane was considered in Chapter 1. Basically, the cell surface of smooth

Table 6.1 — Comparative responses of Gram-positive and Gram-negative bacteria to some antiseptics, disinfectants and preservatives

Antibacterial agent	MIC^a (μg/ml) against			
	Staph. aureus	E. coli	Ps. aeruginosa	P. vulgaris
Chlorhexidine diacetate	0.5	1	5–60	12.5–25
Propamidine isethionate	1	64	256	256
Dibromopropamidine isethionate	1	4	32	128
Cetrimide	0.4	12.5	64–128	
Hexachlorophane	0.05	100	>100	>100

^{a}MIC, minimum inhibitory concentration.

Gram-negative bacteria is hydrophilic in nature, a property that can be readily demonstrated by measuring the partitioning of cells into a water-miscible hydrocarbon solvent. Deep rough (heptoseless) mutants, on the other hand, tend to be much more hydrophobic. Thus, wild-type (smooth) strains are resistant to hydrophobic biocides (and antibiotics) whereas deep rough mutants are sensitive. The basis of this difference is explained below, from which it will become clear that outer membrane mutants, which are genetically hypersensitive to a biocide, are of considerable value in evaluating the nature of intrinsic resistance in wild-type strains.

A distinction must be drawn between low molecular weight (less than about 600) hydrophilic molecules which can readily enter via the aqueous porins, and hydrophobic molecules which diffuse across the outer membrane bilayer (Fig. 6.1; see also Chapter 2). The porin system is present in both smooth and rough strains and uptake of hydrophilic biocides is thus not impeded by the presence of complete lipopolysaccharide (LPS) molecules. In wild-type bacteria, however, the intact LPS molecules prevent ready access of hydrophobic molecules to the cell interior. In smooth cells, the intact LPS shields phospholipids which are not present in the outer leaflet of the outer membrane (see also Section 6.6, Chapter 5). In deep-rough strains, which lack the O-specific side-chain and most of the core polysaccharide, and in EDTA-treated cells, patches of phospholipid appear in the outer leaflet (Fig. 6.2a,b) thereby permitting diffusion of hydrophobic molecules across what is essentially a phospholipid bilayer.

The role of the outer membrane in intrinsic resistance of enteric bacteria to biocides is illustrated by the quaternary ammonium compounds (QACs) and amidines. These compounds are considerably less active against wild-type than deep rough strains of *E. coli* and *Salm. typhimurium* (Table 6.2). However, in the case of chlorhexidine salts the outer membrane of wild-type *Salm. typhimurium*, but not *E. coli*, confers intrinsic resistance to the antiseptic (Table 6.2).

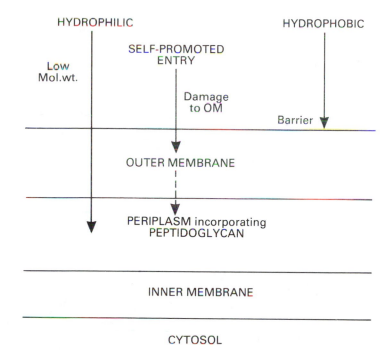

HYDROPHILIC   HYDROPHOBIC

Low
Mol.wt.   SELF-PROMOTED
                               ENTRY

                            Damage
                            to OM
                                        Barrier

                    OUTER MEMBRANE

                    PERIPLASM incorporating
                        PEPTIDOGLYCAN

                    INNER MEMBRANE

                        CYTOSOL

Fig. 6.1 — Interaction of biocides with the Gram-negative cell envelope: Diagrammatic representation of uptake pathways and exclusion barrier. Demonstrated are a hydrophilic biocide of low Mol. wt., a hydrophobic biocide and a biocide that promotes its own entry. OM, outer membrane. For additional information, see Fig. 6.2.

2.2.1 Outer membrane barrier and intrinsic resistance to membrane-active biocides

It was pointed out in Chapter 3 that biocides with a target site in the cytoplasmic (inner) membrane are usually, if rather loosely, termed 'membrane-active' agents. For these compounds to reach their target, they must traverse the outer membrane. Limitation of their access by the outer membrane may result in intrinsic resistance.

2.2.1.1 Parabens

The parabens (Chapter 3) are widely used preservatives in the food, pharmaceutical and cosmetic industries. They are inhibitory to Gram-positive and Gram-negative bacteria but their bactericidal activity is slow. Activity is increased as the homologous series of methyl (Me), ethyl (Et), propyl (Pr) and butyl (Bu) esters of *para*(4)-hydroxybenzoic acid is ascended, but this is accompanied by a corresponding decrease in solubility. Wild-type strains of *E. coli* and *Salm. typhimurium* are intrinsically more resistant to the four esters than are deep rough mutants, with the Me ester the least, and the Bu ester the most, active against any individual strain. Uptake probably proceeds by a general dissolution of an ester into the cell with no specific sites existing for binding at the cell surface. The deficiency of LPS in deep

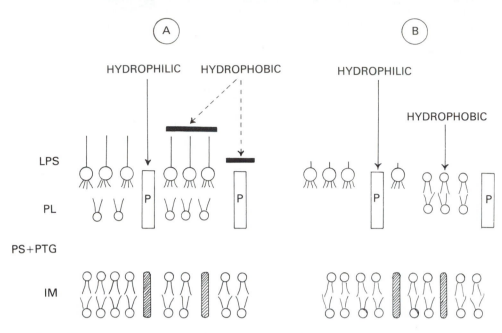

Fig. 6.2 — Comparison of intracellular penetration of hydrophilic and hydrophobic molecules into (A) smooth, (B) deep rough Gram-negative bacteria. P, porin; LPS, lipopolysaccharide; PL, phospholipid; PS, periplasmic space (periplasm); PTG, peptidoglycan; IM, inner membrane; ▬▬ barrier; ▨ inner membrane protein.

Table 6.2 — Susceptibility of wild-type and envelope mutant strains of Gram-negative bacteria to QACs, chlorhexidine and amides

Type of biocide	*E. coli*	*Salm. typhimurium*
QACs ⎫ Amidines ⎭	Deep rough mutants much more sensitive	
Chlorhexidine	Deep rough mutants and wild-type strain show same order of sensitivity	Deep rough mutants rather more sensitive than wild-type

rough mutants resulting in decreased intrinsic resistance, i.e. increased sensitivity, to the parabens, is due to phospholipid patches appearing in the outer leaflet of the outer membrane. These aid the penetration of an ester, and especially the most hydrophobic one (the Bu ester), across the outer membrane to the target site at the inner membrane. The composition of LPS from *E. coli* and *Salm. typhimurium* is shown in Figs 6.3 and 6.4, respectively.

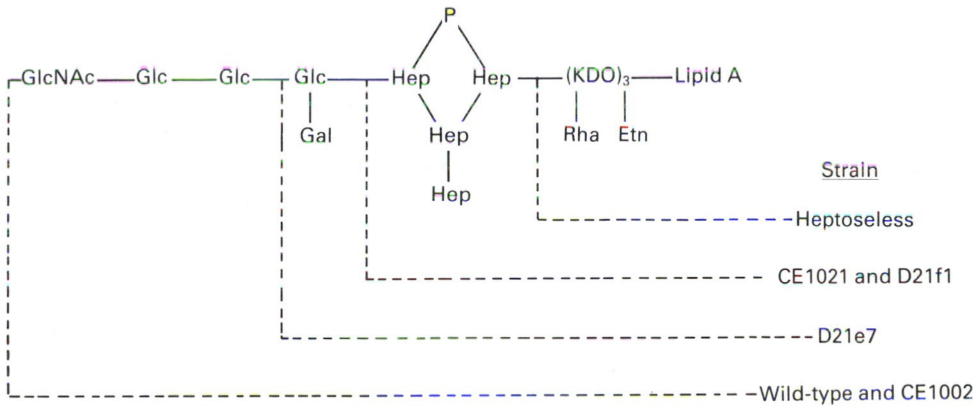

Fig. 6.3 — Lipopolysaccharide (LPS) of wild-type and envelope mutant strains of *E. coli*. Abbreviations: GlcNAc, *N*-acetylglucosamine; Hep, L-glycero-D-mannoheptose; KDO, 2-ketodeoxyoctonate; Rha, rhamnose; Etn, ethanolamine; P, phosphate. (The chemical structure of LPS is based on Van Alphen *et al.*).

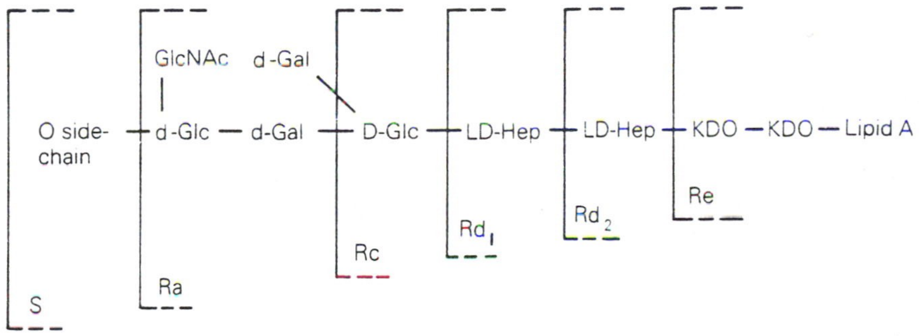

Fig. 6.4 — LPS of wild-type and envelope mutant strains of *Salm. typhimurium*. Abbreviations: as for *E. coli* LPS (Fig. 6.3). Additionally, d-Gal is D-galactose.

2.2.1.2 *Phenols and cresols*
Bacterial resistance to phenolics decreases in the order phenol > cresol > chlorocresol. Intrinsic resistance in Gram-negative bacteria is probably related to the ease with

which these compounds cross the outer membrane, since deep rough mutants are more sensitive to an individual phenolic, and especially the most hydrophobic (chlorocresol) of the three cited, than are wild-type strains.

2.2.1.3   Chlorhexidine

Chlorhexidine is an important, widely used antiseptic, disinfectant and preservative that is effective against Gram-negative and Gram-positive bacteria, except mycobacteria (Section 2.4) and bacterial spores (Chapter 7). Differences in response of most staphylococcal strains and a Gram-negative organism such as *E. coli* are not great, relative MICs being about 0.5 and 1–2 µg/ml, respectively. These, and other data, suggest that the biguanide readily penetrates the *E. coli* outer membrane, i.e. that this structure does not confer substantial intrinsic resistance to chlorhexidine. This contrasts markedly with the situation for other cationic agents such as the QACs (Section 2.2.1.4) and amidines (Section 2.2.2.1). However, certain Gram-negative bacteria, e.g. *Providencia stuartii*, exhibit high levels of intrinsic resistance to chlorhexidine. Here, intrinsic resistance is probably related to the nature of the outer membrane, but the basis of resistance is unknown.

2.2.1.4   Quaternary ammonium compounds

The LPS in the outer membrane acts as a barrier to the entry of QACs into Gram-negative bacteria. This has been demonstrated by comparing the sensitivity to QACs of wild-type and envelope mutants with deletions in LPS. The barrier mechanism of intrinsic QAC resistance could be the result of a shielding of phospholipid molecules beneath the LPS in wild-type strains or could arise by an interaction of the cationic biocides with anionic groups on LPS thereby reducing the amount of 'free' QAC.

2.2.2   Outer membrane barrier and intrinsic resistance to other biocides

2.2.2.1   Amidines

Gram-negative bacteria are intrinsically resistant to amidines such as propamidine isethionate (PI) or dibromopropamidine isethionate (DBPI). The outer membrane is a permeability barrier to PI and DBPI, a conclusion reached in part from studies with wild-type and LPS mutants of both *E. coli* and *Salm. typhimurium*. The exact mechanism for this intrinsic resistance is unknown.

2.2.2.2   Triphenylmethane dyes

Gram-negative bacteria are intrinsically more resistant to dyes such as crystal violet than are Gram-positive organisms. Crystal violet is a hydrophobic agent and is therefore excluded by the Gram-negative outer membrane (Fig. 6.2). Wild type cells of *Salm. typhimurium* are considerably more resistant than deep rough mutants and these and other findings demonstrate that intrinsic resistance is associated with the outer membrane.

2.2.2.3   Acridines

Some strains of *P. mirabilis* are more resistant to acriflavine than others. The basis of this resistance (apparently intrinsic) has not been investigated.

2.3   Intrinsic resistance of Gram-negative bacteria

Having discussed the general role of the outer membrane as a means of excluding biocide entry, it is now pertinent to consider the extent to which this resistance mechanism contributes towards intrinsic resistance in specific types of Gram-negative bacteria.

2.3.1   Enterobacteriaceae

The family Enterobacteriaceae encompasses a range of important pathogens and spoilage organisms. It includes members of the genera *Escherichia*, *Salmonella*, *Proteus*, *Providencia*, *Serratia*, *Klebsiella*, *Shigella* and *Yersinia*. Generally, they are less sensitive to biocides than Gram-positive bacteria such as *Staphylococcus aureus* but more sensitive than *Pseudomonas aeruginosa* (Table 6.1).

2.3.1.1   Escherichia coli

E. coli is more resistant to QACs, triphenyl methane dyes and diamidines than *Staph. aureus* and markedly more resistant to salicylanilides, carbanilides and hexachlorophane (hexachlorophene). Studies with deep rough *E., coli* mutants demonstrate that this resistance is intrinsic in nature. However, *E. coli* is only slightly less sensitive than *Staph. aureus* to chlorhexidine.

2.3.1.2   Proteus spp.

Members of the genus *Proteus* are unusually intrinsically resistant to high concentrations of chlorhexidine and other cationic bactericides, and are more resistant to EDTA than most other types of Gram-negative bacteria. Intrinsic resistance to (a) the cationic biocides may be due to a less acidic type of LPS, so that biocide binding is reduced and (b) EDTA may be due to reduced divalent cation content of the *Proteus* outer membrane or inaccessibility of these cations to the chelator.

2.3.1.3   Providencia spp.

Prov. stuartii may be a particularly troublesome member of this genus, showing high intrinsic resistance to cationic bactericides, especially chlorhexidine, and frequently to many antibiotics. The basis of intrinsic chlorhexidine resistance is unknown but may relate to the nature of the outer membrane in this organism which effectively excludes the antiseptic.

2.3.1.4   Salmonella spp.

Compared with other members of the Enterobacteriaceae, salmonellae are not especially intrinsically resistant to biocides. Well-defined mutants of *Salm. typhimurium* have, however, provided useful information about the role played by the outer membrane in conferring intrinsic resistance to biocides. In particular, the importance of smooth, Ra, Rd_1 and Re types of LPS has been assessed (Fig. 6.4 and Table 6.2). Deep rough strains, with Re-type LPS, are considerably more sensitive than smooth strains to QACs, diamidines and parabens (especially the butyl ester) and rather more so to chlorhexidine, suggesting that LPS has an important role in intrinsic resistance of wild-type cells to biocides, However, recently isolated super-sensitive mutants of *Salm. typhimurium* have the same LPS composition as the parent strain and similar amounts of LPS are released by EDTA or polycations. This implies that factors other than LPS contribute towards intrinsic resistance to these compounds in *Salm. typhimurium*.

2.3.1.5 Serratia *spp.*
Hospital isolates of *Ser. marcescens* may be highly resistant to chlorhexidine. Furthermore, *Ser. marcescens* has been isolated from hexachlorophane liquid soaps and detergent creams.

The outer membrane is probably the most important single factor determining the response of *Ser. marcescens* to a biocide, although it has been suggested that the inner membrane is associated with the high intrinsic resistance presented to chlorhexidine.

2.3.2 *Pseudomonads*
Considerable differences exist in the responses of pseudomonads to biocides. This is particularly true between *Ps. aeruginosa* and *Ps. cepacia* on the one hand and *Ps. stutzeri* on the other.

2.3.2.1 *Ps. aeruginosa*
Ps. aeruginosa is one of the most antibiotic- and biocide-resistant non-sporing organisms. In many cases, such intrinsic resistance is due to the nature of its cell envelope. In 1951, it was found that solutions of the QAC, cetrimide, were sometimes contaminated with *Ps. aeruginosa* and this was later expanded to include other QACs such as benzalkonium chloride; the organism is capable of surviving in high concentrations of QACs. *Ps. aeruginosa* is also more resistant than many other types of Gram-negative bacteria to chlorhexidine. The question arises as to why *Ps. aeruginosa* exhibits higher intrinsic resistance than other Gram-negative bacteria to many biocides. As with other Gram-negative organisms, the outer membrane is undoubtedly responsible for conferring intrinsic resistance. There are differences in LPS composition and it is now believed that general diffusion may not occur via porins in *Ps aeruginosa* (see Section 6.7, Chapter 5). A factor of considerable importance is the cation content of the outer membrane, Mg^{2+} content being greatest in *Ps. aeruginosa*. This aids in producing strong LPS–LPS links which may relate to resistance to some biocides.

2.3.2.2 *Ps. cepacia*
Ps. cepacia has been recovered from benzalkonium chloride solutions associated with hospital outbreaks of urinary tract infections, surgical wound and respiratory infections. Chlorhexidine solutions contaminated with this organism have also been found. *Ps. cepacia* is often considerably more resistant in the hospital environment than under laboratory conditions.

2.3.2.3 *Ps. stutzeri*
Ps. stutzeri is mentioned here not because of intrinsic resistance but because strains are often, but not invariably, intrinsically sensitive to a range of biocides (including chlorhexidine and QACs) and antibiotics. *Ps. stutzeri* contains less wall muramic acid than other strains of pseudomonads and appears to stand apart on the basis of its

envelope structure. Additional comparative studies with *Ps. stutzeri* and other pseudomonads could yield useful information about mechanisms(s) of intrinsic resistance in the latter organisms.

2.4   Intrinsic resistance of mycobacteria to biocides

2.4.1   Cell wall composition

Mycobacteria are generally more resistant than other non-sporing bacteria to bactericides. This intrinsic resistance is undoubtedly linked to their cell wall composition; they possess a high wall lipid content and their high resistance appears to be related to the amount of waxy material present. Mycobacterial walls contain several components:

(a) a covalent skeleton comprising two covalently linked polymers, peptidoglycan and an arabinogalactan mycolate (Fig. 6.5; Table 6.3);

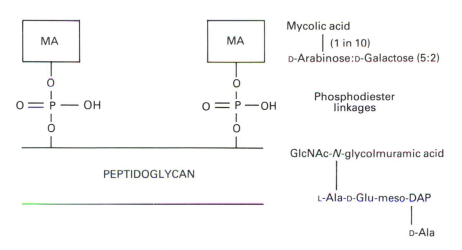

Fig. 6.5 — Cell wall skeleton of mycobacteria. MA, mycolate of arabinolactan.

(b) free lipids, which can be removed by neutral solvents;
(6) peptides which can be removed by proteolytic enzymes.

In some strains, a glucan may be present. The related genera, *Nocardia* and *Corynebacterium*, possess a covalent skeleton with the same general structure.

Mycobacterial peptidoglycan consists of glycan strands substituted by partly cross-linked tri- or tetra-peptides. However, N-glycolylmuramic acid is present instead of the usual N-acetylmuramic acid (see Chapter 1) and there are two kinds of interpeptide linkages, namely D-Ala-meso-DAP and meso-DAP-meso-Dap (D-Ala representing D-alanine, and meso-DAP being α, ε-diaminopimelic acid).

The arabinogalactan is a highly branched polymer containing D-arabinose and D-galactose (approximate ratio 5:2) and about 1 in ten of the arabinose residues is

Table 6.3 — Cell wall composition of mycobacterial strains

Cell wall component	Chemical composition	Comment
Covalent skeleton	Peptidoglycan	Contains N-glycolmuramic acid Two types of interpeptide linkage
	Arabinogalactan mycolate	D-arabinose, D-galactose and mycolic acid
Lipids	Free lipids Wax D Cord factors	
Peptides	Non-peptidoglycan amino acids Poly-α-L-glutamic acid	Removed by treatment with proteolytic enzymes
Glucan		Present in some strains

esterified by a molecule of mycolic acid (an α-branched ß-hydroxy-acid containing 60–90 carbon atoms). Arabinogalactan molecules are covalently linked to peptidoglycan by phosphodiester linkages.

Free lipids account for about 25–30% of the weight of the cell walls of mycobacteria. These comprise Wax D and cord factors. Wax D, which is considered to be an autolysis product of the cell wall of *M. tuberculosis* strains, consists of an arabinogalactan esterified by mycolic acids that is linked to a peptidoglycan that contains N-acetylglucosamine and N-glycolylmuramic acid and L-Ala, D-Ala, meso-DAP and D-glutamic acid. Cord factors, so named because of the tendency of pathogenic mycobacteria to form 'cords' when grown on the surface of a liquid medium, are dimycolates of α, α^1-D-trehalose.

2.4.2   Biocide resistance

There are wide responses to biocides within the mycobacteria. *M. tuberculosis* is the most significant human pathogen, and QACs and chlorhexidine are inhibitory (tuberculostatic) but not tuberculocidal. Alcohols, formaldehyde, formaldehyde-alcohol and iodine-alcohol are tuberculocidal and glutaraldehyde, despite earlier conflicting reports, is also considered to be in this category.

Another significant pathogen, predominantly with AIDS patients, is the *M. avium intracellulare* group (or MAIS group). MAIS are considered to be more than 10 times as resistant to glutaraldehyde as *M. tuberculosis*. *M. smegmatis* is more susceptible than *M. tuberculosis* to chemical disinfectants, whereas *M. terrae* has a similar resistance to *M. tuberculosis*.

The mechanism of high intrinsic resistance to biocides amongst mycobacteria is not precisely known, but the hydrophobic nature of the cell wall (see Section 2.4.1) is believed in some way to exclude many compounds. No investigations have yet been made, however, to correlate particular components with expression of intrinsic resistance to biocides.

2.5   Role of the glycocalyx and biofilm production in intrinsic resistance to biocides
The interaction of bacteria with surfaces is initially reversible and eventually irreversible. Irreversible adhesion is initiated by the binding of bacteria to the suface by means of expolysaccharide glycocalyx polymers. Sister cells are then produced as a result of cell division and are bound within the glycocalyx matrix. The development of adherent microcolonies is thereby initiated, leading eventually to the production of a continuous biofilm on the colonized surface. Bacteria within such a biofilm reside in a specific microenvironment that differs from cells grown in batch culture under ordinary laboratory conditions.

Bacteria within biofilms are much more resistant to biocides (and to antibiotics) than are cells in batch-type culture (Fig. 6.6(a),(b)). There are two possible reasons

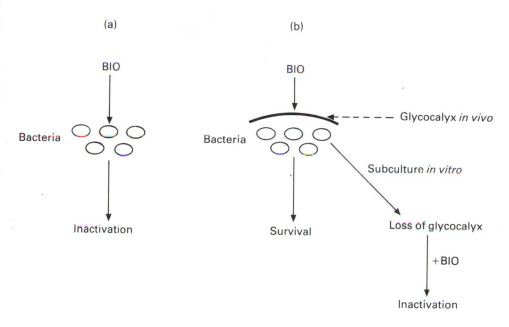

Fig. 6.6 — Comparison of absence (a) and presence (b) of glycocalyx in bacterial response to a biocide (BIO).

for this:

(a) physiological changes in the cells,
(b) penetration barriers presented by the exopolysaccharide matrix, as depicted in Fig. 6.6(b).

The latter is probably more important in relation to intrinsic resistance since subculture of cells *in vitro* often results in loss of the glycocalyx and reimposition of biocide sensitivity (Fig. 6.6(b)). Exopolysaccharide formation may be responsible for the failure of biocides in both industrial and clinical applications.

The importance of the glycocalyx in conferring intrinsic resistance is illustrated by several examples: (1) A glycocalyx associated with *Ps. aeruginosa* shields the cells from the inimical effects of iodophors. (2) Chlorine-resistant strains of *Staph. aureus* have been isolated from poultry processing plants; resistance has been ascribed to biofilm production since bacteria *in vitro* remain fully sensitive to the disinfectant. (3) *Ps. cepacia* is often considerably more resistant in the hospital environment than it is in artificial culture media and a glycocalyx may be associated with intrinsic resistance of this organism to chlorhexidine. (4) *Legionella pneumophila* is often found in hospital water distribution systems and cooling towers. Chlorination is the most effective disinfectant measure for incoming water in combination with continuous heating of hot water heaters to 60°C. Contaminating organisms, because of biofilm production, may be less susceptible to this treatment than those studied in the laboratory.

In conclusion, it is likely that biofilm production associated with a bacterial glycocalyx will assume increasing importance as a mechanism of intrinsic resistance to biocides.

2.6 Role of slime in intrinsic resistance to biocides

In nature, *Staph. aureus* may exist as mucoid strains, with a slime layer around the cells. Non-mucoid strains are killed more rapidly than mucoid strains when chloroxylenol, cetrimide and chlorhexidine are used, but there is little difference in response with phenols or chlorinated phenols. Washing of mucoid cells to remove slime renders them as sensitive as non-mucoid organisms. Slime therefore has a protective role, and is an effective resistance mechanism employed by pathogenic staphylococci. This could act either (a) as a physical barrier to biocide penetration or (b) as a loose layer interacting with, or absorbing, the biocide. The addition of crude slime to non-mucoid strains does not confer resistance, from which it may be concluded that the first hypothesis is correct.

2.7 Enzymatic degradation as a basis for intrinsic resistance to biocides

Enzymatic degradation of biocides is responsible for intrinsic biocide resistance in only a few cases.

Some *Ps. aeruginosa* are able to degrade the methyl ester of *para*-hydroxybenzoic acid which is used by the organism as a carbon source. It is not known whether this is a significant factor in the undoubtedly higher resistance of *Ps. aeruginosa* to the parabens when compared with other organisms. Phenol-decomposing bacteria have also been isolated but phenol degradation is not considered to be responsible for resistance.

Several types of preservatives and disinfectants are readily metabolized by many bacteria. They include QACs, benzoic acid, chlorhexidine and phenylethanol but this metabolism occurs only at concentrations well below inhibitory or 'in-use' concentrations. It is thus unlikely that this metabolism of biocides confers intrinsic resistance on a bacterial cell.

However, intrinsic formaldehyde resistance in some *Pseudomonas* spp. is linked to the presence of an aldehyde dehydrogenase which is expressed constitutively at high levels in these resistant strains. Other aldehydes are also reduced, to the corresponding acid, by aldehyde dehydrogenase but there is no evidence to suggest that intrinsic resistance to the most important aldehyde, glutaraldehyde, occurs by this mechanism.

3. ACQUIRED BIOCIDE RESISTANCE

Acquired resistance to biocides results from genetic changes in a cell and arises either by mutation or by the acquisition of genetic material from another cell as described for antibiotics in Chapter 5.

3.1 Plasmid-mediated resistance

Plasmid-encoded resistance to antibiotics has been widely studied (Chapter 5). Resistance to antibiotics in bacteria causing hospital infections is frequently determined by transmissible plasmids. A considerable amount of research has also been conducted on the role of plasmids and transposons in resistance of bacteria to metals, including inorganic and organic mercury compounds. There is, however, comparatively little information about the role of plasmids to most other biocides, with the exception of recent findings that suggest that antiseptic resistance in staphylococci may be plasmid-linked.

3.1.1 *Heavy metal resistance*

Genetic determinants of resistance to heavy metals are often found on plasmids and transposons and this resistance occurs with high frequency. Heavy metal resistance may be associated with antibiotic resistance but this does not necessarily always occur.

3.1.1.1   *Resistance to mercury*

Because of its toxicity, mercuric chloride is no longer widely used as a disinfectant. Some organomercury compounds such as phenylmercuric nitrate (PMN), phenylmercuric acetate (PMA) and thiomersal are, however, widely used as preservatives in injectable and ophthalmic preparations (PMN, PMA) and in immunological products (thiomersal). Merbromin (mercurochrome) is a weak disinfectant.

Mercury resistance is plasmid-borne, not chromosomal, and may be transferred from donor to recipient cells by conjugation or transduction. Inorganic (Hg^{2+}) and organomercury resistance is a common property of clinical isolates of *Staph. aureus* containing penicillinase plasmids and plasmids in Gram-negative bacteria may also carry genes conferring resistance to antibiotics and in some cases to cobalt (Co^{2+}), nickel (Ni^+), cadmium (Cd^{2+}) and arsenate (AsO_4^{3-}). Mercury resistance is inducible.

Plasmids conferring resistance to mercurials are of two types:

(a) 'Narrow-spectrum' plasmids: these are responsible for resistance to Hg^{2+} (by reduction to, and vaporization of, metallic mercury: see Fig. 6.7) and to the organomercury compounds merbromin and fluorescein mercuric acetate (pro-

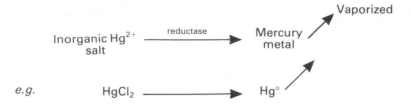

Fig. 6.7 — Biochemical mechanism of resistance to inorganic mercury compounds.

bably by exclusion) in *E. coli*. Such plasmids do not, however, confer resistance to methylmercury, ethylmercury, PMN, PMA, *p*-hydroxymercuribenzoate (PHMB) and thiomersal.

(b) 'Broad-spectrum' plasmids: these specify resistance to all the compounds listed in (a). Hydrolysis of an organomercury compound by a hydrolase (lyase) to inorganic ionic mercury (Hg^{2+}) may be followed by rapid enzymatic reduction to metallic mercury which is readily vaporized (Fig. 6.8). This volatilization does

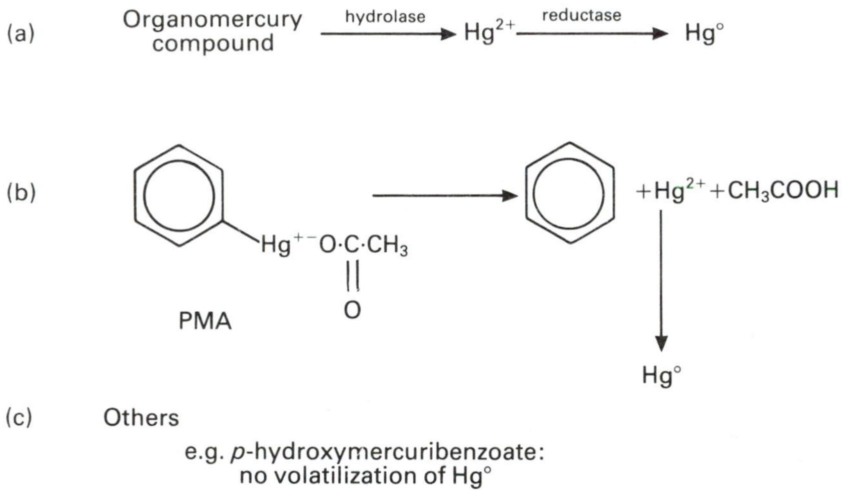

(a)   Organomercury compound $\xrightarrow{\text{hydrolase}}$ Hg^{2+} $\xrightarrow{\text{reductase}}$ Hg°

(b) PMA → $+Hg^{2+}+CH_3COOH$ → Hg°

(c)   Others
e.g. *p*-hydroxymercuribenzoate:
no volatilization of Hg°

Fig. 6.8 — Biochemical mechanisms of resistance to organic mercury compounds. (a) General pattern, (b) *Ps. aeruginosa* (broad-spectrum plasmid), (c) other organomercury derivatives. Permeability barriers may play a role in resistance of Gram-negative bacteria. *Note*: Hg° formation does not necessarily confer resistance. PMA, phenylmercuric acetate.

not, however, occur with all organomercury compounds (Fig. 6.8, Table 6.4). Table 6.4 summarizes these data.

Considerable progress has been made in examining the genes responsible for various functions. The most widely studied plasmid is R-100 which confers Hg^{2+}

Table 6.4 — Plasmid-encoded resistance to mercury compounds[a]

Organism	Plasmid-specified resistance to		Comment
	Hg^{2+}	Organomercurials	
E. coli	+	+	Narrow- or broad-spectrum plasmids
Salm. typhimurium	+	−	
Proteus spp.	+	−	
Providencia spp.	+	−	
Ps. aeruginosa	+	+	Narrow- or broad-spectrum plasmids
Staph. aureus	+	+	Broad-spectrum plasmids

[a]Note: (1) Host cell background might affect resistance pattern.
   (2) Although Hg° may be formed by volatilization from a number of organomercury substrates, this does not necessarily indicate that resistance is conferred. Seemingly, a threshold level of Hg° must be formed which, if exceeded, confers resistance.
   (3) Resistance to an organomercury compound does not necessarily involve volatilization of Hg°: cell impermeability responsible?

but not organomercury resistance. The genes are as follows (see Fig. 6.9 for genetic map):

(i) *merR* regulatory gene, the product of which is a *trans*-acting inducer-repressor, i.e. positive and negative regulation. This is followed by a promoter-operator region (*cis*-acting mutations only),

(ii) *merT* is responsible for an Hg^{2+} transport system that brings extracellular mercury into the cell,

(iii) *merP*, the product of which is a periplasmic Hg^{2+}-binding protein (encoded by Tn 501),

(iv) *merC*, whose function is uncertain, but which is not considered to be essential for Hg^{2+} resistance because it is absent from Tn*501*,

(v) *merA*, whose gene product is a subunit of mercuric reductase,

(vi) *merB*, the determinant of organomercury lyase. This gene, if present, lies between *merA* and *merD* and confers resistance to phenylmercury and other organomercurials,

(vii) *merD*, a gene defined by mutations distal to *merA*. Like *merC*, its function is uncertain, but loss of its activity leads to decreased Hg^{2+} resistance.

3.1.1.2   Resistance to silver

In the context of hospital infection, plasmid-mediated resistance to silver salts is particularly interesting because silver nitrate and silver sulphadiazine (AgSu) have been used topically for preventing infections in severe burns. The former is used for this purpose in the form of compresses soaked in a 0.5% solution. AgSu is a topical antimicrobial agent used as a prophylactic cream for application to burns; it is relatively water-soluble, is bactericidal in action and appears to bind firmly to DNA.

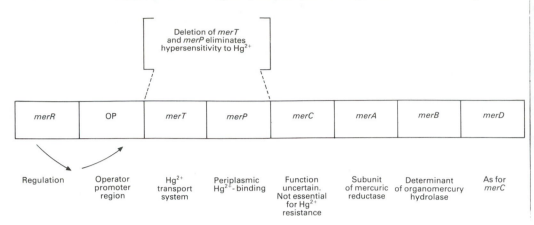

Fig. 6.9 — Genetic map of the mercury resistance of determinant of Tn 501.

Plasmid-determined Ag^+ resistance is demonstrated by the very wide ratio (>100:1) of MICs for silver-resistant and silver-sensitive cells. It is often, however, difficult to transfer silver resistance from Ag^R to Ag^S cells. Silver reduction is not the basis of resistance. The current hypothesis is that sensitive cells bind silver so tightly that they extract it from silver chloride whereas resistant cells do not complete successfully with Ag^+-halide complexes for Ag^+.

3.1.1.3   Resistance to other cations and to anions
Plasmid-encoded resistance to cations other than mercury and to anions may occur as demonstrated in Table 6.5.

Table 6.5 — Plasmid-encoded resistance to cations and anions

Anion or cation	Plasmid-specified resistance in
Ag^+	*E. coli, Salm. typhimurium*
Cd^{2+}	*Staph. aureus*
Co^{2+}	*E. coli*
Ni^+	*E. coli*
Zn^{2+}	*Staph. aureus*
Pb^{2+}	*Staph. aureus*
Cu^{2+}	*E. coli*
Arsenate, arsenite, antimony (III)	*E. coli, Staph. aureus*
CrO^{2-}	*Pseudomonas* strains, *Strep. lactis*
Tellurate, tellurite	*Alcaligenes* strains

Resistances to arsenate (AsO_4^{3-}), arsenite (AsO_3^{3-}) and antimony (III) are encoded by an inducible operon-like system in both *E. coli* and *Staph. aureus*. Interestingly, any of the three ions induces resistance to all three. The mechanism of arsenate resistance involves energy-dependent efflux of inhibitor, producing a reduced net accumulation. This efflux system is mediated by an ATPase transport system.

The plasmid-located genes are known as *ars*. In *E. coli*, phosphate transport systems are responsible for accumulating arsenate, and this organism possesses two such constitutive systems, Pit (Pi transport) and Pst (phosphate specific transport). Both are responsible for arsenate uptake although Pit has a lower affinity for phosphate. Three *ars*-encoded polypeptides are involved in the expression of resistance to arsenicals in *E. coli*: ArsA (Mol. wt. 63000), a catalytic subunit of arsenical-transducing ATPase; ArsB (Mol. wt. 45000), a membrane-located component of the arsenic pump; ArsC (Mol. wt. 15000) which modifies ArsA and ArsB to allow efflux of arsenate. The result is that imported arsenate is rapidly pumped out of resistant cells by a plasmid-encoded system that behaves like an ATPase (Fig. 6.10).

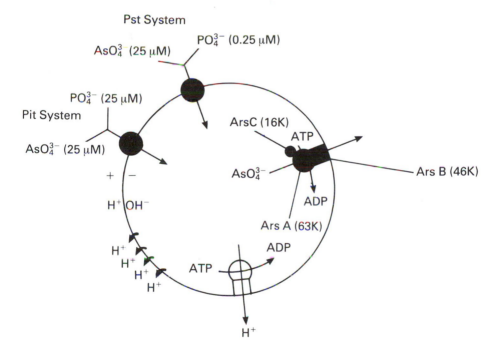

Fig. 6.10— Accumulation of phosphate and arsenate by *E. coli*. The upper left-hand side of the diagram shows the Pst (phosphate specific transport) and Pit (Pi transport) systems, both of which can accumulate phospate and arsenate ions. The values of 0.25 μM or 25 μM where indicated are the Km values for phosphate, or the Ki values for arsenate as a competitive inhibitor of phosphate transport. Beneath the Pit system is illustrated the electrogenic extrusion of protons, catalysed by the respiratory chain, which establishes the electrochemical proton gradient with the indicated polarity. The lower portion of the diagram shows the FOF1 proton translocating ATPase; above this the ATPase mediating arsenical efflux is illustrated. It is believed to consist of three polypeptides ArsA, ArsB and ArsC.

It must be pointed out that this ATPase differs from that involved in cadmium resistance (this section, below).

In contrast, plasmid-mediated chromate (CrO_4^-) resistance which is found in several *Pseudomonas* strains is expressed at the level of uptake rather than efflux, i.e. a decreased uptake, since there is no difference in efflux between sensitive and resistant cells.

Tellurite and tellurate resistances are plasmid-encoded, but the resistance mechanisms are as yet unknown.

At least four plasmid-determined systems confer cadmium (Cd^{2+}) resistance. The first two, and the most widely studied, are the *cadA* and *cadB* systems unique to staphylococcal plasmids. The *cadA* gene specifies an approximately 100-fold increase in Cd^{2+} resistance which occurs as a consequence of Cd^{2+} efflux, whereas the *cadB*$^+$ locus provides a smaller (10-fold) increase detectable in *cadA*$^-$ mutants. cadA-mediated resistance results from an energy-dependent efflux system whereby Cd^{2+} is expelled. Cd^{2+} is transported into the cell by an energy-dependent, chromosomally-determined manganese (Mn) transport system which is highly specific for Cd and Mn ions (Fig. 6.11, A). A specific efflux ATPase, involving a $Cd^{2+}/2H^+$

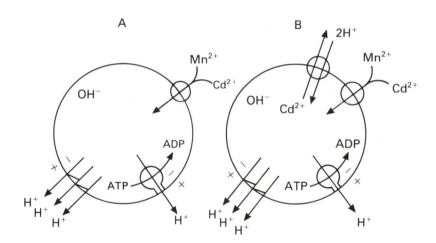

Fig. 6.11 — Accumulation of manganese and cadmium ions by *Staph. aureus* (A) illustrates cadmium and manganese co-transport into a cadmium-sensitive cell. (B) also illustrates transport of these cations, but in addition shows the *cadA*-encoded cadmium efflux protein in a cadmium resistant cell which promotes electroneutral cadmium/proton exchange. For other details see the text and the legend to Fig. 6.10. From Tynecka *et al.*, 1981: reproduced with permission from the *Journal of Bacteriology*, **147**, 313–319.

exchange, is present in resistant cells but absent from sensitive cells, and is responsible for conferring resistance (Fig. 6.11, B). As noted above, this ATPase differs from that involved in arsenate resistance.

These *cadA* and *cadB* systems also confer resistance to several other heavy metals. The third system has a cadA type mechanism but differs in that it confers Cd^{2+} resistance only. A fourth system, found in an *Alcaligenes* strain, involves a plasmid locus simultaneously conferring resistance to Cd^{2+}, Zn^{2+} and Co^{2+}. However, the mechanism of resistance is unknown.

Plasmid-determined copper (Cu^{2+}) resistance has been reported on an antibiotic resistance plasmid in some Gram-negative bacteria. In *E. coli* plasmid Rtsl encodes resistance to copper ostensibly by a decreased accumulation process. Whether this is the basis of resistance is, however, doubtful because considerable amounts of Cu^{2+} are accumulated by resistant cells although much less than by sensitive ones. In *M. scrofulaceum*, two resistance mechanisms have been proposed, involving removal of copper from culture media by (a) a sulphate-dependent precipitation as copper sulphide and (b) a sulphate-independent mechanism. In *Ps. syringae* pv tomato, possible copper-binding sites in proteins implicated in resistance have been identified. Clearly, further studies are necessary to elucidate plasmid-mediated mechanism of Cu^{2+} resistance.

In conclusion, it is apparent that studies of plasmid-encoded resistance to anions and cations are entering a particularly exciting period and that further useful evidence about mechanisms of resistance is likely to follow in the near future. Such findings will also provide further information about bacterial physiology, in particular about the properties and functions of different ATPases. It must, however, be emphasized that although the anions and cations described in this section are biocidal, they do not have major practical applications as antibacterial agents.

3.1.2   *Resistance to other biocides*
The role of plasmids in bacterial resistance to biocides has not been studied extensively. Consequently, the amount of information about possible plasmid-mediated resistance is sparse. It is convenient to consider the available data by examining first Gram-negative and then Gram-positive bacteria.

3.1.2.1   *Gram-negative bacteria*
Transferable resistance to formaldehyde and formaldehyde-releasing agents has been described in *Ser. marcescens*. Although the mechanism of resistance is unclear, it has been proposed that surface changes are induced in resistant cells; this does not involve the LPS of the outer membrane but rather the proteins, sensitive strains having a higher content of 40 and 45 kD proteins than resistant strains. Another suggestion has been that resistant strains take up less formaldehyde than isogenic, plasmid-less strains, metabolism of the aldehyde by resistant strains also contributing to for its lack of biocidal activity.

In *Ps. aeruginosa*, plasmid RPl has been claimed to confer resistance to hexachlorophane, albeit by an unknown mechanism.

Col V plasmids confer F-like transfer properties on enterobacteria and permit the bacteria to synthesize the colicin V toxin as well as an outer membrane protein known as VmpA. When attached to glass beads, Col[+] strains are more resistant than unattached bacteria to chlorine, a finding that might be of significance for bacterial survival during water chlorination.

Plasmids of different incompatibility groups have been inserted into plasmid-less members of the Enterobacteriaceae. Antibiotic resistance may then be expressed, depending on the plasmid (Chapter 5). However, the response to biocides depends mainly on the host strain, and although plasmid-encoded surface properties may change (as described above for *Ser. marcescens* and formaldehyde resistance) there is scant evidence to suggest that plasmid acquisition *per se* confers resistance to biocides. Strains of *Prov. stuartii* isolated from paraplegic patients often harbour plasmids conferring resistance to Hg^{2+} and several antibiotics and the organisms may also express resistance to cationic biocides. However, attempts to transfer chlorhexidine and QAC resistance to suitable recipients have failed and the occurrence of a plasmid-linked association between antibiotic and antiseptic resistance has not been shown (see also Chapter 8 for a fuller discussion).

In laboratory experiments, resistance to some biocides has been transferred from *Staph. aureus* to *E. coli* by recombinant techniques. In some reports, high level QAC resistance has been expressed in *E. coli*. In others, low-level plasmid-mediated resistance to chlorhexidine and QACs (MICs of resistant *Staph. aureus* only twice those of sensitive *Staph. aureus* strains) has been transferred, as has higher-level resistance to acriflavine and ethidium bromide (Table 6.6). The resistance levels of

Table 6.6 — Plasmid-mediated resistance to cationic bactericides in *Staphylococcus aureus* and *Escherichia coli*[a]

Bactericide	*Staph. aureus* MIC ratio (P^+/P^-)[b]	*E. coli* MIC ratio (P^+/P^-)[b]
Chlorhexidine gluconate	2	4–8
Benzalkonium chloride	2	4
Acriflavine	128	8
Ethidium bromide	64	16

[a] Based on data of T. Yamamoto *et al.* (1988).
P^+, P^- ... plasmid-bearing and isogenic plasmid-less strains, respectively.
[b] *E. coli* P^+ strain ... strain carrying recombinant plasmid with genetic material from *Staph. aureus* resistance plasmids.

the *E. coli* strain carrying recombinant plasmids are some 4- to 16-fold higher than for isogenic plasmid-free strains. The mechanism of resistance expressed in *E. coli* is unclear. One possibility is the presence of a biocide efflux system, similar to that found in resistant staphylococci which expel certain cationic bactericides (Section 3.1.2.2).

In conclusion, it is clear that plasmids are not generally involved in resistance of Gram-negative bacteria to biocides and that any such resistance is intrinsic and not transferable. There is, nevertheless, evidence that some plasmids are responsible for producing surface changes in cells which may be responsible for slight alterations in sensitivity or resistance and that the response depends not only on the plasmid but on the host cells. There is little evidence, apart from mercury compounds (Section 3.1.1.1) and a few reports with formaldehyde, that plasmid-mediated resistance to biocides is due to their degradation.

3.1.2.2   Staphylococci

Staph. aureus is a major cause of surgical sepsis, septicaemia and bacteraemia in hospitals. Methicillin-resistant *Staph. aureus* (MRSA) strains first appeared in the 1960s but by the mid-1970s the 'hospital staphylococcus' was considered to be in decline. The re-emergence in 1976 of MRSA strains which were in addition resistant to gentamicin led to staphylococcal outbreaks throughout Europe and Australia (see Chapter 8 for further details).

In Australia an analysis of MRSA strains showed them to be closely related and to contain only two classes of R plasmids:

(a) small (4.5 kb) chloramphenicol resistance plasmids, varying in the carriage of additional determinants for resistance to aminoglycoside antibiotics (gentamicin, kanamycin, tobramycin), penicillins and trimethoprim;

(b) larger (20–36 kb) plasmids encoding resistance to antiseptics, disinfectants and dyes such as acriflavine, QACs, ethidium bromide (EB) and diamidines (e.g. propamidine isethionate, PI).

The majority of the gentamicin R plasmids also possesed a determinant encoding resistance to QACs and this was originally referred to as QA-r. This determinant conferred resistance to the other cationic agents referred to in (b) above, all of which bind to nucleic acids so that it is now termed a nucleic acid-binding resistance (NAB-r) determinant. Two such NAB-r determinants have been found:

(i) known as NAB-r, it confers a broad spectrum of resistance to EB, QACs, acriflavine, PI and crystal violet;

(ii) termed EB-r, it confers resistance to all of these agents *except* PI.

Thus, two resistance genes are involved, one specifying resistance to diamidines and the second to other NAB agents. The NAB-r determinant is contained in a 2.3 kb sequence whereas the EB-r determinant is present in a 1.1 kb sequence. Both determinants have been cloned and expressed in *E. coli*. Resistance to EB results from an efflux system whereby EB is exported from the cell interior; the same mechanism applies for QAC resistance.

The above findings must, however, be put into perspective. The MIC values quoted by Australian workers for methicillin-sensitive *Staph. aureus* (MSSA) and MRSA strains are, respectively, 1.56 and 6.25 μg/ml for cetyltrimethylammonium bromide (CTAB) and 16 and 512 μg/ml for propamidine isethionate (PI). Not all workers agree that there is an increase in resistance to CTAB and this 4-fold increase, is, anyway, extremely small. There is general agreement about a considerable increase in resistance to PI and to the more antibacterially effective dibromopropamidine isethionate (DBPI). MRSA strains may be about 2–4 times more resistant to chlorhexidine, but when MIC values for MSSA strains are of the order of 1 μg/ml, it is clear that differences are not large. MSSA and MRSA strains show equal sensitivity to phenols, cresols and parabens.

3.2   Resistance acquired by transformation

There has been one report of transferability of chlorhexidine resistance by genetic transformation. DNA from chlorhexidine-resistant mutants of *Streptococcus sanguis* (isolated by step-wise inoculation of chlorhexidine-containing media: see Fig. 6.12) has been found to transform competent sensitive *Strep. sanguis* to chlorhexidine resistance. The basis of this resistance is unknown and its clinical significance unproven.

3.3   Resistance determined by chromosomal gene mutation

Chromosomal mutation to antibiotic resistance has been recognized in bacteria for many decades (Chapter 5). In contrast, fewer studies have been made with antiseptics, disinfectants and preservatives to determine whether chromosomal mutations confer resistance. However, some 50 years ago it was demonstrated that *Ser. marcescens*, normally inhibited by a QAC at <100 µg/ml, could adapt to grow in the presence of 100 mg/ml of that compound. Resistant and sensitive cells showed different surface properties, the former possessing an increased lipid content. Resistance was unstable, however, being lost when the resistant cells were grown in QAC-free media, presumably by back mutation.

Resistance to chlorhexidine can readily develop in some bacteria, e.g. *E. coli*, *P. mirabilis*, *Ps. aeruginosa* and *Ser. marcescens*, but may or may not be stable when the resistant cells are incorporated into biocide-free media (Fig. 6.12). Chlorhexidine-

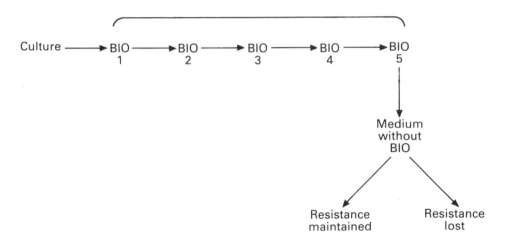

Fig. 6.12 — Laboratory-acquired resistance to a biocide by stepwise subculture. This is assumed to occur by a series of mutations in one or more chromosomal genes. In this case, expression of resistance is unstable and removal of selection pressure usually leads to back-mutations and re-expression of a sensitive phenotype. BIO, biocide.

resistant strains may also show increased resistance to QACs. Chloroxylenol-resistant strains of *Ps. aeruginosa* have been isolated by repeated subculture in media containing gradually increasing concentrations of the xylenol. Again, however, resistance is unstable.

Outer membrane chromosomally resistant mutants of *Ps. aeruginosa* produced by stepwise exposure (FIg. 6.12) to polymyxin are resistant to both polymyxin and EDTA, having a defective self-promoted uptake pathway and containing increased amounts of a major outer membrane protein (H1) with a corresponding decrease in enveloping Mg^{2+}. Identical phenotypes appear in cells growing in Mg^{2+}-deficient media and it has been proposed that protein H1 may replace Mg^{2+} at cross-bridging sites with LPS, these sites normally being those at which interaction occurs with Mg^{2+} (e.g. EDTA) or at which displacement of Mg^{2+} takes place (polymyxin).

Bacterial resistance to heavy metals arises by different mechanisms. Internal transformation of metal ions to more volatile compounds is plasmid-mediated (Section 3.1.1) but decreased uptake can be the result of either decreased permeability or plasmid-encoded efflux. Although resistance to cadmium is usually plasmid-mediated (see Section 3.1.1.3), examples of chromosomal mutation to resistance are also known. A chromosomal mutation in *B. subtilis* involves the membrane manganese (Mn^{2+}) transport system, which normally transports Mn^{2+} and Cd^{2+}, so that Cd^{2+} is no longer accumulated.

Resistance to acridines can develop as a result of mutation, but the basis of this is unknown.

The lipid bilayer of the cytoplasmic membrane is the target for alcohols and other low molecular weight solvents. Resistant *E. coli* mutants have been isolated in which resistance is due to a decrease in the ratio of inner membrane phosphatidylethanolamine to anionic phospholipids (phosphatidylglycerol and diphosphatidylglycerol).

Chromosomal mutation to chlorhexidine resistance has been described in *Prov. stuartii*, but there is no evidence that an efflux mechanism is responsible, or that the biguanide is inactivated. An osmotic shocking procedure, which removes periplasmic proteins, sensitizes the cells to the biocide, resistance being restored when the cells are allowed to revive in growth medium. It is tentatively concluded that mutant periplasmic protective proteins bind or trap chlorhexidine preventing it from reaching its target site.

4. GENERAL CONCLUSIONS

From the foregoing, it is apparent that several mechanisms of resistance might occur with non-sporing bacteria (Table 6.7). These can be summarized as follows, with specific examples being presented above:

(i) Intrinsic resistance of Gram-negative bacteria: a comparison of barriers presented by smooth and rough cells to hydrophobic and hydrophilic molecules is given in Fig. 6.2 (A, B). The specific roles of glycocalyx and slime were dealt with in Sections 2.5 and 2.6 respectively.

(ii) Intrinsic resistance of mycobacteria: the waxy cell wall presents a formidable hydrophobic barrier to many biocides (see also Section 2.4).

Table 6.7 — Possible mechanisms[a] of resistance to biocides found in non-sporing bacteria

Biocide(s)	Intrinsic resistance		Acquired resistance	
	Impermeability	Enzyme inactivation	Plasmid-encoded	Mutation
Acridines	OM? (3a)		Efflux in MRSA (3b)	
Alcohols				Altered phospholipids in inner membrane
Anions				
Arsenate			Efflux by ATPase pump (3b)	
Chlorhexidine	OM, GCX (3a)		Efflux in MRSA? (3b)	Prov. stuartii: periplasmic protective proteins?
Chlorine	SL (3a)			
Crystal violet	OM (3a)		Efflux in MRSA (3b)	
Diamidines	OM (3a)		Efflux in MRSA (3b)	
Ethidium bromide			Efflux in MRSA (3b)	
EDTA				Altered H1 OM protein in Ps. aeruginosa (2)
Formaldehyde		Dehydrogenase (1)		
Hexachlorophane	GCX (3a)		Mechanism unknown	
Iodine				
Metals				
Cadmium			cadA system (Staph. aureus): Efflux by ATPase pump (3b)	Cd^{2+} not accumulated (3a)
Mercury (inorganic)			Reduction to Hg° and vaporization Hydrolase then reductase (1)	
Mercury (organic)			Decreased uptake (3a)	
Silver				
Parabens	OM (3a)	(+) (1)		
Phenols	OM (3a)	(+) (1)		
QACs	OM (3a)		Efflux in MRSA (3b)	Altered lipid content

[a]OM, outer membrane of Gram-negative bacteria: GCX, glycocalyx; SL, slime layer; MRSA, methicillin-resistant Staph. aureus strains.
(+) Not conclusively established as a basis for resistance.
Numbers in brackets classify the resistance mechanisms in the context of those described for antibiotics in Table 5.3 (Chapter 5).

(iii) Plasmid-mediated resistance to biocides in Gram-negative bacteria: this is responsible for resistance to silver compounds and inorganic and organic mercurials but is rare in other cases. Further studies are needed to evaluate the nature and extent of plasmid-mediated formaldehyde resistance.

(iv) Plasmid-mediated resistance to biocides in staphylococci: this has been found in plasmid-containing MRSA strains. The most important type of biocide is the QAC type but resistance to QACs, although transferable, is low-level.

 (v) Expulsion of biocide from resistant cells. The clinical significance of this type of resistance mechanism is, at present, unknown.

(vi) Resistance occurring by chromosomal mutation: such resistance is known but is generally unstable.

Studies on the biochemical mechanism of resistance to biocides are not as advanced as those on antibiotics (see Chapter 5). However, at this stage, there is no evidence for changes at the target site as a basis either of plasmid- or chromosomally-determined acquired resistance. Since the target of biocide action is frequently the bacterial cytoplasmic membrane, changes at this level to confer resistance may not be compatible with cell survival.

FURTHER READING

General reviews on antiseptics, disinfectants and preservatives

Russell, A. D. (1990). Principles of antimicrobial activity. In *Disinfection, Sterilization and Preservation* (ed. S. S. Block) 4th edition. Lea & Febiger, Philadelphia.

Wallhäuser, K. H. (1984). Antimicrobial preservatives used by the cosmetic industry. In *Cosmetic and Drug Preservation: Principles and Practice* (ed. J. J. Kabara) pp. 605–745. Marcel Dekker, New York.

Reviews on bacterial surfaces

Benz, R. (1988). Structure and function of porins from Gram-negative bacteria. *Annual Review of Microbiology* **42**, 359–393.

Hammond, S. M., Lambert, P. A. & Rycroft, A. N. (1984). *The Bacterial Cell Surface*. Croom Helm, London.

Lambert, P. A. (1988). Enterobacteriaceae: composition, structure and function of the cell envelope. *Journal of Applied Bacteriology Symposium Supplement* **65**, 21S–34S.

Reviews on bacterial resistance

Brown, M. R. W. & Williams, P. (1985). The influence of environment on envelope properties affecting survival of bacteria in infection. *Annual Review of Microbiology* **39**, 527–556.

Chopra, I. (1988). Efflux of antibacterial agents from bacteria. *FEMS Symposium*

No. 44: Homeostatic Mechanisms of Microorganisms, pp. 146–158. Bath University Press, Bath.

Costerton, J. W., Cheng, K.-J., Geesey, G. G., Ladd, T. I., Nickel, J. C., Dasgupta, M. & Marrie, T. J. (1987). Bacterial biofilms in nature and disease. *Annual Review of Microbiology* **41** 435–464.

Foster, T. J. (1983). Plasmid-determined resistance to antimicrobial drugs and toxic metal ions in bacteria. *Microbiological Reviews* **47**, 361–409.

Heinzel, M. (1988). The phenomena of resistance to disinfectants and preservatives. In *Industrial Biocides*. Critical Reports on Applied Chemistry, Vol. 23. (Ed. K. R. Payne) pp. 52–67. John Wiley & Sons, Chichester.

Lyon, B. R. & Skurray, R. A. (1987). Antimicrobial resistance of *Staphylococcus aureus*: genetic basis. *Microbiological Reviews* **51**, 88–134.

Nikaido, H. & Vaara, T. (1985). Molecular basis of bacterial outer membrane permeability. *Microbiological Reviews* **49**, 1–32.

Russell, A. D. (1985). The role of plasmids in bacterial resistance to antiseptics, disinfectants and preservatives. *Journal of Hospital Infection* **6**, 9–19.

Russell, A. D. & Gould, G. W. (1988). Resistance of Enterobacteriaceae to preservatives and disinfectants. *Journal of Applied Bacteriology Symposium Supplement* **65,** 167S–195S.

Russell, A. D., Hammond, S. A. & Morgan, J. R. (1986). Bacterial resistance to antiseptics and disinfectants. *Journal of Hospital Infection* **7**, 213–225.

Silver, S. & Misra, S. (1988). Plasmid-mediated heavy metal resistances. *Annual Review of Microbiology* **42**, 717–743.

Silver, S., Nucifora, G., Chu, L. & Misra, T. K. (1989). Bacterial ATPases: primary pumps for exporting toxic cations and anions. *Trends in Biochemical Sciences* **14**, 76–80.

Bacterial resistance: selected research papers

Gillespie, M. T., May, J. W. & Skurray, R. A. (1986). Plasmid-encoded resistance to acriflavine and quaternary ammonium compounds in methicillin-resistant *Staphylococcus aureus*. *FEMS Microbiology Letters* **34**, 47–51.

LeChevalier, M. W., Cawthorn, C. D. & Lee, R. G. (1988). Inactivation of biofilm bacteria. *Applied and Environmental Microbiology* **54**, 2492–2499.

Marrie, T. J. & Costerton, J. W. (1981). Prolonged survival of *Serratia marcescens* in chlorhexidine. *Applied and Environmental Microbiology* **42**, 1093–1102.

Martin, T. D. M. (1969). Sensitivity of the genus *Proteus* to chlorhexidine. *Journal of Medical Microbiology* **2**, 101–108.

Midgley, M. (1986). The phosphonium ion efflux system of *Escherichia coli*: a relationship to the ethidium efflux system and energetic studies. *Journal of General Microbiology* **132**, 3187–3193.

Midgley, M. (1987). An efflux system for cationic dyes and related compounds in *Escherichia coli*. *Microbiological Sciences* **4**, 125–127.

Nikaido, H. (1976). Outer membrane of *Salmonella typhimurium*. Transmembrane diffusion of some hydrophobic substances. *Biochimica et Biophysica Acta* **433**, 118–132.

Roussow, F. T. & Rowbury, R. J. (1984). Effects of the resistance plasmid R124 on the level of the OmpF outer membrane protein and on the response of *Escherichia coli* to environmental agents. *Journal of Applied Bacteriology* **56**, 63–79.

Russell, A. D., Furr, J. R. & Pugh, W. J. (1985). Susceptibility of porin- and lipopolysaccharide-deficient mutants of *Escherichia coli* to a homologous series of esters of *p*-hydroxybenzoic acid. *International Journal of Pharmaceutics* **27**, 263–273.

Stickler, D. J., Thomas, B., Clayton, J. C. & Chawla, J. A. (1983). Studies on the genetic basis of chlorhexidine resistance. *British Journal of Clinical Practice Symposium Supplement* **25**, pp. 23–28.

Yamamoto, T., Tamura, Y. & Yokota, T. (1988). Antiseptic and antibiotic resistance plasmid in *Staphylococcus aureus* that posseses ability to confer chlorhexidine and acrinol resistance. *Antimicrobial Agents and Chemotherapy* **32**, 932–935.

7

Mechanisms of spore resistance to biocides

1. INTRODUCTION

Bacterial spores are generally considerably more resistant to biocides than are germinated spores or non-sporulating bacteria (Fig. 7.1). As demonstrated in

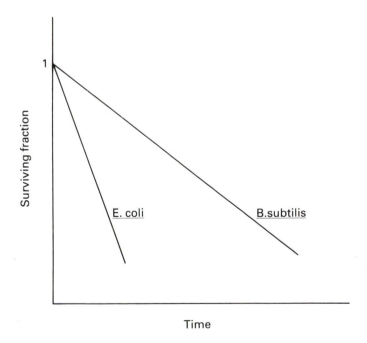

Fig. 7.1 — Comparative responses of non-sporing (*Escherichia coli*) and sporing (*Bacillus subtilis*) organisms to a bactericidal and sporicidal agent.

Chapter 4, there are several stages during sporulation subject to inhibition by antibacterial agents. Conversely, there are also several stages where resistance of spores to chemicals may arise. This is undoubtedly of potential significance in the context of food and medical microbiology.

2. EXPERIMENTAL ASPECTS

Various techniques have been employed to investigate the mechanism by which spores resist chemical inhibitors. These include the use of sporulation (Spo⁻) and other mutants, an examination of the changes in sensitivity that occur during sporulation and the use of specific agents that are known to have an effect on the spore coat or coats. Theoretical aspects of each approach will be considered below leading on to some general conclusions that may be reached.

2.1   Use of Spo⁻ mutants

The use of Spo⁻ mutants of *B. subtilis* strain 168 for studies on resistance is increasing. These mutants are unable to develop beyond a certain stage in the sporulation process (Table 7.1) and are consequently of value in correlating

Table 7.1 — Use of sporulation (Spo⁻) mutants of *Bacillus subtilis* in studying development of resistance to biocides

B. subtilis strain	Characteristics
Wild type	Develops into mature spores
IV mutants	Do not develop beyond Stage IV
V mutants	Do not develop beyond Stage V
VI mutants	Do not develop into fully mature spores

structural changes and biochemical characteristics with response to antibacterial compounds (Table 7.2) (or to physical processes such as heat, ultraviolet or ionizing radiations).

Table 7.2 — Onset of resistance to antibacterial agents during the sporulation process

Agent	Sporulation stage	
	At which resistance develops	Where resistance is fully developed
Toluene	Late Stage III	Early Stage IV
Chlorhexidine	Stage IV	Stage V
Heat	Stage V	Stage IV
Lysozyme	Middle of Stage V	Stage VI
Glutaraldehyde	Late Stage V	Stage VI completed

Studies with these Spo⁻ mutants reveal that resistance to toluene develops early in sporulation, whereas resistance to lysozyme is a late event. Toluene cannot, of course, be considered as a useful antibacterial agent and lysozyme is rarely used as such. Both can, however, be regarded as useful markers. Resistance to chlorhexidine occurs later than toluene and just before heat resistance, whereas glutaraldehyde resistance is a very late event, occuring after the development of lysozyme resistance (Table 7.2). This view is reinforced by studies on wild-type (Spo$^+$) cultures of *B. subtilis* 168 (see Section 2.3 and Figs 7.2 and 7.3).

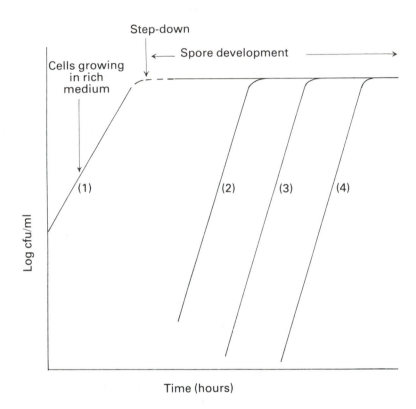

Fig. 7.2 — Diagrammatic representation of sporulation and development of resistance. (1) Cells growing in nutritionally rich medium are suddenly transferred to a nutritionally poor medium ('step-down' procedure). During sporulation, samples are removed and exposed to various inhibitors. Early, intermediate and late development of resistance is shown to inhibitors (2), (3) and (4), respectively.

2.2   Use of Dap$^-$ mutants

Conditional spore cortex-less mutants of a strain of *B. sphaericus* have been described. These are deficient in the synthesis of *meso*-diaminopimelic acid (Dap), and the muramic lactam and hence cortex content increases with an increase in the external concentration of Dap (see Chapter 1 for details of muramic lactam). Spores with varying cortical contents can thus be obtained by growth in media containing different Dap concentrations. Characteristic spore properties are associated with

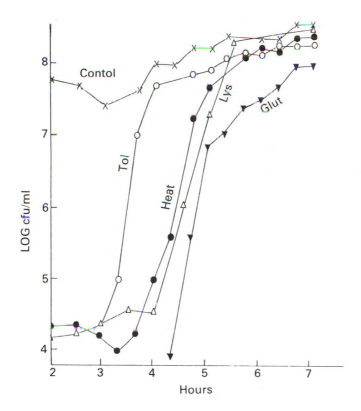

Fig. 7.3 — Development of resistance to glutaraldehyde (Glut) and other agents during sporulation of *B. subtilis* strain 168. Tol, toluene; Lys, lysozyme.

different amounts of cortex, e.g. 25% of maximal cortex content to show octanol resistance but 90% is needed to demonstrate heat resistance.

Unfortunately changes may occur elsewhere in the spore and thus conclusions reached by this approach must be made with caution.

2.3 Development of resistance during sporulation

Useful information can be obtained by attempting to correlate resistance to chemicals (or physical agencies) with structural and other changes that occur during sporulation (Figs 7.2, 7.3). Results obtained by this type of approach substantiate those obtained with Spo⁻ mutants (Section 2.1).

Some twelve polypeptides found in the spore coat of *B. subtilis* are synthesized at different times and incorporated into the spore during stages V and VI. One polypeptide, molecular weight 36 000 (36K) which is formed very late in sporulation, may have a direct role in conferring lysozyme resistance upon the spores. However, the late development of resistance to glutaraldehyde is probably not concerned with the deposition of a single, specific spore coat protein because of the highly reactive nature of the dialdehyde molecule with proteins in general.

2.4   Coat-less spores

Even when the inner and outer spore coats are removed, spores remain viable. Thus, to examine the role of the coats in resistance, an obvious approach is to compare the sensitivity of intact spores with that of spores from which the spore coats have been removed.

UDS, a combination of urea, dithiothreitol (DTT) and sodium dodecyl sulphate (SDS) employed at a pH of about 10 is the most widely employed procedure for removing spore coats. DTT is a disulphide bond-reducing agent that, used alone, substantially removes the outer coat; it can be replaced by another disulphide bond-reducing agent, mercaptoethanol. SDS, an anionic surfactant, dissociates acidic polypeptides in the inner coat. By selective use of these agents, therefore, it is possible to produce spores lacking outer coat as well as spores devoid of both coats (Table 7.3). UDS-treated spores are rendered highly sensitive to glutaraldehyde,

Table 7.3 — Removal of outer and inner spore coats

Chemical agent(s)[a]	Properties	Function
DTT	Disulphide bond-reducing agent	Removal of outer spore coat
SDS	Dissociates polypeptides	Dissociation of inner spore coat
UDS	Urea+DTT+SDS	Removal of inner and outer spore coats.

[a]DTT, dithiothreitol; SDS, sodium dodecyl sulphate.

iodine, hydrogen peroxide, ozone, chlorine dioxide and chlorine. Thus, the spore coats must have an important role to play in rendering intact spores less susceptible to these disinfectants. However, whether spore coats play a role in the resistance of spores to ethylene oxide is unclear. Ethylene oxide, $(CH_2)_2O$, is a comparatively small molecule (Mol. wt. 44) that might be expected to enter spores freely. It seems unlikely that Mol. wt. is, however, an important factor in governing spore permeability, since the coats play an important role in limiting entry to other small molecule inhibitors, as noted above. The comparatively high resistance of bacterial spores to ethylene oxide is not lost during germination, so that hydration of the spore core and alteration of spore coat layers do not appear to be linked to sensitivity to this gaseous disinfectant.

In some organisms, the spore coats offer better protection than in others. For example, the spore coat offers a protective barrier against peroxide in *Clostridium bifermentans* but is much less effective in conferring resistance in *B. cereus*. This probably results from differences in the composition of the coats in different species.

3.   CONCLUSIONS

Comparative resistance to some sporicides develops during sporulation and is lost during germination and/or outgrowth (Chapter 4). Resistance is not associated with biodegradation of antibacterial agents by sporulating cells or by mature spores and indeed it would be surprising if this were the case. A possible alternative explanation would be an alteration in the nature of a target site during sporulation. Although there is little evidence for this, it should be noted that at the level of DNA organization spore DNA *in vivo* (but not *in vitro*) is present in the A-form rather than the normal B-form (see Chapter 1). Possibly the A-conformation is associated with the resistance of spores to some agents interacting with DNA.

The sporicides discussed in this chapter are quite distinct from antibiotics and

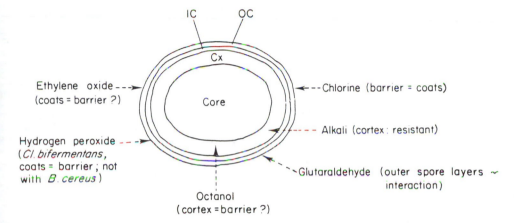

Fig. 7.4 — Possible spore barriers to specific non-antibiotic agents. OC, outer spore coat; IC, inner spore coat: CX, cortex.

Table 7.4 — Mechanisms of spore resistance to antibacterial agents

Antibacterial agent	Spore component	Comment[a]
Alkali	Cortex	
Lysozyme	Coat(s)	
Hypochlorites, chlorine dioxide	Coat(s)	UDS spores highly sensitive
Glutaraldehyde	Coat(s)	
Iodine	Coat(s)	
Hydrogen peroxide	Coat(s)	Varies with strain
Chlorhexidine	Coat(s)	UDS spores rather more sensitive
Ethylene oxide	Coat(s)?	Exact relationship unclear
Octanol	Cortex	Dap⁻ mutants of
Xylene	Cortex	B. sphaericus used[b]
Ozone	Coat(s)	UDS spores highly sensitive

[a]UDS Urea+dithiothreitol+sodium lauryl sulphate.
[b]Changes may occur in cortex *and* other parts of spore.

chemotherapeutic agents. The latter tend to have very specific sites of action (Chapter 2) and target site mutations that lead to resistance in vegetative bacteria are therefore feasible and do indeed occur (Chapter 5). Sporicides, however, are much less specific in their actions (see, for example, aldehydes and alkylating agents already referred to in the present chapter), and the most likely mechanism responsible for the comparative resistance to inhibitors of spores is the inaccessibility of target sites. Obviously, spore coats have an important role to play here, and the synthesis of specific spore coat proteins is associated with the development during sporulation of resistance to lysozyme.

Fig. 7.4 and Table 7.4 provide a summary of the barriers presented by various spore components to the intracellular penetration of inhibitory agents.

FURTHER READING

General works on spore resistance to biocides

Gould, G. W. (1985). Modification of resistance and dormancy. In *Fundamental and Applied Aspects of Bacterial Spores* (eds G. J. Dring, D. J. Ellar and G. W. Gould) pp. 371–382. Academic Press, London.

Foegeding, P. M. (1983). Bacterial spore resistance to chlorine compounds. *Food Technology* **37** (11), 100–104.

Hurst, A. & Gould G. W. (eds) (1983). *The Bacterial Spore,* Vol. 2. Academic Press, London.

Russell, A. D. (1982). *The Destruction of Bacterial Spores.* Academic Press, London.

Stevenson, K.E. & Shafer, B. D. (1983). Bacterial spore resistance to hydrogen peroxide. *Food Technology* **37** (11), 111–114.

Waites, W. M. (1982). Resistance of bacterial spores. In *Principles and Practice of Disinfection, Preservation and Sterilisation* (eds A. D. Russell, W. B. Hugo and G. A. J. Ayliffe) pp. 207–220. Blackwell Scientific Publications, Oxford.

Spore resistance to biocides: selected papers

Dadd, A. H. & Daly, G. M. (1982). Role of the coat in resistance of bacterial spores to inactivation by ethylene oxide. *Journal of Applied Bacteriology* **53**, 109–116.

Jenkinson, H. F. (1981). Germination and resistance defects in spores of a *Bacillus subtilis* mutant lacking a coat of polypeptide. *Journal of General Microbiology* **127**, 81–91.

Jenkinson, H. F., Sawyer, W. D. & Mandelstam, J. (1981). Synthesis and order of assembly of spore coat proteins in *Bacillus subtilis. Journal of General Microbiology* **123**, 1–16.

Power, E.G. M., Dancer, B. N. & Russell, A. D. (1988). Emergence of resistance to glutaraldehyde in spores of *Bacillus subtilis* 168. *FEMS Microbiology Letters* **50**, 223–226.

Shaker, L. A., Furr, J.R., & Russell, A. D. (1988). Mechanism of resistance of *Bacillus subtilis* spores to chorhexidine. *Journal of Applied Bacteriology* **64**, 531–539.

Shaker, L. A., Dancer, B. N., Russell, A. D. & Furr, J. R. (1988). Emergence and development of chlorhexidine resistance during sporulation of *Bacillus subtilis* 168. *FEMS Microbiology Letters* **51**, 73–76.

Waites, W. M. & Bayliss, C. E. (1979). The effect of changes in the spore coat on the destruction of *Bacillus cereus* spores by heat and chemical agents. *Journal of Applied Biochemistry* **1**, 71–76.

8

Impact on society of bacterial resistance to antibiotics and biocides and ways of counteracting it

1. INTRODUCTION

Previous chapters have dealt with the genetic and biochemical basis of resistance to antibiotics and biocides expressed by bacteria and their spores. In this chapter the social implications of bacterial resistance, particularly in the contexts of human medicine and hygiene, are considered. Later sections deal with strategies for counteracting resistance to antibacterial agents.

2. IMPACT OF BACTERIAL RESISTANCE TO CHEMOTHERAPEUTIC ANTIBIOTICS

2.1 Consequences for therapy of infectious diseases: overview

As mentioned in Chapter 5, acquired rather than intrinsic antibiotic resistance usually poses the greatest threat to successful chemotherapy. Table 8.1 gives specific

Table 8.1 — Valuable treatments under threat or no longer available

Type of infection	Treatments under threat	Treatment no longer available
Meningococcal meningitis and septicaemia		Sulphonamides (for initial treatment)
H. influenzae infections	Chloramphenicol	Ampicillin (for initial treatment)
Urinary infections	Ampicillin, trimethoprim	
Gonorrhoea	'High-dose' penicillin	'Low-dose' penicillin
Pneumococcal infections	Penicillin	
Salmonella infection	Chloramphenicol, co-trimoxazole, amoxycillin	
Methicillin-resistant staphylococcal infection	Many antibiotics	
Hospital coliform infection	Many antibiotics	Ampicillin
Shigellosis		Sulphonamides, ampicillin

Reproduced, with permission, from Lambert (1984).

examples in which the emergence of acquired antibiotic resistance has either eliminated a number of previously valuable treatments, or made treatment more difficult or more costly because alternative agents must now be used. Two of the examples in Table 8.1 are considered in more detail below.

2.1.1   Penicillin resistance in Neisseria gonorrhoeae

Until the mid-1970s single dose oral therapy with penicillins such as ampicillin or amoxycillin was invariably the preferred choice for treatment of *N. gonorrhoeae* infections. However, in 1976, beta-lactamase-producing organisms, with a high level of resistance to penicillins and causing infections refractory to penicillin therapy, emerged in the United Kingdom and United States. These strains have now spread throughout the world and possess plasmids that encode the TEM-1 beta-lactamase. Infections with such organisms are now frequently treated with beta-lactamase-stable cephalosporins such as cefoxitin, cefuroxime and cefotaxime. However, these cephalosporins are considerably more expensive than the penicillins that could be used previously, they have to be given intramuscularly and none is very effective in dealing with pharyngeal infections.

The incidence of beta-lactam-resistant strains of *N. gonorrhoeae* that do not produce beta-lactamase has also increased in recent years. Resistance in such strains is due to mutations in chromosomal genes which either result in the production of altered forms of penicillin-binding proteins (PBPs) that have decreased affinity for beta-lactams, or cause reduced uptake of the antibiotics across the gonococcal outer membrane. The combined effect of such mutations can result in a 1000-fold increase in resistance levels to beta-lactams. This situation has further undermined the use of beta-lactam antibiotics for treatment of gonococcal infections, necessitating the use of other antibiotics which are either more costly or have more pronounced side-effects on the patient than beta-lactams.

2.1.2   Methicillin-resistant staphylococcal infections

As already noted in Chapter 6, staphylococci are members of a group of invasive Gram-positive pathogens known as pyogenic cocci that can cause acute to chronic infections in man ranging from surgical sepsis to generalized septicaemia and bacteraemia.

Prior to introduction of antibiotics in clinical medicine the prognosis for patients with severe staphylococcal infections was very poor. However, the introduction of benzylpenicillin in the 1940s offered effective treatment for severe infections caused by invasive staphylococci, e.g. *Staphylococcus aureus*. Unfortunately, within a few years of the introduction of penicillin the majority of hospital isolates were resistant to the antibiotic, the strains expressing beta-lactamase activity. Thus, soon after the introduction of penicillin for clinical use, a large-scale World Health Organization survey showed that approximately 8% of strains were resistant; by 1956 the value was about 70%. The introduction of other types of antibiotic (e.g. streptomycin, chloramphenicol, tetracycline) for the therapy of staphylococcal infections also resulted in the emergence of strains specifically resistant to these compounds. Furthermore, strains which had acquired resistance to the new antibiotics were also often resistant to penicillin because of beta-lactamase production. Such multiply-resistant *S. aureus* strains were responsible for many outbreaks of hospital infection during the 1950s.

The predominance of beta-lactamase producing staphylococci in the 1950s led to an urgent search for beta-lactamase-stable penicillins that could be used for chemotherapy. The discovery and introduction of such compounds, e.g. methicillin caused a major decline in the incidence of multiply resistant *S. aureus* strains during the 1960s. However, during the late 1970s and early 1980s strains of *S. aureus* resistant to multiple antibiotics including methicillin and gentamicin emerged that were responsible for outbreaks of hospital infections throughout the world (e.g. see Table 8.2 and Section 3.1.2.2, Chapter 6). Such strains, referred to as MRSA (methicillin-resistant *S. aureus*) not only cause difficulty in hospitals, but spread from them to nursing homes and to surrounding communities. The pattern of resistance exhibited by MRSA imposes serious constraints upon the choice of antibiotics for therapy since the organisms involved are resistant to virtually all the antibiotics available to clinicians. Vancomycin, which is a somewhat toxic antiobiotic requiring intravenous administration is often the only drug effective against such staphylococci. Clearly this antibiotic is only suitable for use in hospitals.

3. STRATEGIES FOR COUNTERACTING RESISTANCE TO CHEMOTHERAPEUTIC ANTIBIOTICS

From the foregoing examples it is clear that the emergence of acquired antibiotic resistance in bacteria has frequently had a profound impact on the treatment of bacterial infections with antibiotics: resistance has rendered useless a number of previously valuable treatments and in other cases has made treatment more difficult or more expensive. Consequently, strategies for counteracting and/or minimizing resistance to antibiotics have been sought.

3.1 Antibiotics stable to enzymatic inactivation

As noted in Chapter 5, enzymatic inactivation is an important mechanism of resistance in the case of beta-lactams, chloramphenicol, AGAC and MLS group antibiotics. In several cases enzyme-stable analogues have been developed, most notably with the beta-lactams.

3.1.1 *Beta-lactam antibiotics*

As mentioned in Section 2.1.2, the increase in the frequency of penicillin-resistant strains of *S. aureus* throughout the world during the 1950s led to the development of methicillin, an antibiotic stable to attack by staphylococcal beta-lactamases. Methicillin (a derivative of 6-aminopenicillanic acid (6-APA), where

Fig. 2.25, Chapter 2), is stable to attack by staphylococcal beta-lactamase because its side-chain (structure above) causes the antibiotic to have very poor affinity with the enzyme. Further work with penicillins stable to staphylococcal beta-lactamase led to the development of other 6-APA derivatives. Particularly important are the so-called isoxazolyl series comprising

oxacillin

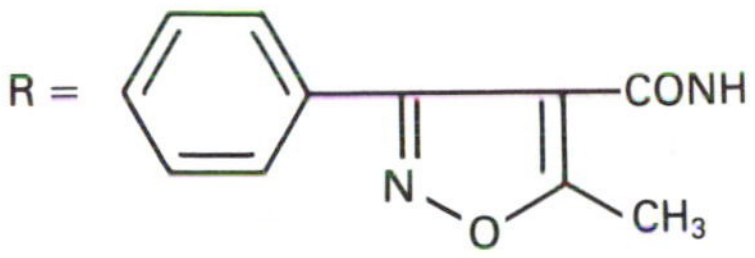

R =

—CONH

N—O   CH$_3$

cloxacillin

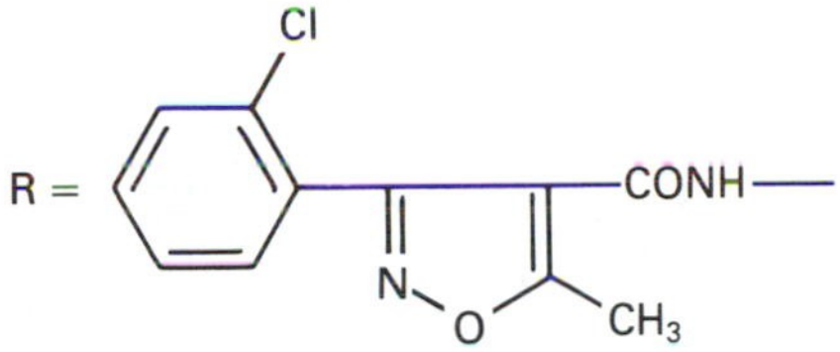

R =

Cl

—CONH—

N—O   CH$_3$

dicloxacillin

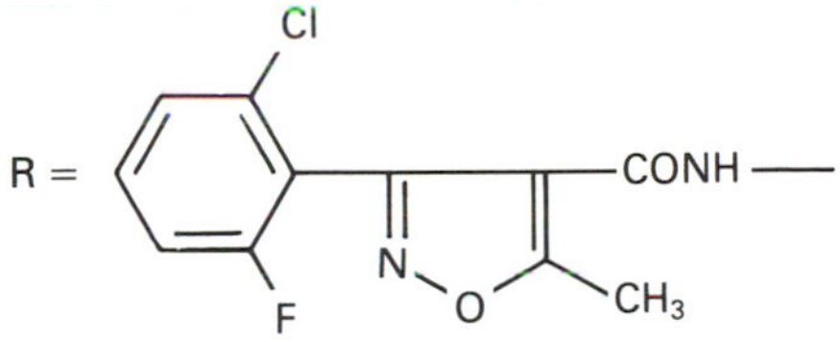

R =

Cl

—CONH—

N—O   CH$_3$

F

and

flucloxacillin

Cl

—CONH—

N—O   CH$_3$

Cl

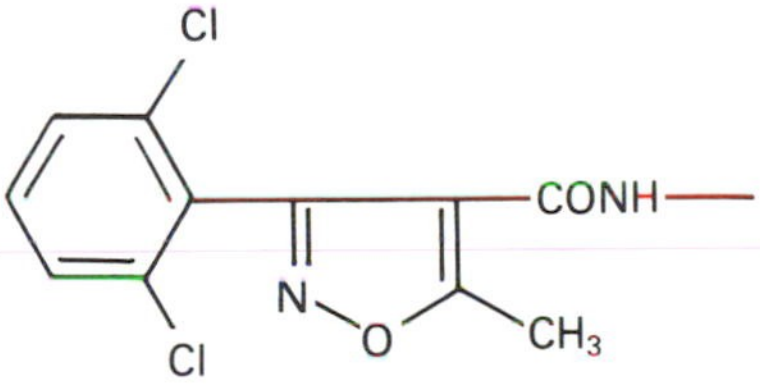

Agents exhibiting stability to enterobacterial beta-lactamases have also been developed, e.g. cefoxitin and temocillin (Fig. 2.25, Chapter 2). The presence of methoxy side chains in these compounds results in a very high degree of stability to the beta-lactamases produced by Gram-negative bacilli. Monobactams (Fig. 2.25, Chapter 2), a recently discovered group of naturally-occurring beta-lactams also display stability to enterobacterial beta-lactamases.

3.1.2   AGAC group antibiotics
As discussed in Chapter 5, resistance to these antibiotics can result from the production of enzymes that acetylate, adenylylate or phosphorylate the antibiotics. Compounds stable to individual, but not all, modifying enzymes have been developed. These compounds lack certain hydroxyl and amino groups so that complex

patterns of resistance may exist in individual strains depending on the enzymes involved (Table 5.4, Chapter 5). Therefore the ability to administer an enzyme-stable AGAC antibiotic for therapy depends upon the prevalence and type of AGAC resistance encountered.

3.1.3 Chloramphenicol

As noted in Chapter 5, chloramphenicol is inactivated by chloramphenicol acetyl-transferases. Chemical modification of chloramphenicol to produce antibiotically-active, enzyme resistant molecules has proved difficult. However, 3-fluoro-3-deoxy derivatives have been synthesized which are resistant to modification by chloram-phenicol acetyl transferases. Unfortunately, these derivatives may be toxic.

3.2   Enzyme inhibitors

The principle of using one agent to inhibit an enzyme that would otherwise inactivate a partner drug has been successfully applied to the beta-lactam antibiotics.

The suggestion that beta-lactamase inhibitors might extend the action of penicil-lin to organisms not otherwise susceptible first arose during the 1940s. However, it was not until the 1970s that such inhibitors were discovered. Clavulanic acid (Fig. 2.25; Chapter 2), first described in 1977, exhibits weak antibacterial activity, but binds with high affinity and essentially irreversibly to many bacterial beta-lactamases (see Table 5.6, Chapter 5). Clavulanic acid protects many beta-lactam antibiotics from destruction and has now been introduced commercially in combination with amoxycillin (Augmentin) and ticarcillin (Timentin). Recently, another beta-lacta-mase inhibitor, sulbactam (a penicillanic acid sulfone) was discovered. However, it is less potent than clavulanic acid.

3.3   Enhancement of permeability

The concept of using one antibiotic to promote entry of another to an otherwise inaccessible target site could, in principle, be applied to overcome acquired and intrinsic resistance due to mechanism 3a described in Table 5.3, Chapter 5. Agents interfering with bacterial peptidoglycan synthesis or outer membrane integrity are the most likely antibiotics to facilitate entry of other agents normally excluded.

This approach has proved useful in the treatment of streptococcal endocarditis where penicillin, by promoting cell envelope damage, enhances uptake of AGAC antibiotics. However, the use of outer membrane-disrupting agents, e.g. polymyxin B nonapeptide, to enhance uptake of other antibiotics into bacteria has not proved promising in terms of likely clinical application (see the article by Lam and co-workers listed in 'Further Reading' at the end of this chapter).

3.4   Other strategies for counteracting antibiotic resistance

As already noted in Chapter 5, the emergence of acquired resistance to antibiotics results from the selective pressure imposed by antibiotic usage. This alters the natural ecological balance which otherwise favours the predominance of antibiotic-susceptible bacteria. Because the use of antibiotics is related to the emergence of bacterial resistance, the ways in which these drugs are prescribed has been closely scrutinized. Several studies have indicated excessive use of antibiotics, particularly for surgical prophylaxis. A consensus is now emerging that greater effort must be devoted to limiting antibiotic usage for essential therapeutic purposes. Various antibiotic management systems have been proposed and many hospitals now exert some degree of control over the prescribing of antibiotics. Control of antibiotic usage also applies to agricultural meat production where the practice of using therapeutic antibiotics as growth promoters in animal feeds has been restricted in many countries for fear that antibiotic-resistant organisms arising in animals may be transferred to humans.

In addition to controls on antibiotic use, it is clear that effective measures to prevent cross-infection between hospital patients limits the spread of antibiotic-resistant organisms in the hospital environment. Various procedures can be adopted (for further details see the article by Lambert listed at the end of this chapter). The success of procedures to limit cross-infection is dramatically illustrated by the decline in MRSA isolation rates in West Lambeth (London) hospitals in 1986 (Table 8.2).

Table 8.2 — Yearly isolation rates of MRSA in West Lambeth Health Authority

Year	Total isolates"	% MRSA
1969	1109	2.00
1970	1128	1.00
1971	1414	1.00
1972	1759	1.00
1973	1476	2.00
1974	1441	1.00
1975	1348	0.40
1976	1782	0.40
1977	2305	<0.05
1978	1842	0.00
1979	1982	1.20
1980	2180	0.90
1981	2338	0.90
1982	2492	0.68
1983	2181	0.18
1984	2378	11.14
1985	2733	15.59
1986	2533	1.34

"All *S. aureus* isolates from patients or staff in three hospitals of the West Lambeth Health Authority.
Reproduced, with permission, from Cookson & Phillips (1988).

4.   IMPACT OF BACTERIAL RESISTANCE TO ANTISEPTICS, DISINFECTANTS AND PRESERVATIVES

4.1   Biocide resistance

As already noted in Chapter 3, non-antibiotic antibacterial agents are widely used as antiseptics, disinfectants and preservatives. Furthermore, they may also be utilized as so-called chemosterilizer systems for delicate medical equipment that cannot be sterilized by physical procedures such as heat, e.g. endoscopes which are disinfected between patient usage. Both intrinsic and acquired transferable resistance to biocides can significantly influence the effectiveness of these agents as inhibitors of bacterial growth or killing agents. Some examples are given below.

Hospital isolates of Gram-negative bacteria often show above-average resistance to disinfectants, which may reflect the wide usage of these agents in the hospital environment. In particular, disinfectants of the QAC type have been contaminated with such bacteria. This has required the introduction of more hygienic methods of preparation and storage of formulated solutions. Some MRSA strains are slightly more resistant to cationic disinfectants than other staphylococci. Although it has been claimed that this property confers a selective advantage in survival when these disinfectants are employed clinically, this claim needs to be substantiated. The widespread use of chlorhexidine and QACs may be correlated with the emergence of resistant strains of Gram-negative bacteria in paraplegic patients; these bacteria may also be resistant to multiple antibiotics. Such organisms can be difficult to control, e.g. a hospital outbreak caused by a strain of *P. mirabilis* that was resistant to chlorhexidine and to several antibiotics, including gentamicin, has been described.

Chlorhexidine bladder washouts are currently believed to be unsuitable for eliminating established infections with Gram-negative bacteria that occur in patients with indwelling bladder catheters. Such organisms are often able to grow as micro-colonies embedded in a polysaccharide matrix and thus resist the biguanide. Industrially, too, biofilms are frequently a problem and have been held responsible for resistance of *Staph. aureus* to chlorine in poultry processing plants, of various types of biofilm bacteria to chlohexidine, hypochlorites and monochloramine and of *Ser. marcescens* to chlorhexidine. *Ps. cepacia* is frequently highly resistant to biocides *in vivo*, but less so *in vitro* and *L. pneumophila* also is more sensitive under laboratory conditions than in cooling towers. The problems of resistance associated with biofilm development have necessitated the incorporation of biocides into biomaterials. Biocide molecules leach from these materials thereby decreasing bacterial adhesion and subsequent biofilm formation.

Virucidal agents are outside the scope of this book. However, patients with AIDS (acquired immune deficiency syndrome) caused by HIV (human immunodeficiency virus) are highly susceptible to bacterial and fungal infections. Transmission of such infection may be prevented by disinfection of inanimate objects. In this context, *M. avium intracelulare* is a potentially problematic organism because it is even more resistant to disinfectants than other mycobacteria.

4.2   Possible relationship between antibiotic and biocide resistance
In the majority of cases, the genetic determinants responsible for acquired resistance to antibiotics and biocides are unrelated. There have been specific instances, however, when biocides have been claimed to select for antibiotic-resistant strains. This potentially alarming situation was first suggested when it was found that about 15% of Gram-negative strains (*Ps. aeruginosa, P. mirabilis* and *Prov. stuartii*) isolated from urinary tract infections in a paraplegic unit expressed resistance to cationic bactericides (QACs, chlorhexidine) and concomitantly to at least five

antibiotics. This led to the proposal that the widespread use of chlorhexidine might be responsible for selecting antibiotic-resistant strains, i.e. that the various resistance determinants might reside on a common plasmid. However, all attempts to demonstrate a plasmid-linked association between antibiotic and chlorhexidine resistance have been unsuccessful. Furthermore, chlorhexidine-resistant mutants have been derived from chlorhexidine-sensitive *E. coli*, but they do not show enhanced resistance to antibiotics. The association between chlorhexidine and multiple antibiotic resistance in *Prov. stuartii* strains isolated from paraplegic patients has yet to be fully explained. However, it is possible that chlorhexidine-resistant strains act as more efficient recipients of plasmids conferring antibiotic resistance.

Bacteria expressing multiple antibiotic resistance have been isolated from drinking water. It has already been pointed out that disinfection and purification of water may augment the occurrence of antibiotic-resistant bacteria and that chlorination may select or induce such changes. The finding that *E. coli* containing a virulence plasmid (CoIV) is better able to attach to particles and exhibits increased chlorine resistance is another example of a potential public health hazard. Also, in this context, natural waters exposed to toxic chemical wastes show a higher incidence of antibiotic-resistant and plasmid-bearing strains than samples of clean ocean waters. Moreover, treated sewage contains large numbers of bacteria that simultaneously possess antibiotic and biocide resistances together with multiple plasmids. Obviously, as in the case of chlorhexidine and antibiotic resistance, the basis of 'linked' biocide/antibiotic resistance in organisms isolated from aquatic sources is of potential clinical and public health importance.

5.   STRATEGIES FOR COUNTERACTING RESISTANCE TO BIOCIDES

Methods for counteracting resistance to biocides usually involve a combined system. In practice the following are used:

(1) Inclusion of an agent for enhancement of permeability (cf. Section 3.3 above). Agents such as EDTA, polylysine, lactoferrin and transferrin all potentiate antibiotic activity *in vitro*. EDTA also potentiates the efficacy of various biocides against Gram-negative bacteria, but the other compounds have not yet been examined in detail for possible synergistic activity with biocides.
(2) Using preservatives in foods that rely on the combined effects of physical factors such as suboptimal pH, temperature and water activity, as well as the chemical preservative itself, to inhibit microbial growth. Citric acid, a naturally occurring acidulant in many foods, can also act synergistically with other added biocides. Many of these combination systems act by placing additional energy demands on cells through interference with energy-requiring homeostatic mechanisms.

In addition, the possibility of using a combination of preservatives in pharmaceutical and other products is currently under investigation.

6.   IMPACT OF SPORE RESISTANCE ON SOCIETY

Under conditions of limitation of carbon, nitrogen or phosphorus, some bacteria, notably the genera *Bacillus* and *Clostridium*, can form highly resistant, dehydrated spores. These spores are amongst the most resistant forms to biocides and to physical agents such as heat, radiation, drying and freezing and are well adapted for long periods of survival under adverse conditions. Medically, spores are important because they are responsible for the dissemination of some serious diseases, e.g. botulism, tetanus, gas gangrene, anthrax and food poisoning.

It is particularly important that spores are excluded from medical appliances intended for introduction into the human or animal body. Since certain medical equipment of this type cannot be sterilized by physical processes, chemical sporicides must be used. However, the high resistance of bacterial spores to biocides has meant that comparatively few chemicals are sufficiently toxic against spores to be employed in this context. Indeed, glutaraldehyde, ethylene oxide and formaldehyde (the last, sometimes with low temperature steam) are essentially the only sporicides available for sterilization of such medical equipment.

7. STRATEGIES FOR COUNTERACTING RESISTANCE OF SPORES TO CHEMICALS

As already noted, bacterial spores are amongst the most resistant forms of microbial life to both chemical and physical processes. There are, however, various procedures for counteracting the high tolerance of spores, although not all have practical applications.

7.1   Use of heat treatment with biocides
It was pointed out in Chapter 3 (Section 2.3) that the activity of most antibacterial agents is potentiated at high temperatures. Until 1988 certain parenteral and ophthalmic products were sterilized by heating at 98–100°C in the presence of a specified phenolic or organomercury compound. Although this method had been widely used in the UK for many years, doubts had frequently been expressed about its efficiency as a true sterilization procedure. Consequently, heating in an autoclave (in the absence of biocide) which employs a temperature of 121°C, is now the recommended pharmacopoeial method for sterilizing thermostable solutions.

In the food industry, a process known as acid-heat treatment has long been used as a sterilizing procedure. This depends upon spores being more heat-sensitive at low, rather than high, pH.

7.2   Use of chemical combinations
Two or more biocides (or antibiotics) in combination may produce a synergistic response against non-sporing bacteria. It is logical, therefore, to consider whether the same principle applies to bacterial spores. The subject has not, however, been approached in a rational manner and the results have therefore tended to be haphazard and not always well explained. Examples to date are as follows:

(1) Combinations of aldehydes: some disinfectant formulations are available which contain more than one aldehyde. Their sporicidal activity is claimed to be greater than that observed with a single aldehyde. It is difficult to explain this observation unless there is greater overall uptake into the spore with the combined formulation.

(2) Glutaraldehyde plus surface-active agents and metals: (a) the sporicidal action of the dialdehyde may be potentiated by non-ionic surfactants and by metal divalent cations, (b) inorganic cation-anionic surfactant combinations greatly increase dialdehyde activity at acid pH, possibly as a result of effects on the spore surface resulting in greater aldehyde uptake.

(3) Hypochlorite plus methanol: the hypochlorites are sporicidal, but this activity is enhanced in the presence of methanol or other alcohols. Methanol is claimed to modify the spore coats, thereby allowing increased hypochlorite penetration. This hypothesis has yet to be substantiated.

(4) Acid-alcohol treatment: alcohol is not sporicidal, and only high concetrations (9%) of hydrochloric acid are sporicidal. Acid alcohol (1% HCl in 70% alcohol) will, however, kill spores within a few hours. The reason for this is unknown, but spore permeability is probably affected by some, as yet unknown, mechanism.

It is clear from the above that little is known about the basis of improved sporicidal activity when combinations of chemical agents are used. Increased penetration of one or both agents is an obvious possibility, but evidence to support this contention is often lacking. It is not yet known how to design specific sporicidal molecules that would be able to penetrate efficiently the spore coats.

7.3   Chemical plus ultraviolet radiation

Ultraviolet light and hydrogen peroxide are synergistic when used in combination. This probably results from the formation of hydroxyl ($\cdot$OH) radicals that damage spore DNA.

8.   CONCLUSIONS

This chapter has indicated the impact of antibiotic resistance on mankind and some of the strategies that have been used to circumvent, or control, it. Undoubtedly further attempts to control the problem will be made in the future. For instance, within the context of plasmid-and transposon-encoded resistance, procedures might be developed to interrupt the spread of resistance genes in or between bacteria. At present bacteria can sometimes be cured of their plasmids by chemical or physical means, but for clinical application it would be necessary for all cells in a bacterial population to be cured on exposure to the (hypothetical) drug. Presently no means are known to prevent the spread of transposons and this again, may be a useful area in which to concentrate efforts on drug development. Inhibition of plasmid transfer between donor and recipient cells might provide a further means of controlling the spread of resistance genes. Indeed, some advances in this direction have already been made since polycations, such as the non-toxic compound polymyxin B nona-peptide that disorganize the outer membrane of Gram-negative organisms, inhibit conjugal DNA transfer.

FURTHER READING

Books

Russell, A. D. (1982). *The Destruction of Bacterial Spores*. Academic Press, London.

Review articles/reports

Easmon, C. S. F. (1985). Gonococcal resistance to antibiotics. *Journal of Antimicrobial Chemotherapy* **16**, 409–412.

Gould, I. M. (1988). Control of antibiotic use in the United Kingdom. *Journal of Antimicrobial Chemotherapy* **22**, 395–397.

Greenwood, D. (1986). Strategies for counteracting resistance to antibacterial agents. *Journal of Antimicrobial Chemotherapy* **18**, Supplement B, 141–151.

Gustafson, R. H. & Kiser, J. S. (1985). Nonmedical uses of the tetracyclines. In *The Tetracyclines, Handbook of Experimental Pharmacology*, Volume 78 (eds J. J. Hlavka & J. H. Boothe) pp. 405–446. Springer-Verlag, Berlin.

Hawkey, P. M. (1984). *Providencia stuartii*: a review of multiply antibiotic-resistant bacteria. *Journal of Antimicrobial Chemotherapy* **13**, 209–226.

Lambert, H. P. (1984). Impact of bacterial resistance to antibiotics on therapy. *British Medical Bulletin* **40**, 102–106.

Report (1969). Joint Committee on the use of Antibiotics in Animal Husbandry and Veterinary Medicine. HMSO, London.

Report (1986). Guidelines for the control of epidemic methicillin-resistant *Staphylococcus aureus*. *Journal of Hospital Infection* **7**, 193–201.

Rolinson, G. N. (1988). The influence of 6-aminopenicillanic acid on antibiotic development. *Journal of Antimicrobial Chemotherapy* **22**, 5–14.

Sykes, R. B. & Bonner, D. P. (1984). Counteracting antibiotic resistance: new drugs. *British Medical Bulletin* **40**, 96–101.

Research papers

Cookson, B. D. & Phillips, I. (1988). Epidemic methicillin-resistant *Staphylococcus aureus*. *Journal of Antimicrobial Chemotherapy* **21**, Supplement C, 57–65.

Ellison, R. T., Giehl, T. J. & LaForce, F. M. (1988). Damage of the outer membrane of enteric Gram-negative bacteria by lactoferrin and transferrin. *Infection and Immunity* **56**, 2774–2781.

Lam, C., Hildebrandt, J., Schutze, E. & Wenzel, A. F. (1986). Membrane-disorganizing property of polymyxin B nonapeptide. *Journal of Antimicrobial Chemotherapy* **18**, 9–15.

Marples, R. R. & Cooke, E. M. (1988). Current problems with methicillin-resistant *Staphylococcus aureus*. *Journal of Hospital Infection* **11**, 381–392.

Shanson, D. C. (1987). Staphylococcal infection in hospitals. *British Journal of Hospital Medicine* **35**, 312–320.

Stickler, D. J. & Chawla, J. C. (1987). The role of antiseptics in the management of patients with long-term indwelling bladder catheters. *Journal of Hospital Infection* **10**, 28–39.

Stickler, D. J., Clayton, C. L. & Chawla, J. C. (1987). The resistance of urinary tract pathogens to chlorhexidine bladder washouts. *Journal of Hospital Infection* **10**, 28–39.

Vaara, M., & Vaara, T. (1983a). Polycations sensitise enteric bacteria to antibiotics. *Antimicrobial Agents and Chemotherapy* **24**, 107–113.

Vaara, M. & Vaara, T. (1983b). Polycations as outer membrane-disorganizing agents. *Antimicrobial Agents and Chemotherapy* **24** 114–122.

Viljanen, P. (1987). Polycations which disorganize the outer membrane inhibit conjugation in *Escherichia coli*. *Journal of Antimicrobial Chemotherapy* **13**, 209–226.

Index